THE BEGINNINGS OF MODERN SCIENCE

THE BEGINNINGS OF
MODERN SCIENCE

Scientific Writings of the 16th,
17th and 18th Centuries

Edited by

HOLMES BOYNTON

Published for the Classics Club ® by

WALTER J. BLACK, INC. · ROSLYN, N. Y.

Acknowledgments

THE editor is indebted to several great libraries and their librarians for making available to him their wealth of source literature. The Medical Historical and Sterling Memorial libraries at Yale University provided most of the material used for this book from their great collections. The Engineering Societies Library in New York City brought forth all five editions of Franklin's *Experiments and Observations in Electricity*, and other rare works. The Smith-Plimpton Collection at Columbia University, the J. P. Morgan Library, and the library of the United States Department of Agriculture also were generous in their offer of resources.

Among the individuals whose good advice was sometimes taken were the following: Dr. Roy H. Miner, Director Emeritus of the American Museum of Natural History; Dr. Edward C. Streeter; Dr. John H. Fulton, Sterling Professor of Physiology at Yale University; Miss Madeleine Stanton, Secretary of the Historical Library, Yale School of Medicine; and Dirk H. van der Stucken of Phillips Academy, Andover. A particularly great debt is owed to Miss Louise R. Loomis, advisory editor for this series, who offered excellent suggestions at every turn. Thanks are due also to Miss Faith Maris, editor of Classics Club; to Edda Kvaran and to Gudmundur Arnason for sharing in the burden of manuscript preparation; to Richard Loving, artist, for redrawing and preparing for reproduction the woodcuts and engravings used as illustrations; and especially to my wife, Beatrice Sigurbjorg Gislason, for her inspiring confidence and her material aid during the year that the preparation of this volume was our most absorbing interest.

For permission to reprint material to which they hold copyright, we thank the following publishers and translators: Columbia University Press (*Physical Treatises of Pascal, Three Copernican Treatises* and extracts from Vesalius, from the Proceedings of the Charaka Club); Paul B. Hoeber (*A Source Book of Medical History* and *The Life and Times of Ambroise Paré*); Herbert Hoover (*De Re Metallica*); McGraw Hill Book Co. (*A Source Book of Physics, A Source Book of Astronomy,* and *A Source Book of Geology*); Macmillan (Galileo's *Dialogues Concerning Two New Sciences*); Reynal and Hitchcock (*The Notebooks of Leonardo da Vinci*); Charles C. Thomas (*Readings in the History of Physiology* and Harvey's *On the Motion of the Heart and Blood*); University of California Press (Newton's *Principia Mathematica*); E. P. Dutton and Co. (Descartes' *A Discourse on Method*).

Foreword

In December 1942 when the first chain-reacting pile became self-operative under the West Stands of the Athletic Field of the University of Chicago, mankind entered upon a new era. As months and years slip by we become more and more concerned as to what use will be made of the tremendous possibilities for good or for evil that were again fore-shadowed in the unbelievable power behind the pillars of cloud and of water lifted above Bikini Lagoon in the summer of 1946.

Only a greater and more widespread understanding of Science and of its way of working and a more universal appreciation of why it has achieved its swift advance within the past century or so can awaken the peoples of this earth and their leaders to a determination that more of good and far less of evil shall be its future fruit.

It would be fantastic to hope that any significant number of our adult population or of their children can quickly become familiar with much of the many-storied structure of modern science. For the long years of study and training necessary to this, there is no substitute. But the few already launched on this hard trail need the support, the understanding and, maybe, some guidance from the many for whom this path is impossible. Common reactions among the latter are that science is something utterly apart from their own lives, repellent to their tastes, or hopelessly beyond their comprehension. To help overcome such negative attitudes the simple stories as written by the early masters of science and collected in this volume can be of great value.

The beginnings of almost every aspect of pure science are here to be found—from the constructions and the motions of the stars to the foundations of atomic theory; from the nature and the mass of the earth, its atmosphere, its storms, its rain, to that of heat and electricity; from the breathing and the sexes of plants to the doorlets in veins and the circulation of the blood.

Just as one can more fully appreciate a great telescope like the one on Mt. Palomar after the first simple glass of Galileo has been held in one's hand and looked through, so does the historical approach through the early stages of a great branch of science inspire interest, enthusiasm, and confidence in spite of the lack of any full understanding of details. The conviction is born that the details may well be left to their modern masters and that perhaps we have too few of the latter. These men indeed may still fumble with words, ideas, and inadequate equipment as did their early predecessors, but today the layman *cannot* follow the struggles of his contemporary scientists. On the other hand, he does know so much more about so many more things than did the early masters that he can read their first reports of exploration with more than a fair understanding. Then, in following their cautious, tentative approach, he discovers how nothing should be accepted without careful control and checking and he thus begins to understand the power of science and to acquire a new respect for the method through which it has so far outstripped other human studies and activities.

Thus we hope that the potent ferment of this method will be transferred into a more active molding of individual human thought and trust that the collective impact of more universal thinking in this fashion may lead towards the betterment of human life.

HARVEY BRACE LEMON

Contents

I

MATTER AND MOTION   1

II

LIGHT, HEAT, AND FIRE   129

III

THE STUDY OF AIR AND OF
CHEMISTRY   207

VI

HOW PLANTS GROW 389

VII

THE STRUCTURE OF THE
HUMAN BODY   463

VIII

THE SCIENCE OF HEALING   527

IX

SCIENTISTS THINK ABOUT SCIENCE   579

Introduction

To GIVE THE general reader with an interest in the subject a better understanding of modern science is the purpose of this book. At first sight it may seem paradoxical to attempt to do this through the writings of men who lived as long ago as the sixteenth, seventeenth, and eighteenth centuries, but there are a number of reasons for selecting this method.

President James Bryant Conant of Harvard University, a leader in the research for and development of the atomic bomb, in a recent series of lectures at Yale gave one of these reasons. In order, he said, to appreciate the true nature of science, it is more important to gain a feeling for the special manner in which a scientist approaches a problem in a new era than it is to know the latest fruits of science. For the layman who wishes to learn how science differs from other forms of intellectual activity, it is more valuable to understand the long-time characteristics of scientific tactics and strategy in general than it is to memorize a given number of specific, scientific rules. There is no better way of gaining this understanding than to study by the case method a few phases of the scientific history of these early modern centuries, when scientists were making revolutionary discoveries in every field.

Moreover, these earlier scientists for the most part wrote more interestingly about their work than do the highly accomplished specialists of more recent days. Up to the year 1800, the large majority of scientists were amateurs. They wrote for each other and the general, intelligent public, because there were few professional scholars to read their reports. Consequently, they made them as lucid, detailed, and simple as they

xvii

could. They were charting a course through strange seas and were thrilled by the sense of adventure. They were often unsophisticated in their approach, and sometimes uncertain in their method, so no detail of their experiments, observations, and conclusions was too minute to record. They carried the excitement of new discovery into their writings, for it was not yet considered bad scientific form to betray feeling in reports of laboratory findings. As a result, these reports are now far better reading than the strictly condensed, unemotional accounts of more modern scientific work, which usually need a skillful interpreter to make them intelligible to the layman.

Today's experts address their writings to each other, and the cold, impartial, technical facts are left to speak for themselves. Galileo, Newton, and Franklin were speaking to the world, and let themselves be openly enthusiastic about their discoveries. So they wrote freshly, in a style that for the most part the world can understand.

Another reason for turning back to the pioneers of modern science in a book for the present-day reader is that the first steps in any new field are the least mathematical. It is one of the noteworthy characteristics of science that in due course, for the sake of universality, impartiality, and economy, it tends to reduce every possible relationship between things to mathematical terms. But in its earlier stages, while it is dealing with the more simple relations, such mathematics as it uses is simpler and more easily grasped by a reader without advanced mathematical training.

Many centuries ago, of course, in the period we now call antiquity, there were individuals who had something of the modern attitude toward science; men who observed, experimented, and measured as best they could with the limited tools they possessed. Dr. Otto Neugebauer of Brown University has translated Babylonian tablets which compute astronomical cycles with almost unbelievable accuracy. Among the ancient Greeks, Aristarchus made brilliant applications of mathematics to astronomy, and even proposed the idea that the earth revolved about the sun. Aristotle carried on extensive researches in biology, psychology, and physics. Archimedes was famous for his discoveries in the realms of physics and mechanics. Eratosthenes, a geographer, figured out with a high degree of precision both the size of the earth and its distance from the sun. The atomic philosophers, Leucippus, Democritus, Epicurus, and Lucretius, framed hypotheses about the structure of matter that strikingly suggest our modern theories.

But during the early Middle Ages, when for a long time conditions of life were hazardous and poor, and feeble rulers were unable to keep order, the work of the ancient scientists was largely lost and forgotten, and ignorance and superstition prevailed over most of Western Europe. The only educated men were in the Church, and the questions they asked, when they looked at the world of nature, were mainly religious and moral ones. "*Why* did God make the earth and man as he did?" "*What divine purpose* may we perceive in this or that?" However, as time passed, life grew gradually more secure again, wealth increased and governments were stronger. Learning revived and men became interested once more in the study of actual nature, the materials of its structure, and the way in which particular objects moved and lived in it. The questions they now began to ask were, "*Of what* are things made?" "*How* do they act, grow, flourish, and die as they do?" Modern science was born when men began to ask *what* and *how*, for to these questions they could find answers, while it is given to God only to answer questions of *why*.

During the three centuries from 1500 to 1800, modern science, under the name of "natural philosophy," grew from infancy to young manhood. At first, nature was still regarded as a sphere of constant, supernatural intervention. Spirits, good and evil, were everywhere, and only to be controlled by secret, mystical, or magical formulae, as we may see in the brief excerpt which we have taken from Paracelsus. Faith in witchcraft was never stronger than in the sixteenth century. All that came and went on the earth was influenced by the fateful powers of the stars. Chemistry was undifferentiated from alchemy and the search for the wonder-working stone that could turn whatever it touched into gold.

Many of the men we think of as audaciously modern were yet far from free of all the older patterns of thought. Kepler's mystical theory of numbers led him at one time to force the solar system into a geometrical form—five regular polyhedrons fitted one inside the other. His distinction as a scientist was due to his conviction that to be true a theory must tally with the observed facts. "I shunned no toil of reckoning," he wrote, "spent days and night in calculation, until I could see whether my hypothesis would agree with the orbits of Copernicus, or whether my joy was to vanish into thin air." But his preoccupation with the search for ultimate causes prevented him from developing even further than he did. Galileo, who spent his life combatting some errors of Aristotle, accepted other errors without challenge. Astrology was taken seriously by the youthful Newton.

During the whole era, as knowledge increased and more adequate tools —the telescope, the microscope, the thermometer, the watch—were invented, the supernatural and the magical disappeared from one area of the universe after another. The year 1543, which saw the publication of Copernicus' momentous book on *The Revolutions of the Heavenly Bodies* and of Vesalius' on *The Structure of the Human Body*, is the date commonly set for the appearance of modern science, for by then speculation about nature had begun to follow observation and experiment instead of preceding them. From Newton's time onward, the world came more and more definitely to be looked at as one vast, well-constructed mechanism, run on principles no more mysterious than those that kept a clock going, once its skillful maker had fabricated and wound it up. The laws that governed its operations were all physical, and their workings as impersonal, regular, and unalterable as those that compelled the cogs of the clock's wheels to turn on one another.

As Laplace wrote, at the end of the era, given an intelligence equipped to comprehend all the forces by which nature is animated and the respective situations of all the objects, great and small, that compose it, both the past and the future would be open to his eyes, since the present state of the universe is nothing but the effect of its previous state, and the cause of that which is to follow. Hence, phenomena that had once seemed supernatural, mystifying, and portentous, having now been shown to be parts of the automatic, undeviating order of the cosmos, ceased to be terrifying. They might even indeed be made useful. For nature, being more and more sharply investigated, weighed, measured, and understood, could be mastered and used for the enrichment of human life. By 1800 the scientific method was fully developed and broadly accepted, and the world was ready for another rapid technological advance.

The present volume contains an account of historical progress in nine areas of modern science, told in the words of the men who brought it about. In general, the plan has been to choose reports on related topics, in order to show step by step the growth of analytical thought on the same subject and the improvement in techniques of experimentation, rather than to compile merely a random series of interesting essays. Many of the scientists whose work is presented here were men of great genius, and their contribution was as much or more in a new attitude towards nature and method as in the actual discoveries which they made. Their story of achievement in this period gives us not only much curious information as to the difficulties against which they struggled in their efforts to reach the truth about our universe but also a real insight into what makes a modern scientist.

HOLMES BOYNTON

Editorial note: In an anthology such as this, that contains works composed over a period of three centuries, and translated from many languages, there are bound to be divergencies in spelling and usage. English spelling of this period was very free, and in general there has been no attempt to make it consistent.

I

Matter and Motion

IT SEEMS to be a universal trait of human beings that we all naturally tend to believe that we ourselves are standing at the motionless center of the universe. Certainly the first people to watch the starry skies assumed that their own position was fixed and immovable, and that the motions they discovered in the heavens above them were real motions. There are still persons today who hold this view.

The apparent movements of the stellar bodies fascinated both shepherds and sages, and from the dawn of history man has made attempts to reduce them to a system. Those of the ancients who were interested in the calculation of time (and it is astonishing to note that some of the most intelligent Greeks showed no great interest in that direction) found stellar motion extremely useful in making up their calendars.

If we take for the moment the earth-centered view, the most obvious fact about the stars is that except for the planets, Venus, Mercury, Mars, Jupiter, and Saturn, there is no visible change in the relation of stars to each other, or the all-over pattern of the heavens, from day to day or from year to year. This fact was expressed somewhat poetically in the idea that the stars were fixed on a distant crystal sphere, which revolved as a whole about the central earth. Other readily observable facts were that this sphere appeared to revolve about the earth one more time each year than the sun did; and, further, that the planets had their own independent irregular motions and appearances. For example, they seemed to be continually losing the race with the stars, except for brief periods when they held their ground and even made a little headway. Venus and Mercury, the morning and evening stars, were never visible late at night. Mars and Jupiter appeared larger and brighter at the season when they were overhead at midnight than when they were seen near dawn or sunset.

Thus many separate facts were known, but the underlying explanation was not recognized. To be sure, the ancients had a few far-sighted geniuses, who made interesting speculations. Heraclitus, and after him the Pythagorean school, imagined a vague "central fire," around which the heavenly bodies revolved. Aristarchus held the opinion that the earth turned daily on its axis and revolved around the sun. But the most revered authorities, Aristotle (384-322 B.C.) and Ptolemy of Alexandria (2nd century A.D.), kept to the earth-centered theory, which was to prevail for many centuries longer. They accounted for the apparent irregularities of the planets by supposing that each of them moved through various small secondary orbits or epicycles, as well as through its great primary orbit around the earth. Aristotle set the total number of orbits described by the seven planets at fifty-five, and as new variations were later noted, observers increased this number to seventy-seven.

Antiquity and the Middle Ages passed before a hypothesis was worked out which explained all the known phenomena in a plain and simple manner. Not until the sixteenth century, greatest of all centuries in the development of the science of astronomy, was the order of the solar system finally understood. Copernicus was the first modern scientist to propose the theory that the planets, including our earth, revolve around the sun, thus reviving the conjecture of Aristarchus that "the fixed stars and the sun alone remain unmoved, while the earth revolves around the sun in the circumference of a circle, the sun lying in the middle of that orbit." The idea was of course incompatible with church teaching, since the authors of the Bible had known only the earth-centered theory. How could Joshua have made the sun to stand still if it did not move? However, the Church for some time placed no obstacles in the way of the publication of Copernicus' treatise. But other astronomers either rejected Copernicus' work with contempt or tried to sidestep the issue by intricate explanations which were meant to reconcile the new view with the old. For instance, the Danish astronomer Tycho Brahe, friend of the half-scientific, half-superstitious Emperor Rudolf II, after a long study of the heavens, developed the compromise theory that every stellar body except the earth and the moon revolved around the sun, and that the sun, carrying with it the rest of the universe, revolved about the earth.

But Johann Kepler took Copernicus' conclusions and Tycho Brahe's accurate observations of the planets, and tried nineteen possible systems for reducing still further the complexity of astronomical theory. Eventually he found that one additional assumption, namely, that the planetary orbits were elliptical instead of circular, made possible a simplification of the Copernican hypothesis by eliminating all epicycles or secondary orbits.

Galileo, the first astronomer to possess a telescope, was the first to see the moons of Jupiter and the spots on the sun, things which had no right to exist according to mediaeval conceptions of celestial symmetry and perfection. The Roman court of the Inquisition forbade him to go on with his astronomical researches, but did not object to his working in physics. He then began discovering the laws of gravitation by measuring the acceleration in velocity of balls rolling down slanting planes. Jeremiah Horrox, who died the same year as Galileo, started the formulation of the laws that govern the ocean tides as derived from the work of Galileo and Kepler.

Newton, with his law of universal gravitation, is the focal point of this section of our history; the men before him led up to him, those who came after explained him and developed his methods. Hooke's discovery that coiled springs could be used to determine the relative force of gravity seems in itself trivial, but it serves as an example of the fertility of the time in developing new experimental apparatus. Maskelyne, Cavendish, and Laplace, each in turn, made fresh applications of the law of universal attraction.

One hundred and fifty-one years after Galileo's condemnation by the Roman Inquisition came Herschel's almost casual announcement that he had just observed four hundred new nebulae. One hundred and ninety-nine years after the burning of the Dominican monk, Giordano Bruno (1548-1600), for spreading the Copernican doctrine came the publication of Laplace's comprehensive *Celestial Mechanics*. In that interval scientific thought had become free. The news of the four hundred new nebulae and of the formulation of a completely mechanical world system were hailed with genuine enthusiasm. Neither Herschel nor Laplace was threatened with loss of freedom or of life for stating the facts as he saw them.

NICOLAUS COPERNICUS

1 4 7 3 · 1 5 4 3

NIKLAS COPPERNICK, better known as Copernicus, a Pole of German descent, was born on the Vistula River in 1473. During three years at the University of Cracow he became interested in mathematics and astronomy. He then went south to study law, medicine, and astronomy at the Italian universities of Bologna, Padua, and Ferrara.

The rest of his life Copernicus spent chiefly in the Prussian city of Frauenburg, where he filled the post of canon at the cathedral, sharing in the duties and activities of the chapter. His medical skill was always at the service of the poor, but his prime concern was always his astronomical and mathematical studies. Following out some suggestions found in the writings of the old Greek scientists, he slowly developed the laborious calculations which showed that the motions of the planets could be more simply explained if they were assumed to rotate about the sun rather than about the earth. Aware that there might be ecclesiastical disapproval of so startling a view, he postponed publication of his momentous book, On the Revolutions of the Heavenly Bodies, until his seventieth year. The first printed copy reached him barely in time to be laid on his death-bed. However, some fifteen years earlier he had allowed his friends to see a briefer manuscript, Commentariolus, which set forth his system, though without his full mathematical verification. We quote here from the latter work, of which two copies have survived. The translation is by Edward Rosen, in Three Copernican Treatises (Columbia University Press, 1939).

5

HYPOTHESES FOR
THE HEAVENLY MOTIONS

OUR ANCESTORS assumed, I observe, a large number of celestial spheres for this reason especially, to explain the apparent motion of the planets by the principle of regularity. For they thought it altogether absurd that a heavenly body, which is a perfect sphere, should not always move uniformly. They saw that by connecting and combining regular motions in various ways they could make any body appear to move to any position.

Callippus [fourth century B.C.] and Eudoxus [about 409-356 B.C.], who endeavored to solve the problem by the use of concentric spheres, were unable to account for all the planetary movements; they had to explain not merely the apparent revolutions of the planets but also the fact that these bodies appear to us sometimes to mount higher in the heavens, sometimes to descend; and this fact is incompatible with the principle of concentricity. Therefore it seemed better to employ eccentrics and epicycles, a system which most scholars finally accepted.

Yet the planetary theories of Ptolemy [second century B.C.] and most other astronomers, although consistent with the numerical data, seemed likewise to present no small difficulty. For these theories were not adequate unless certain equants were also conceived; it then appeared that a planet moved with uniform velocity neither on its deferent nor about the center of its epicycle. Hence a system of this sort seemed neither sufficiently absolute nor sufficiently pleasing to the mind.

Having become aware of these defects, I often considered whether there could perhaps be found a more reasonable arrangement of circles, from which every apparent inequality would be derived and

6

in which everything would move uniformly about its proper center, as the rule of absolute motion requires. After I had addressed myself to this very difficult and almost insoluble problem, the suggestion at length came to me how it could be solved with fewer and much simpler constructions than were formerly used, if some assumptions (which are called axioms) were granted me. They follow in this order.

Assumptions

1. There is no one center of all the celestial circles or spheres.

2. The center of the earth is not the center of the universe, but only of gravity and of the lunar sphere.

3. All the spheres revolve about the sun as their mid-point, and therefore the sun is the center of the universe.

4. The ratio of the earth's distance from the sun to the height of the firmament [1] is so much smaller than the ratio of the earth's radius to its distance from the sun that the distance from the earth to the sun is imperceptible in comparison with the height of the firmament.

5. Whatever motion appears in the firmament arises not from any motion of the firmament, but from the earth's motion. The earth together with its circumjacent elements performs a complete rotation on its fixed poles in a daily motion, while the firmament and highest heaven abide unchanged.

6. What appear to us as motions of the sun arise not from its motion but from the motion of the earth and our sphere, with which we revolve about the sun like any other planet. The earth has, then, more than one motion.

7. The apparent retrograde and direct motion of the planets arises not from their motion but from the earth's. The motion of the earth alone, therefore, suffices to explain so many apparent inequalities in the heavens.

[1] The firmament here means the outermost crystalline sphere in which the fixed stars were supposed to be set. Copernicus did nothing to alter the conception of this sphere or of the stars set in it, except to call them all immovable and increase immensely their distance from the earth.

Having set forth these assumptions, I shall endeavor briefly to show how uniformity of the motions can be saved in a systematic way. However, I have thought it well, for the sake of brevity, to omit from this sketch mathematical demonstrations, reserving these for my larger work. But in the explanation of the circles I shall set down here the lengths of the radii; and from these the reader who is not unacquainted with mathematics will readily perceive how closely this arrangement of circles agrees with the numerical data and observations.

Accordingly, let no one suppose that I have gratuitously asserted, with the Pythagoreans, the motion of the earth; strong proof will be found in my exposition of the circles. For the principal arguments by which the natural philosophers attempt to establish the immobility of the earth rest for the most part on the appearances; it is particularly such arguments that collapse here, since I treat the earth's immobility as due to an appearance.

The Order of the Spheres

The celestial spheres are arranged in the following order. The highest is the immovable sphere of the fixed stars, which contains and gives position to all things. Beneath it is Saturn, which Jupiter follows, then Mars. Below Mars is the sphere on which we revolve; then Venus; last is Mercury. The lunar sphere revolves about the center of the earth and moves with the earth like an epicycle. In the same order also, one planet surpasses another in speed of revolution, according as they trace greater or smaller circles. Thus Saturn completes its revolution in thirty years, Jupiter in twelve, Mars in two and one-half, and the earth in one year; Venus in nine months, Mercury in three.

The Apparent Motions of the Sun

The earth has three motions. First, it revolves annually in a great circle about the sun in the order of the signs, always describing equal arcs in equal times; the distance from the center of the circle to the center of the sun is one twenty-fifth of the radius of the circle.

The radius is assumed to have a length imperceptible in comparison with the height of the firmament; consequently the sun appears to revolve with this motion, as if the earth lay in the center of the universe. However, this appearance is caused by the motion not of the sun but of the earth, so that, for example, when the earth is in the sign of Capricorn [2] [the Goat], the sun is seen diametrically opposite in Cancer [the Crab], and so on. On account of the previously mentioned distance of the sun from the center of the circle, this apparent motion of the sun is not uniform, the maximum inequality being two and one-sixth degrees. The line drawn from the sun through the center of the circle is invariably directed toward a point of the firmament about ten degrees west of the more brilliant of the two bright stars in the head of Gemini [the Twins]; therefore when the earth is opposite this point, and the center of the circle lies between them, the sun is seen at its greatest distance from the earth. In this circle, then, the earth revolves together with whatever else is included within the lunar sphere.

The second motion, which is peculiar to the earth, is the daily rotation on the poles in the order of the signs, that is, from west to east. On account of this rotation the entire universe appears to revolve with enormous speed. Thus does the earth rotate together with its circumjacent waters and encircling atmosphere.

The third is the motion in declination. For the axis of the daily rotation is not parallel to the axis of the great circle, but is inclined to it at an angle that intercepts a portion of a circumference, in our time about twenty-three and one-half degrees. Therefore, while the center of the earth always remains in the plane of the ecliptic,[3]

[2] The ancients had divided the zones of the sky through which the sun seemed to pass on its yearly journey around our globe into twelve regions, the so-called houses of the Zodiac. Each house was named after the sign or emblem supposedly formed by the pattern of a constellation included in it. The Goat, the Crab, and the Twins were all signs of the Zodiac.
[3] The great circle mentioned here, on which the earth moves around the sun, is called the ecliptic. The plane of the equator is tipped about twenty-three and one-half degrees from the plane of the ecliptic.

that is, in the circumference of the great circle, the poles of the earth rotate, both of them describing small circles about centers equidistant from the axis of the great circle. The period of this motion is not quite a year and is nearly equal to the annual revolution on the great circle. But the axis of the great circle is invariably directed toward the points of the firmament which are called the poles of the ecliptic. In like manner the motion in declination, combined with the annual motion in their joint effect upon the poles of the daily rotation, would keep these poles constantly fixed at the same points of the heavens, if the periods of both motions were exactly equal. Now with the long passage of time it has become clear that this inclination of the earth to the firmament changes. Hence it is the common opinion that the firmament has several motions in conformity with a law not yet sufficiently understood. But the motion of the earth can explain all these changes in a less surprising way. I am not concerned to state what the path of the poles is. I am aware that, in lesser matters, a magnetized iron needle always points in the same direction. It has nevertheless seemed a better view to ascribe the changes to a sphere, whose motion governs the movements of the poles. This sphere must doubtless be sublunar.

Equal Motion Should Be Measured Not By the Equinoxes but by the Fixed Stars

Since the equinoxes and the other cardinal points of the universe shift considerably, whoever attempts to derive from them the equal length of the annual revolution necessarily falls into error. Different determinations of this length were made in different ages on the basis of many observations. Hipparchus computed it as 365¼ days, and Albategnius the Chaldean as 365 days, 5 hours, 46 minutes, that is, 13⅗ minutes or 13⅓ minutes less than Ptolemy. Hispalensis increased Albategnius' estimate by the twentieth part of an hour, since he determined the tropical year as 365 days, 5 hours, 49 minutes.[4]

Lest these differences should seem to have arisen from errors of observation, let me say that if anyone will study the details carefully, he will find that the discrepancy has always corresponded to the motion of the equinoxes. For when the cardinal points moved one degree in one hundred years, as they were found to be moving in the age of Ptolemy, the length of the year was then what Ptolemy stated it to be. When, however, in the following centuries they moved with greater rapidity, being opposed to lesser motions, the year became shorter; and this decrease corresponded to the increase in precession. For the annual motion was completed in a shorter time on account of the more rapid recurrence of the equinoxes. Therefore the derivation of the equal length of the year from the fixed stars is more accurate. I used Spica Virginis and found that the year has always been 365 days, 6 hours, and about 10 minutes, which is also the estimate of the ancient Egyptians. The same method must be employed also with the other motions of the planets, as is shown by their apsides, by the fixed laws of their motion in the firmament, and by heaven itself with true testimony. [We omit twenty-two pages here and come to the conclusion.]

Then Mercury runs on seven circles in all; Venus on five; the earth on three, and round it the moon on four; finally Mars, Jupiter, and Saturn on five each.[5] Altogether, therefore, thirty-four circles suffice to explain the entire structure of the universe and the entire ballet of the planets.

[4] Hipparchus (about 160-125 B.C.) was a Greek astronomer, Albategnius (about 850-929 A.D.) an Arab, and Hispalensis, or Jabir ibn Aflah (13th century), a Spanish Moslem, who was born or lived in Seville. The last in his treatise on astronomy criticized the Ptolemaic theory of the planets.
[5] That is, Copernicus still believed that Mercury traversed six smaller eccentric orbits in the course of its main rotation around the sun. Venus four, the earth two, etc.

TYCHO BRAHE

1 5 4 6 · 1 6 0 1

THROUGH GREAT precision, diligence, and ingenuity, the talented Dane, Tycho Brahe (pronounced Tyko Brä), succeeded in reducing the errors in astronomical observations to a fraction of the best his predecessors had done. At the age of seventeen he noticed the discrepancy between the actual position of the planets and their positions as calculated from the most accurate tables then available, and began to build larger instruments with better scales. At twenty-two, he constructed a quadrant of seasoned oak so heavy that it took twenty men to carry it to the top of a hill. It was there, four years later, that he caught sight of a "new star" in Cassiopeia.

Meanwhile, the young scientist studied mathematics and astronomy at the universities of Copenhagen, Leipzig, Rostock, and Augsburg. In 1576 King Frederick II of Denmark bestowed on him for life the island of Hveen in the Baltic, and built for him there a remarkable observatory, so designed that all parts of the heavens could be under observation at the same time. It was divided into five chambers, each opening into a central study in such a way that five observers could work simultaneously, and yet not be able to compare notes until their observations were completed. Here Tycho collected a great mass of accurate stellar and planetary data, and developed the idea of averaging readings. Among his activities was the preparation of a catalogue of 777 stars.

But after the death of King Frederick in 1586, Tycho lost the support of the Danish crown, in part through his own extravagance and tactlessness. In 1599 he accepted the invitation of the German emperor, Rudolf II, to go to Prague as imperial mathematician.

There, during the last year of his life, he was assisted by the young German astronomer, Johann Kepler, who, on his death, succeeded to his position.

From time to time a new star, not previously seen, makes a sudden brilliant appearance in the sky and then, after a time, fades out. This phenomenon had not been noted before Tycho Brahe's observation of the "nova" in 1572. It startled the scientific world, which had always believed that the heavens were fixed and immutable, save for occasional comets, and, of course, the wandering planets. Hence Tycho spent much time and pains on proving that his star was too distant and too constant in position to be a comet.

This translation of Tycho's De Stella Nova (On a New Star), 1573, was made by John H. Walden for a Source Book in Astronomy, edited by Harlow Shapley and Helen E. Howarth (McGraw-Hill Book Co., 1929).

ON A NEW STAR,

NOT PREVIOUSLY SEEN WITHIN THE MEMORY OF ANY AGE SINCE THE BEGINNING OF THE WORLD

ITS FIRST APPEARANCE IN 1572 Last year [1572], in the month of November, on the eleventh day of that month, in the evening after sunset, when, according to my habit, I was contemplating the stars in a clear sky, I noticed that a new and unusual star, surpassing the other stars in brilliancy, was shining almost directly above my head; and since I had, almost from boyhood, known all the stars of the heavens perfectly (there is no great difficulty in attaining that knowledge), it was quite evident to me that there had never before been any star in that place in the sky, even the smallest, to say nothing of a star so conspicuously bright as this. I was so astonished at this sight that I was not ashamed to doubt the trustworthiness of my own eyes. But when I observed that others, too, on having the place pointed out to them, could see that there was really a star there, I had no further doubts. A miracle indeed, either the greatest of all that have occurred in the whole range of nature since the beginning of the world, or one certainly that is to be classed with those attested by the Holy Oracles, the staying of the Sun in its course in answer to the prayers of Joshua, and the darkening of the Sun's face at the time of the Crucifixion.

For all philosophers agree, and facts clearly prove it to be the case, that in the ethereal region of the celestial world no change, in the way either of generation or of corruption, takes place; but that the heavens and the celestial bodies in the heavens are without increase or diminution, and that they undergo no alteration, either in number or in size or in light or in any other respect; that

14

they always remain the same, like unto themselves in all respects, no years wearing them away. Furthermore, the observations of all the founders of the science, made some thousands of years ago, testify that all the stars have always retained the same number, position, order, motion, and size as they are found, by careful observation on the part of those who take delight in heavenly phenomena, to preserve even in our own day. Nor do we read that it was ever before noted by any one of the founders that a new star had appeared in the celestial world, except only by Hipparchus, if we are to believe Pliny. For Hipparchus, according to Pliny (Book II of his *Natural History*), noticed a star different from all others previously seen, one born in his own age. . . .

Its Position with Reference to the Diameter of the World and Its Distance from the Earth, the Center of the Universe. It is a difficult matter, and one that requires a subtle mind, to try to determine the distances of the stars from us, because they are so incredibly far removed from the earth; nor can it be done in any way more conveniently and with greater certainty than by the measure of the parallax [diurnal], if a star have one. For if a star that is near the horizon is seen in a different place than when it is at its highest point and near the vertex, it is necessarily found in some orbit with respect to which the Earth has a sensible size. . . .

In order, therefore, that I might find out in this way whether this star was in the region of the Element [1] or among the celestial orbits, and what its distance was from the Earth itself, I tried to determine whether it had a parallax, and, if so, how great a one; and this I did in the following way. I observed the distance between this star and Schedir of Cassiopeia (for the latter and the new star were both nearly on the meridian), when the star was at its nearest point to the vertex, being only 6 degrees removed from the zenith itself. . . . I made the same observation when the star was farthest from the zenith and at its nearest point to the horizon, and in each case I found that the distance from the above-mentioned fixed star

[1] That is, the region of the air, between the earth and the moon.

was exactly the same, without the variation of a minute, namely 7 degrees and 55 minutes. Then I went through the same process, making numerous observations with other stars. Whence I conclude that this new star has no diversity of aspect, even when it is near the horizon. For otherwise in its least altitude it would have been farther away from the above-mentioned star in the breast of Cassiopeia than when in its greatest altitude. Therefore, we shall find it necessary to place this star, not in the region of the Element, below the Moon, but far above, in an orbit with respect to which the Earth has no sensible size. For if it were in the highest region of the air, below the hollow region of the Lunar sphere, it would, when nearest the horizon, have produced on the circle a sensible variation of altitude from that which it held when near the vertex. . . .

Therefore, this new star is neither in the region of the Element, below the Moon, nor among the orbits of the seven wandering stars, but it is in the eighth sphere,[2] among the other fixed stars, which was what we had to prove. Hence it follows that it is not some peculiar kind of comet or some other kind of fiery meteor become visible. For none of these are generated in the heavens themselves, but they are below the Moon, in the upper region of the air, as all philosophers testify; unless one would believe with Albategnius that comets are produced, not in the air, but in the heavens. For he believes that he has observed a comet above the Moon, in the sphere of Venus. That this can be the case, is not yet clear to me. But, please God, sometime, if a comet shows itself in our age, I will investigate the truth of the matter.

Even should we assume that it can happen (which I, in company with other philosophers, can hardly admit), still it does not follow that this star is a kind of comet; first, by reason of its very form, which is the same as the form of the real stars and different from the form of all the comets hitherto seen, and then because, in such a length of time, it advances neither latitudinally nor longi-

[2] The so-called eighth sphere of the heavens was the crystalline sphere in which the fixed stars were set, outside the sphere of the farthest planet, Saturn.

tudinally by any motion of its own, as comets have been observed to do. For, although these sometimes seem to remain in one place several days, still, when the observation is made carefully by exact instruments, they are seen not to keep the same position for so very long or so very exactly. I conclude, therefore, that this star is not some kind of comet or a fiery meteor, whether these be generated beneath the Moon or above the Moon, but that it is a star shining in the firmament itself—one that has never previously been seen before our time, in any age since the beginning of the world.

JOHANN KEPLER

1571 - 1630

KEPLER'S LIFE work consisted of a tremendous volume of mathematical calculation, based on the systematic and accurate observations he had inherited from his patron and teacher, Tycho Brahe. Kepler was obsessed with the idea of finding the mathematical harmonies present in the mind of the Creator and computed incessantly through thirty years of illness, poverty, and misfortune. He was born at Württemberg and educated at first for the ministry, but later, as a student at the University of Tübingen, he became interested in the theories of Copernicus. Abandoning the idea of the ministry, he accepted the chair of science at Gratz, and began his labors in the fields of astrology, mathematics, and astronomy. Later, as Tycho Brahe's assistant and as his successor at Prague, he developed his own theories further.

A mystical attitude towards numbers, derived from the Greeks, led him at first into fruitless by-ways. After reading Gilbert on magnetism, he attempted to explain planetary motions as magnetic phenomena instead of using the ideas on force being worked out by his friend Galileo. But his great achievement, his discovery that planets move in ellipses, within whose common focus the sun is situated, swept away at last the involved systems of circles and epicycles which had been part of all previous astronomical thinking, including that of Copernicus and Tycho Brahe. Like other of his conclusions, however, it was forced on him only after he had investigated wellnigh every other possibility.

"Truth comes out of error more easily than out of confusion," said Francis Bacon. There was certainly no confusion in Kepler's data, nor in his conviction that the universe was orderly. Nor did his errors hinder him from laying an important foundation for Newton's greater work.

The first excerpt below, a defense of Copernicus against religious objectors, is taken from the "Introduction to Mars," translated by Thomas Salusbury in 1661, and included in Salusbury's Mathematical Collections and Translations. The second, longer excerpt, containing a statement of Kepler's first law of planetary motion, is from De harmonice mundi, published in 1619, and was translated by John H. Walden in 1928. It is contained in A Source Book in Astronomy, edited by Harlow Shapley and Helen E. Howarth (McGraw-Hill Book Co., 1929).

SCRIPTURE AND THE DOCTRINE
OF THE EARTH'S MOBILITY

IT MUST BE confessed that there are very many who are devoted to Holiness, that dissent from the Judgement of *Copernicus*, fearing to give the Lye to the Holy Ghost speaking in the Scriptures, if they should say, that the Earth moveth, and the Sun stands still. But let us consider, that since we judge of very many, and those the most principal things by the Sense of Seeing, it is impossible that we should alienate our Speech from this Sense of our Eyes. Therefore, many things daily occur, of which we speak according to the Sense of Sight, when as we certainly know that the things themselves are otherwise. An example whereof we have in that Verse of Virgil:

Provehimur portu, Terraeque urbesque recedunt . . .

[Forth we sail from the harbor, the land and the cities recede.]

And I do also beseech my Reader, not forgetting the Divine Goodnesse conferred on Mankind, the consideration of which the Psalmist doth chiefly urge, that when he returneth from the Temple, and enters into the School of *Astronomy*, he would with me praise and admire the Wisdome and Greatnesse of the Creator, which I discover to him by a more narrow explication of the World's Form, the Disquisition of Causes, and Detection of the Errours of Sight. And so he will not onely extoll the Bounty of God in the preservation of Living Creatures of all kindes, and establishment of the Earth; but even in its Motion also, which is so strange, so admirable, he will acknowledge the Wisdome of the Creator.

But he who is so stupid as not to comprehend the Science of

Astronomy, or so weak and scrupulous as to think it an offence of Piety to adhere to *Copernicus,* him I advise, that leaving the Study of *Astronomy,* and censuring the opinions of Philosophers at pleasure, he betake himself to his own concerns, and that desisting from further pursuit of these intricate Studies, he keep at home and manure his own Ground; and with those Eyes wherewith alone he seeth, being elevated towards this to be admired Heaven, let him pour forth his whole heart in thanks and praises to God the Creator; and assure himself that he shall therein perform as much Worship to God, as the *Astronomer,* on whom God hath bestowed this Gift, that though he seeth more clearly with the Eye of his Understanding, yet whatever he hath attained to, he is both able and willing to extoll his God above it.

And thus much concerning the Authority of Sacred Scripture. Now as touching the opinions of the Saints about these Natural Points. I answer in one word, That in Theology the weight of Authority, but in Philosophy the weight of Reason is to be considered. Therefore Sacred was *Lactantius* [early 4th century A.D.], who denied the earth's rotundity; Sacred was *Augustine* [354-430 A.D.], who granted the Earth to be round, but denied the *Antipodes;*[1] Sacred is the Liturgy (Officium) of our Moderns, who admit the smallnesse of the Earth, but deny its Motion. But to me more sacred than all these is Truth, who, with respect to the Doctors of the Church, do demonstrate from Philosophy that the Earth is both round, circumhabited by *Antipodes,* of a most contemptible smallnesse and in a word, that it is ranked amongst the Planets.

[1] Augustine did not believe the opposite or under side of the earth could be inhabited.

THE DISCOVERY OF
THE LAWS OF PLANETARY MOTION

CHIEF POINTS OF ASTRONOMICAL LEARNING,
NECESSARY FOR THE CONTEMPLATION
OF THE CELESTIAL HARMONIES

IN THE BEGINNING let my readers understand this: that the old astronomical hypotheses of Ptolemy [second century A.D.] as they are set forth in the *Theoriae* of Purbach and the writings of the other epitomizers, are to be kept far from the present enquiry and banished wholly from the mind; for they fail to give a true account either of the arrangement of the heavenly bodies or of the laws governing their motions.

In their place I cannot do otherwise than substitute simply Copernicus's theory of the universe, and (were it possible) convince all men of its truth; but, since among the mass of students the idea is still unfamiliar, and the theory that the Earth is one of the planets and moves among the stars about the Sun, which is stationary, sounds to the most of them quite absurd, let those who are offended by the strangeness of this doctrine know that these harmonic speculations hold a place even among the hypotheses of Tycho Brahe. While that author agrees with Copernicus in regard to everything else which concerns the arrangement of the heavenly bodies and the laws governing their motions, the annual motion of the Earth alone, as held by Copernicus, he transfers to the whole system of the planetary orbits and to the Sun, which, according to both authors, is the center of the system. For from this transference, motion results just the same, so that, if not in that utterly vast and immense space of the sphere of the fixed stars, at least in the system of the planetary world, the Earth holds at any one time the same place according to Brahe as is given to it by Copernicus.

Furthermore, just as he who draws a circle on paper moves the writing foot of the compass around, while he who fastens the paper or a board to a revolving wheel keeps the foot of the compass or the style stationary and draws the same circle on the moving board, so also in the present case; for Copernicus, the Earth measures out its orbit between the outer circle of Mars and the inner circle of Venus, by the real motion of its own body, while for Tycho Brahe the whole planetary system (in which among the other orbits are also those of Mars and Venus) turns around like the board on the wheel and brings to the stationary Earth, as to the style of the turner, the space between the orbits of Mars and Venus; and from this motion of the system it results that the Earth, itself remaining stationary, marks on space the same course around the Sun, between Mars and Venus, which, according to Copernicus, it marks by the real motion of its own body with the system at rest.

Since, then, the harmonic speculation considers the eccentric motions of the planets, as seen from the Sun, one can easily understand that, if an observer were on the Sun, however great the Sun's motion, the Earth, although it were at rest (to grant this for the moment to Brahe), would, nevertheless, seem to him to run its annual course in the space between the planets, and also in a time between the planet's times. Although, therefore, a man may be weak in faith and so unable to conceive of the motion of the Earth among the stars, he may still find it possible to take pleasure in the exalted contemplation of this most divine mechanism; he needs but to apply whatever he hears about the daily motions of the Earth in its eccentric to the appearance of those motions on the Sun, as even Tycho Brahe presents it with the Earth at rest.

The true followers of the Samian philosophy,[2] however, have no just cause for envying such men this participation in a most delightful speculation, for if they accept also the immovability of the Sun and the motion of the Earth, their pleasure will be more exquisite in many ways, since it will be derived from the very consummated perfection of contemplation.

In the first place, therefore, let my readers understand that at the present day among all astronomers it is held to be a well established fact that all the planets except the Moon, which alone has the Earth as its center, revolve around the Sun; the Moon's orbit or course, be it said, is not large enough to enable it to be drawn on this chart in proper relation to the other orbits. To the other five planets, therefore, is added the Earth as sixth, which, either by its own motion, with the Sun stationary, or, itself being at rest while the whole planetary system is in revolution, describes its orbit, the sixth, about the Sun.

Secondly, the following fact is also established: that all the planets revolve in eccentric orbits; that is, they alter their distances from the Sun, so that in one part of the orbit they are very remote from the Sun, while in the opposite part they come very near the Sun. . . .

Thirdly, let the reader recall from my *Mysterium Cosmographicum*, which I published twenty-two years ago, that the number of the planets, or orbits about the Sun, was derived by the most wise Creator from the five solid figures, about which Euclid so many centuries ago wrote the book which, since it is made up of a series of propositions, is called Elementa. That there cannot be more regular bodies, that regular plane figures, that is, cannot unite into a solid in more than five ways, was made clear in the second book of the present work.

Fourthly: [The ratios between the sizes of the orbits of the planets correspond to the ratio between the five regular Euclidean solids.]

[2] That is, the theory of Aristarchus of Samos, the Greek astronomer of the third century b.c., who propounded the idea that the sun and not the earth was the center of our universe. See above, p. 2.

. . . It is reasonable to believe, however, that the Creator, if he paid attention to the relation of the orbits in their general aspect, paid attention also to the relation of the varying distances of the individual orbits in detail, and that these acts of attention were the same in both cases and were connected with each other. When we duly consider this fact, we shall certainly arrive at the conclusion that for establishing the diameters and the eccentricities of the orbits there are required several principles in combination, besides the principle of the five regular bodies.

Fifthly, to come to the motions, among which are established the harmonies, I again impress upon the reader the fact that it has been shown by me in my Commentaries on Mars, from the exceedingly accurate observations of Brahe, that equal diurnal arcs on one and the same eccentric are not traversed with equal velocities, but that these different times *in equal parts of the eccentric are to each other as the distances from the Sun*, the source of the motion; and, on the other hand, that, the times being supposed equal, as, for instance, one natural day in each case, *the true diurnal arcs corresponding to them in a single eccentric orbit are inversely proportional to the two distances from the Sun*. It has likewise been shown by me that *the orbit of a planet is elliptical, and the Sun, the source of motion, is in one of the foci of this ellipse*. . . .

Eighthly, thus far we have dealt with the various times of arcs of one and the same planet. Now we must deal also with the motions of the planets taken two at a time and compare these motions with each other . . . Again, therefore, a part of my *Mysterium Cosmographicum*, suspended twenty-two years ago, because I did not then see my way clear, must be completed and introduced here. For, after I had my unceasing toil through a long period of time, using the observations of Brahe, discovered the true distances of the orbits and, if you ask for the exact time . . . conceived [my theory] on the eighth of March of this year, 1618. I unsuccessfully brought it to the test and for that reason rejected it as false; but finally returning on the fifteenth of May, by a new onset it overcame by storm the shadows of my mind, with such fullness of agreement between my seventeen years' labor on the observations of Brahe and this present study of mine that at first I believed that I was dreaming and was assuming as an accepted principle what was still a subject of enquiry. But the principle is unquestionably true and quite exact: *the periodic times of any two planets are to each other exactly as the cubes of the square roots of their median distances.* [That is, the square of the time of revolution of each planet is proportional to the cube of its mean distance from the sun.]

GALILEO GALILEI

1 5 6 4 · 1 6 4 2

HISTORY's fables are both useful and deceiving. The story that
Galileo dropped cannon balls from the leaning Tower of Pisa to
measure their velocity or their acceleration is an example; while
there is no evidence from his own writings, or from any contemporary witness, that he actually performed this experiment, it
resembles the experiments he is known to have made and well illus-
trates his rebellion against the tradition of subservience to Aristotle.
Equally apocryphal may be the legend that after recanting his
theory that the earth moved round the sun, he muttered, "Nevertheless it moves." But through all his later years he acted as if he knew
it moved.

Galileo inherited from his father, an impoverished nobleman of
Pisa, a great interest in music and mathematics. At the University
of Pisa he made a special study of mathematics and physics. In
1589 he was appointed lecturer there in these subjects, but his out-
spoken opposition to Aristotelian doctrine made him unpopular
with his colleagues, and in 1592 he went on to a post in the more
liberal University of Padua, where he taught for eighteen years. Not
only did Galileo advocate substituting firsthand observation and
experiment for the authority of the ancients as the basis of future
science, but with the aid of his new telescope he upheld Copernicus'
sun-centered astronomy. As a result, he was tried by the Inquisition,
compelled to recant verbally his belief in the Copernican theory,
and forced to live in retirement the rest of his life.

Galileo's work shook the scientific world in two ways. First, his
discovery through the telescope of the moons of Jupiter increased

from the mystical and "perfect" seven the number of ethereal bodies moving inside the celestial sphere, and proved also that there were bodies revolving around something besides the earth. Second, his later discovery that force was not necessary merely to keep a body in motion, that, in fact, force applied to a body would cause it to move with a new velocity, revolutionized all previous ideas of movement in nature.

The first of the selections below is taken from "The Sidereal Messenger," 1610, translated from the Latin by E. S. Carlos, in 1880. The title page told in Galileo's own words what the book was about: "The Sidereal Messenger, unfolding great and marvelous sights, and proposing them to the attention of everyone, but especially philosophers and astronomers, being such as have been observed by Galileo Galilei, a gentleman of Florence, Professor of Mathematics in the University of Padua, with the aid of a telescope lately invented by him. Respecting the Moon's Surface, an innumerable number of Fixed Stars, the Milky Way, and Nebulous Stars, but especially respecting Four Planets which revolve around the Planet Jupiter at different distances and in different periodic times, with amazing velocity, and which after remaining unknown to this day, the Author recently discovered, and determined to name the Medicean Stars. Venice, 1610."

The second selection is from the Dialogues Concerning Two New Sciences,[1] Leyden, 1638, translated by H. Crew and A. de Salvio (Macmillan, 1914; Northwestern University, 1939). It contains Galileo's solution of the problem of moving bodies, his anticipation of Newton's first two laws, and his recognition of gravity as the force that causes acceleration in bodies rolling downhill. His mechanistic conception of the nature of the world is apparent throughout. "Increases take place," he says, "in a manner which is exceedingly simple and rather obvious to everybody." In discussing the nature of his laws, however, he is still somewhat inclined to mix argument with the reports of his own experimentation; whereas later scientists tend

[1] For another selection from the same Dialogue, see below, p. 219.

to describe their experiments first, and to give their theoretical arguments later.

Three speakers carry on the dialogue. The two, who between them present the scientific case for Galileo's position, bear the names of Galileo's warm friends, Filippo Salviati of Florence and Giovanni Sagredo of Venice. Salviati is a professed advocate of the Copernican doctrine. Sagredo is an open-minded student, ready to be convinced. He supplies the lively illustrations and makes the important objections. The third speaker, Simplicio, has the name of a sixth-century commentator on Aristotle. He repeats the time-worn arguments of the followers of Aristotle, and when these fail to persuade, reverts to pure sophistry.

THE DISCOVERY OF
JUPITER'S SATELLITES

IN THE PRESENT small treatise I set forth some matters of great interest for all observers of natural phenomena to look at and consider. They are of great interest, I think, first, from their intrinsic excellence; secondly, from their absolute novelty; and lastly, also on account of the instrument by the aid of which they have been presented to my apprehension.

The number of the fixed stars which observers have been able to see without artificial powers of sight up to this day can be counted. It is therefore decidedly a great feat to add to their number, and to set distinctly before the eyes other stars in myriads, which have never been seen before, and which surpass the old, previously known stars in number more than ten times.

Again, it is a most beautiful and delightful sight to behold the body of the moon, which is distant from us nearly sixty semidiameters of the earth, as near as if it was at a distance of only two of the same measures; so that the diameter of this same moon appears about thirty times larger, its surface about nine hundred times, and its solid mass nearly twenty-seven thousand times larger than when it is viewed only with the naked eye: and consequently anyone may know with the certainty that is due to the use of our senses that the moon certainly does not possess a smooth and polished surface, but one rough and uneven, and, just like the face of the earth itself, is everywhere full of vast protuberances, deep chasms, and sinuosities.

Then to have got rid of disputes about the Galaxy, or Milky Way, and to have made its nature clear to the very senses, not to say to the understanding, seems by no means a matter which ought to be considered of slight importance. In addition to this, to point out, as with one's finger, the nature of those stars which every one of the astronomers up to this time has called *nebulous*, and to demonstrate that it is very different from what has hitherto been believed, will be pleasant, and very fine. But that which will excite the greatest astonishment by far, and which indeed especially moved me to call the attention of all astronomers and philosophers, is this, namely, that I have discovered four planets, neither known nor observed by any one of the astronomers before my time, which have their orbits round a certain bright star, one of those previously known, like Venus and Mercury round the sun, and are sometimes in front of it, sometimes behind it, though they never depart from it beyond certain limits. All which facts were discovered and observed a few days ago by the help of a telescope devised by me, through God's grace first enlightening my mind.

Perchance other discoveries still more excellent will be made from time to time by me or other observers, with the assistance of a similar instrument, so I will first briefly record its shape and preparation, as well as the occasion of its being devised, and then I will give an account of the observations made by me.

About ten months ago a report reached my ears that a Dutchman [1] had constructed a telescope, by the aid of which visible objects, although at a great distance from the eye of the observer, were seen distinctly as if near; and some proofs of its most wonderful performances were reported, which some gave credence to, but others contradicted. A few days after, I received confirmation of the report in a letter written from Paris by a noble Frenchman, Jacques Badovere, which finally determined me to give myself up first to inquire into the principle of the telescope, and then to consider the means by which I might compass the invention of a similar instrument, which after a little while I succeeded in doing, through deep

[1] Hans Lippershey.

study of the theory of refraction; and I prepared a tube, at first of lead, in the ends of which I fitted two glass lenses, both plane on one side, but on the other side one spherically convex and the other concave. Then, bringing my eye to the concave lens, I saw objects satisfactorily large and near, for they appeared one third of the distance off and nine times larger than when they are seen with the natural eye alone. I shortly afterward constructed another telescope with more nicety, which magnified objects more than sixty times. At length, by sparing neither labor nor expense, I succeeded in constructing for myself an instrument so superior that objects seen through it appear magnified nearly a thousand times, and more than thirty times nearer than if viewed by the natural powers of sight alone.

It would be altogether a waste of time to enumerate the number and importance of the benefits which this instrument may be expected to confer, when used by land or sea. But without paying attention to its use for terrestrial objects, I betook myself to observations of the heavenly bodies; and first of all I viewed the moon as near as if it was scarcely two semidiameters of the earth distant. After the moon, I frequently observed other heavenly bodies, both fixed stars and planets, with incredible delight; and, when I saw their very great number, I began to consider about a method by which I might be able to measure their distances apart, and at length I found one. And here it is fitting that all who intend to turn their attention to observations of this kind should receive certain cautions. For, in the first place, it is absolutely necessary for them to prepare a most perfect telescope, one which will show very bright objects distinct and free from any mistiness, and will magnify them at least four hundred times, for then it will show them as if only one twentieth of their distance off. For unless the instrument be of such power, it will be in vain to attempt to view all the things which have been seen by me in the heavens, or which will be enumerated hereafter.

But in order that anyone may be a little more certain about the magnifying power of his instrument he shall fashion two circles, or two square pieces of paper, one of which is four hundred times greater than the other, but that will be when the diameter of the greater is twenty times the length of the diameter of the other. Then he shall view from a distance simultaneously both surfaces, fixed on the same wall, the smaller with one eye applied to the telescope, and the larger with the other eye unassisted: for that may be done without inconvenience at one and the same instant with both eyes open. Then both figures will appear of the same size, if the instrument magnifies objects in the desired proportion. . . .

Now let me review the observations made by me during the two months just past, again inviting the attention of all who are eager for true philosophy to the beginnings which led to the sight of most important phenomena.

Let me first speak of the surface of the moon, which is turned toward us. For the sake of being understood more easily I distinguish two parts in it, which I call respectively the brighter and the darker. The brighter part seems to surround and pervade the whole hemisphere; but the darker part, like a sort of cloud, discolors the moon's surface and makes it appear covered with spots. Now these spots, as they are somewhat dark and of considerable size, are plain to everyone, and every age has seen them, wherefore I shall call them *great* or *ancient* spots, to distinguish them from other spots, smaller in size, but so thickly scattered that they sprinkle the whole surface of the moon, but especially the brighter portion of it. These spots have never been observed by anyone before me; and from my observations of them, often repeated, I have been led to that opinion which I have expressed, namely, that I feel sure that the surface of the moon is not perfectly smooth, free from inequalities, and exactly spherical, as a large school of philosophers considers with regard to the moon and the other heavenly bodies, but that, on the contrary, it is full of inequalities, uneven, full of hollows and protuberances, just like the surface of the earth itself, which is varied everywhere by lofty mountains and deep valleys.

The appearances from which we may gather these conclusions are of the following nature. On the fourth or fifth day after new moon, when the moon presents itself to us with bright horns, the boundary which divides the part in shadow from the enlightened part does not extend continuously in an ellipse, as would happen in the case of a perfectly spherical body, but it is marked out by an irregular, uneven, and very wavy line . . . for several bright excrescences, as they may be called, extend beyond the boundary of light and shadow into the dark part, and on the other hand pieces of shadow encroach upon the light—nay, even a great quantity of small blackish spots, altogether separated from the dark part, sprinkle everywhere almost the whole space which is at the time flooded with the sun's light, with the exception of that part alone which is occupied by the great and ancient spots. I have noticed that the small spots just mentioned have this common characteristic always and in every case, that they have the dark part toward the sun's position, and on the side away from the sun they have brighter boundaries, as if they were crowned with shining summits.

Now we have an appearance quite similar on the earth about sunrise, when we behold the valleys, not yet flooded with light, but the mountains surrounding them on the side opposite to the sun already ablaze with the splendor of his beams; and just as the shadows in the hollows of the earth diminish in size as the sun rises higher, so also these spots on the moon lose their blackness as the illuminated part grows larger and larger. Again, not only are the boundaries of light and shadow in the moon seen to be uneven and sinuous, but—and this produces still greater astonishment—there appear very many bright points within the darkened portion of the moon, altogether divided and broken off from the illuminated tract, and separated from it by no inconsiderable interval, which, after a little while, gradually increase in size and brightness, and after an hour or two become joined onto the rest of the main portion, now become somewhat larger; but in the meantime others, one here and another there, shooting up as if growing, are lighted up within the shaded portion, increase in size, and at last are linked onto the same luminous surface, now still more extended. . . .

Now is it not the case on the earth before sunrise that, while the level plain is still in shadow, the peaks of the most lofty mountains are illuminated by the sun's rays? After a little while does not the light spread further, while the middle and larger parts of those mountains are becoming illuminated; and at length, when the sun has risen, do not the illuminated parts of the plains and hills join together? The grandeur, however, of such prominences and depressions in the moon seems to surpass both in magnitude and extent the ruggedness of the earth's surface, as I shall hereafter show. . . .

Hitherto I have spoken of the observations which I have made concerning the moon's body; now I will briefly announce the phenomena which have been, as yet, seen by me with reference to the fixed stars. And first of all the following fact is worthy of consideration. The stars, fixed as well as erratic, when seen with a telescope, by no means appear to be increased in magnitude in the same proportion as other objects, and the moon herself, gain increase of size; but in the case of the stars such an increase appears much less, so that you may consider that a telescope, which (for the sake of illustration) is powerful enough to magnify other objects a hundred times, will scarcely render the stars magnified four or five times. But the reason of this is as follows. When stars are viewed with our natural eyesight they do not present themselves to us of their bare, real size, but beaming with a certain vividness, and fringed with sparkling rays, especially when the night is far advanced; and from this circumstance they appear much larger than they would if they were stripped of those adventitious fringes, for the angle which they subtend at the eye is determined not by the primary disk of the star but by the brightness which so widely surrounds it. . . . A telescope . . . removes from the stars their adventitious and accidental splendors before it enlarges their true disks (if indeed they are of that shape), and so they seem less magnified than other objects, for a star of the fifth or sixth magnitude seen through a telescope is shown as of the first magnitude only.

The difference between the appearance of the planets and the fixed stars seems also deserving of notice. The planets present their disks perfectly round, just as if described with a pair of compasses, and appear as so many little moons, completely illuminated and of a globular shape; but the fixed stars do not look to the naked eye bounded by a circular circumference, but rather like blazes of light, shooting out beams on all sides and very sparkling, and with a telescope they appear of the same shape as when they are viewed by simply looking at them, but so much larger that a star of the fifth or sixth magnitude seems to equal Sirius, the largest of all the fixed stars.

But beyond the stars of the sixth magnitude you will behold through the telescope a host of other stars, which escape the unassisted sight, so numerous as to be almost beyond belief, for you may see more than six other differences of magnitude, and the largest of these, which I may call stars of the seventh magnitude, or of the first magnitude of invisible stars, appear with the aid of the telescope larger and brighter than stars of the second magnitude seen with the unassisted sight. But in order that you may see one or two proofs of the inconceivable manner in which they are crowded together, I have determined to make out a case against two star clusters, that from them as a specimen you may decide about the rest.

As my first example I had determined to depict the entire constellation of Orion, but I was overwhelmed by the vast quantity of stars and by want of time, and so I have deferred attempting this to another occasion, for there are adjacent to or scattered among the old stars more than five hundred new stars within the limits of one or two degrees. For this reason I have selected the three stars in Orion's Belt and the six in his Sword, which have been long well-known groups, and I have added eighty other stars recently discovered in their vicinity, and I have preserved as exactly as possible the intervals between them. The well-known or old stars, for the sake of distinction, I have depicted of larger size, and I have out-

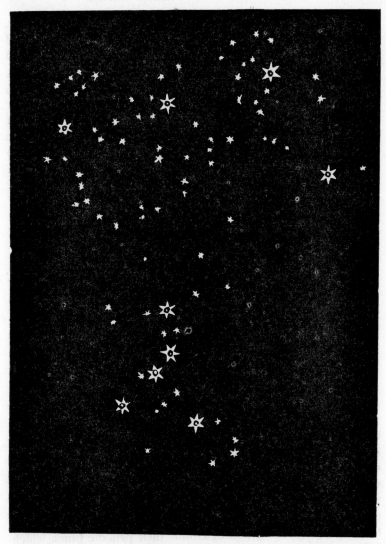

Orion's belt and sword.

lined them with a double line; the others, invisible to the naked eye, I have marked smaller and with one line only. I have also preserved the differences of magnitude as much as I could. As a second example I have depicted the six stars of the constellation Taurus, called the Pleiades (I say *six* intentionally, since the seventh is scarcely ever visible), a group of stars which is enclosed in the heavens within very narrow precincts. Near these there lie more than forty others invisible to the naked eye, no one of which is more than half a degree off any of the aforesaid six; of these I have noticed only thirty-six in my diagram. I have preserved their intervals, magnitudes, and the distinction between the old and the new stars, just as in the case of the constellation Orion.

The next object which I have observed is the essence or substance of the Milky Way. By the aid of a telescope anyone may behold this in a manner which so distinctly appeals to the senses that all the disputes which have tormented philosophers through so many ages are exploded at once by the irrefragable evidence of our eyes, and we are freed from wordy disputes upon this subject, for the Galaxy is nothing else but a mass of innumerable stars planted together in clusters. Upon whatever part of it you direct the telescope, straightway a vast crowd of stars presents itself to view; many of them are tolerably large and extremely bright, but the number of small ones is quite beyond determination. . . . I have now finished my brief account of the observations which I have thus far made with regard to the moon, the fixed stars, and the Galaxy.

There remains the matter, which seems to me to deserve to be considered the most important in this work, namely, that I should disclose and publish to the world the occasion of discovering and observing four *planets*, never seen from the very beginning of the world up to our own times, their positions, and the observations made during the last two months about their movements and their changes of magnitude; and I summon all astronomers to apply themselves to examine and determine their periodic times, which it has not been permitted me to achieve up to this day, owing to

The Pleiades.

the restriction of my time. I give them warning, however, again, so that they may not approach such an inquiry to no purpose, that they will want a very accurate telescope, and such as I have described in the beginning of this account.

On the seventh day of January in the present year, 1610, in the first hour of the following night, when I was viewing the constellations of the heavens through a telescope, the planet Jupiter presented itself to my view, and as I had prepared for myself a very excellent instrument, I noticed a circumstance which I had never been able to notice before, owing to want of power in my other telescope, namely, that three little stars, small but very bright, were near the planet; and although I believed them to belong to the number of the fixed stars, yet they made me somewhat wonder, because they seemed to be arranged exactly in a straight line, parallel to the ecliptic, and to be brighter than the rest of the stars equal to them in magnitude. The position of them with reference to one another and to Jupiter was as follows.

Ori.   *   *   O   *   Occ.

On the east side there were two stars, and a single one toward the west. The star which was furthest toward the east, and the western star, appeared rather larger than the third.

I scarcely troubled at all about the distance between them and Jupiter, for, as I have already said, at first I believed them to be fixed stars; but when on January 8, led by some fatality, I turned again to look at the same part of the heavens, I found a very different state of things, for there were three little stars all west of Jupiter, and nearer together than on the previous night, and they were separated from one another by equal intervals, as the accompanying figure shows.

Ori.   O   *   *   *   Occ.

At this point, although I had not turned my thoughts at all upon the approximation of the stars to one another, yet my surprise began to be excited, how Jupiter could one day be found to the east of all the aforesaid fixed stars when the day before it had been west of two of them; and forthwith I became afraid lest the planet might have moved differently from the calculation of astronomers, and so had passed those stars by its own proper motion. I therefore waited for the next night with the most intense longing, but I was disappointed of my hope, for the sky was covered with clouds in every direction.

But on January 10 the stars appeared in the following position with regard to Jupiter, the third, as I thought, being hidden by the planet. They were situated just as before, exactly in the same straight line with Jupiter, and along the Zodiac.

Ori.　　　　　＊　　＊　　○　　　　　Occ.

When I had seen these phenomena, as I knew that corresponding changes of position could not by any means belong to Jupiter, and as, moreover, I perceived that the stars which I saw had always been the same, for there were no others either in front or behind, within a great distance, along the Zodiac—at length, changing from doubt into surprise, I discovered that the interchange of position which I saw belonged not to Jupiter but to the stars to which my attention had been drawn, and I thought therefore that they ought to be observed henceforward with more attention and precision.

Accordingly, on January 11 I saw an arrangement of the following kind, namely, only two stars to the east of Jupiter, the nearer of

Ori.　　　　　＊　　＊　　○　　　　　Occ.

which was distant from Jupiter three times as far as from the star further to the east; and the star furthest to the east was nearly twice as large as the other one; whereas on the previous night they had appeared nearly of equal magnitude. I therefore concluded, and decided unhesitatingly, that there are three stars in the heavens moving about Jupiter, as Venus and Mercury round the sun; which at length was established as clear as daylight by numerous other subsequent observations. These observations also established that there are not only three but four erratic sidereal bodies performing their revolutions round Jupiter, observations of whose changes of position made with more exactness on succeeding nights the following account will supply. I have measured also the intervals between them with the telescope in the manner already explained. Besides this, I have given the times of observation, especially when several were made in the same night, for the revolutions of these planets are so swift that an observer may generally get differences of position every hour.

January 12. At the first hour of the next night I saw these heavenly bodies arranged in this manner.

Ori.   *   * ○   *   Occ.

The satellite farthest to the east was greater than the satellite farthest to the west; but both were very conspicuous and bright; the distance of each one from Jupiter was two minutes. A third satellite, certainly not in view before, began to appear at the third hour: it nearly touched Jupiter on the east side, and was exceedingly small. They were all arranged in the same straight line, along the ecliptic.

January 13. For the first time four satellites were in view in the following position with regard to Jupiter.

Ori.   *   ○ * *   Occ.

There were three to the west and one to the east; they made a straight line nearly, but the middle satellite of those to the west deviated a little from the straight line toward the north. The satellite farthest to the east was at a distance of 2′ from Jupiter; there were intervals of 1′ only between Jupiter and the nearest satellite, and between the satellites themselves, west of Jupiter. All the satellites appeared of the same size, and though small they were very brilliant and far outshone the fixed stars of the same magnitude. . . .

These are my observations upon the four Medicean planets, recently discovered for the first time by me; and although it is not yet permitted me to deduce by calculation from these observations the orbits of these bodies, yet I may be allowed to make some statements, based upon them, well worthy of attention.

And, in the first place, since they are sometimes behind, sometimes before Jupiter, at like distances, and withdraw from this planet toward the east and toward the west only within very narrow limits of divergence, and since they accompany this planet alike when its motion is retrograde and direct, it can be a matter of doubt to no one that they perform their revolutions about this planet, while at the same time they all accomplish together orbits of twelve years' length about the center of the world. Moreover, they revolve in unequal circles, which is evidently the conclusion to be drawn from the fact that I have never been permitted to see two satellites in conjunction when their distance from Jupiter was great, whereas near Jupiter two, three, and sometimes all four have been found closely packed together. Moreover, it may be detected that the revolutions of the satellites which describe the smallest circles round Jupiter are the most rapid, for the satellites nearest to Jupiter are often to be seen in the east, when the day before they have appeared in the west, and contrariwise. Also the satellite moving in the greatest orbit seems to me, after carefully weighing the occasions of its returning to positions previously noticed, to have a periodic time of half a month.

Besides, we have a notable and splendid argument to remove the scruples of those who can tolerate the revolution of the planets round the sun in the Copernican system, yet are so disturbed by the motion of one moon about the earth, while both accomplish an orbit of a year's length about the sun, that they consider that this theory of the universe must be upset as impossible: for now we have not one planet only revolving about another, while both traverse a vast orbit about the sun, but our sense of sight presents to us four satellites circling about Jupiter, like the moon about the earth, while the whole system travels over a mighty orbit about the sun in the space of twelve years.

THE LAWS OF FALLING BODIES

My PURPOSE is to set forth a very new science dealing with a very ancient subject. There is, in nature, perhaps nothing older than motion, concerning which the books written by philosophers are neither few nor small; nevertheless I have discovered by experiment some properties of it which are worth knowing and which have not hitherto been either observed or demonstrated. Some superficial observations have been made, as, for instance, that the free motion of a heavy falling body is continuously accelerated; but to just what extent this acceleration occurs has not yet been announced; for so far as I know, no one has yet pointed out that the distances traversed, during equal intervals of time, by a body falling from rest, stand to one another in the same ratio as the odd numbers beginning with unity.

It has been observed that missiles and projectiles describe a curved path of some sort; however no one has pointed out the fact that this path is a parabola. But this and other facts, not few in number or less worth knowing, I have succeeded in proving; and what I consider more important, there have been opened up to this vast and most excellent science, of which my work is merely the beginning, ways and means by which other minds more acute than mine will explore its remote corners.

This discussion is divided into three parts; the first part deals with motion which is steady or uniform; the second treats of motion as we find it accelerated in nature; the third deals with the so-called violent motions and with projectiles.

44

UNIFORM MOTION

In dealing with steady or uniform motion, we need a single definition which I give as follows:

Definition

By steady or uniform motion, I mean one in which the distances traversed by the moving particle, during any equal intervals of time, are themselves equal. . . .

NATURALLY ACCELERATED MOTION

The properties belonging to uniform motion have been discussed in the preceding section; but accelerated motion remains to be considered.

And first of all it seems desirable to find and explain a definition best fitting natural phenomena. For anyone may invent an arbitrary type of motion and discuss its properties; thus, for instance, some have imagined helices and conchoids as described by certain motions which are not met with in nature, and have very commendably established the properties which these curves possess in virtue of their definitions; but we have decided to consider the phenomena of bodies falling with an acceleration such as actually occurs in nature, and to make this definition of accelerated motion exhibit the essential features of observed accelerated motions. And this, at last, after repeated efforts, we trust we have succeeded in doing. In this belief we are confirmed mainly by the consideration that experimental results are seen to agree with and exactly correspond with those properties which have been, one after another, demonstrated by us. Finally, in the investigation of naturally accelerated motion we are led, by hand as it were, in following the habit and custom of nature herself in all her various other processes, to employ only those means which are most common, simple and easy. For I think no one believes that swimming or flying can be accomplished in a manner simpler or easier than that instinctively employed by fishes and birds.

When, therefore, I observe a stone initially at rest falling from an elevated position and continually acquiring new increments of speed, why should I not believe that such increases take place in a manner which is exceedingly simple and rather obvious to everybody? If now we examine the matter carefully we find no addition or increment more simple than that which repeats itself always in the same manner. This we readily understand when we consider the intimate relationship between time and motion; for just as uniformity of motion is defined by and conceived through equal times and equal spaces (thus we call a motion uniform when equal distances are traversed during equal time-intervals), so also we may, in a similar manner, through equal time-intervals, conceive additions of speed as taking place without complication; thus we may picture to our mind a motion as uniformly and continuously accelerated when, during any equal intervals of time whatever, equal increments of speed are given to it. Thus if any equal intervals of time whatever have elapsed, counting from the time at which the moving body left its position of rest and began to descend, the amount of speed acquired during the first two time-intervals will be double that acquired during the first time-interval alone; so the amount added during three of these time-intervals will be treble, and that in four, quadruple that of the first time-interval. To put the matter more clearly, if a body were to continue its motion with the same speed which it had acquired during the first time-interval and were to retain this same uniform speed, then its motion would be twice as slow as that which it would have if its velocity had been acquired during *two* time-intervals.

And thus, it seems, we shall not be far wrong if we put the increment of speed as proportional to the increment of time; hence the definition of motion which we are about to discuss may be stated as follows: *A motion is said to be uniformly accelerated, when start-*

ing from rest, it acquires, during equal time-intervals, equal incre-ments of speed.

SAGREDO. Although I can offer no rational objection to this or indeed to any other definition, devised by any author whomsoever, since all definitions are arbitrary, I may nevertheless without offense be allowed to doubt whether such a definition as the above, estab-lished in an abstract manner, corresponds to and describes that kind of accelerated motion which we meet in nature in the case of freely falling bodies. And since the Author apparently maintains that the motion described in his definition is that of freely falling bodies, I would like to clear my mind of certain difficulties in order that I may later apply myself more earnestly to the propositions and their demonstrations.

SALVIATI. It is well that you and Simplicio raise these difficulties. They are, I imagine, the same which occurred to me when I first saw this treatise, and which were removed either by discussion with the Author himself, or by turning the matter over in my own mind.

SAGREDO. When I think of a heavy body falling from rest, that is, starting with zero speed and gaining speed in proportion to the time from the beginning of the motion . . . then there is no degree of speed, however small (or, one may say, no degree of slow-ness however great), with which we may not find this body travel-ling after starting from infinite slowness, i.e., from rest. . . . As the instant of starting is more and more nearly approached, the body moves so slowly that, if it kept on moving at this rate, it would not traverse a mile in an hour, or in a day, or in a year or in a thousand years; indeed, it would not traverse a span in an even greater time; a phenomenon which baffles the imagination, while our senses show us that a heavy falling body suddenly acquires great speed.

SALVIATI. This is one of the difficulties which I also at the begin-ning, experienced, but which I shortly afterwards removed; and the removal was effected by the very experiment which creates the diffi-culty for you. You say the experiment appears to show that immedi-

ately after a heavy body starts from rest it acquires a very considerable speed: and I say that the same experiment makes clear the
fact that the initial motions of a falling body, no matter how heavy,
are very slow and gentle.

Place a heavy body upon a yielding material, and leave it there
without any pressure except that owing to its own weight; it is
clear that if one lifts this body a cubit or two and allows it to fall
upon the same material, it will, with this impulse, exert a new and
greater pressure than that caused by its mere weight; and this effect
is brought about by the [weight of the] falling body together with
the velocity acquired during the fall, an effect which will be greater
and greater according to the height of the fall, that is, according
as the velocity of the falling body becomes greater. From the quality
and intensity of the blow we are thus enabled to accurately estimate the speed of a falling body.

But tell me, gentlemen, is it not true that if a block be allowed to
fall upon a stake from a height of four cubits and drives it into
the earth, say, four finger-breadths, that, coming from a height of
two cubits, it will drive the stake a much less distance, and from the
height of one cubit a still less distance; and finally if the block be
lifted only one finger-breadth how much more will it accomplish
than if merely laid on top of the stake without percussion? Certainly very little. If it be lifted only the thickness of a leaf, the
effect will be altogether imperceptible. And since the effect of the
blow depends upon the velocity of this striking body, can anyone
doubt the motion is very slow and the speed more than small whenever the effect [of the blow] is imperceptible? See now the power
of truth; the same experiment which at first glance seemed to show
one thing, when more carefully examined, assures us of the contrary.

Pray listen, I hardly think you will refuse to grant that the gain of
speed of the stone falling from rest follows the same sequence as
the diminution and loss of this same speed when, by some impelling
force, the stone is thrown to its former elevation; but even if you
do not grant this, I do not see how you can doubt that the ascend-

ing stone, diminishing in speed, must before coming to rest pass through every possible degree of slowness.

SIMPLICIO. But if the number of degrees of greater and greater slowness is limitless, they will never be all exhausted, therefore such an ascending heavy body will never reach rest, but will continue to move without limit always at a slower rate; but this is not the observed fact.

SALVIATI. This would happen, Simplicio, if the moving body were to maintain its speed for any length of time at each degree of velocity; but it merely passes each point without delaying more than an instant: and since each time-interval however small may be divided into an infinite number of instants, these will always be sufficient [in number] to correspond to the infinite degrees of diminished velocity. . . .

SAGREDO. But now, continuing the thread of our talk, it would seem that up to the present we have established the definition of uniformly accelerated motion, which is expressed as follows:

> A motion is said to be equally or uniformly accelerated when, starting from rest, its momentum receives equal increments in equal times.

SALVIATI. This definition established, the Author makes a single assumption, namely,

> The speeds acquired by one and the same body moving down planes of different inclinations are equal when the heights of these planes are equal.

By the height of an inclined plane we mean the perpendicular let fall from the upper end of the plane upon the horizontal line drawn through the lower end of the same plane. Thus, to illustrate, let the line AB be horizontal, and let the planes CA and CD be inclined to it; then the Author calls the perpendicular CB the "height" of the planes CA and CD; he supposes that the speeds acquired by one and the same body, descending along the planes

CA and CD to the terminal points A and D are equal since the heights of these planes are the same, CB; and also it must be understood that this speed is that which would be acquired by the same body falling from C to B.

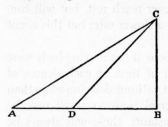

SAGREDO. Your assumption appears to me so reasonable that it ought to be conceded without question, provided of course there are no chance or outside resistances, and that the planes are hard and smooth, and that the figure of the moving body is perfectly round, so that neither plane nor moving body is rough. All resistance and opposition having been removed, my reason tells me at once that a heavy and perfectly round ball descending along the lines CA, CD, CB would reach the terminal points A, D, B, with equal momenta. . . .

Theorem II, Proposition II

The spaces described by a body falling from rest with a uniformly accelerated motion are to each other as the squares of the time-intervals employed in traversing these distances. . . .

SIMPLICIO . . . I am convinced that matters are as described, once having accepted the definition of uniformly accelerated motion. But as to whether this acceleration is that which one meets in nature in the case of falling bodies, I am still doubtful; and it seems to me, not only for my own sake but also for all those who think as I do, that this would be the proper moment to introduce one of those experiments—and there are many of them, I understand—which illustrate in several ways the conclusions reached.

SALVIATI. The request which you, as a man of science, make, is a very reasonable one; for this is the custom—and properly so—in those sciences where mathematical demonstrations are applied to natural phenomena, as is seen in the case of perspective, astronomy, mechanics, music, and others where the principles, once established by well-chosen experiments, become the foundations of the entire superstructure. I hope therefore it will not appear to be a waste of time if we discuss at considerable length this first and most funda- mental question upon which hinge numerous consequences of which we have in this book only a small number, placed there by the Author, who has done so much to open a pathway hitherto closed to minds of speculative turn. So far as experiments go they have not been neglected by the Author; and often, in his company, I have attempted in the following manner to assure myself that the accel- eration actually experienced by falling bodies is that above described.

A piece of wooden moulding or scantling, about 12 cubits long, half a cubit wide, and three finger-breadths thick, was taken; on its edge was cut a channel a little more than one finger in breadth; having made this groove very straight, smooth, and polished, and having lined it with parchment, also as smooth and polished as possible, we rolled along it a hard, smooth, and very round bronze ball. Having placed this board in a sloping position, by lifting one end some one or two cubits above the other, we rolled the ball, as I was just saying, along the channel, noting, in a manner presently to be described, the time required to make the descent. We re- peated this experiment more than once in order to measure the time with an accuracy such that the deviation between two observa- tions never exceeded one-tenth of a pulse-beat. Having performed this operation and having assured ourselves of its reliability, we now rolled the ball only one-quarter the length of the channel; and having measured the time of its descent, we found it precisely one- half of the former. Next we tried other distances, comparing the time for the whole length with that for the half, or with that for two-thirds, or three-fourths, or indeed for any fraction; in such ex- periments, repeated a full hundred times, we always found that the spaces traversed were to each other as the squares of the times, and this was true for all inclinations of the plane, i.e., of the channel along which we rolled the ball. We also observed that the times of descent for various inclinations of the plane bore to one another precisely that ratio which, as we shall see later, the Author had predicted and demonstrated for them.

For the measurement of time, we employed a large vessel of water placed in an elevated position; to the bottom of this vessel was soldered a pipe of small diameter giving a thin jet of water, which we collected in a small glass during the time of each descent, whether for the whole length of the channel or for a part of its length; the water thus collected was weighed, after each descent, on a very accurate balance; the differences and ratios of these weights gave us the differences and ratios of the times, and this with such accuracy that although the operation was repeated many, many times, there was no appreciable discrepancy in the results.

SIMPLICIO. I would like to have been present at these experiments; but feeling confidence in the care with which you performed them, and in the fidelity with which you relate them, I am satisfied and accept them as true and valid. . . .

JEREMIAH HORROX

1 6 1 7 ? - 1 6 4 1

AMONG THE few remaining papers of a brilliant young English curate, is the first telescopic observation of the transit of Venus across the face of the sun, in 1639. Jeremiah Horrox (he spelled his name with an x; some later editors have tried to change it to Horrocks) was born about 1617, in a poor district near Liverpool. He went to Cambridge University, which had then no department of mathematics or astronomy; so these subjects he studied by himself. In 1636, at the age of seventeen or nineteen, he found that his prediction of the position of Venus, computed from existing astronomical tables, did not agree with his own observations, a discovery which made him critical of previous work. In 1639 his own computations showed him what no one else had noticed, that a transit of Venus was about to occur. The account here printed is part of an essay he sent to a friend before his death, thirteen months later, at the age of not over twenty-three.

Horrox's personal library included books by Copernicus, Gassendi, Gemma Frisius, Herodotus, Kepler (four volumes), Mercator, Pliny, Ptolemy of Alexandria, and Tycho Brahe, all in Latin. He wrote much in defense and proof of the Keplerian astronomy. The importance of his work on tides and gravity was acknowledged by Newton. He was the first to show that the nearly circular motion of the moon is actually elliptical.

The essay, The Transit of Venus Across the Sun, was printed in Danzig, 1662, by the great astronomer Hevelius, to whom it had been sent by Huygens; it was translated from the Latin in 1859 by the Rev. A. B. Whatton.

THE TRANSIT OF VENUS

ACROSS THE SUN

ON THE 24TH OF NOVEMBER, 1639

Soon after the commencement of my astronomical studies, and whilst preparing for practical observation, I computed the Ephemerides [1] of several years, from the continuous tables of Lansberg.[2] Having followed up the task with unceasing perseverance, and having arrived at the point of its completion, the very erroneous calculation of these tables, then detected, convinced me that an astronomer might be engaged upon a better work. Accordingly I broke off the useless computation, and resolved for the future with my own eyes to observe the positions of the stars in the heavens; but lest so many hours spent on Lansberg should be entirely thrown away, I made use of my Ephemerides in ascertaining the positions of the distant planets, so that I was enabled to predict their conjunctions, their appulses to the fixed stars, and many other extraordinary phenomena. Delighted for the time with such a foretaste of the science, I took great pains carefully to prepare myself for further observation.

Whilst thus engaged, I received my first intimation of this remarkable conjunction of Venus with the Sun; and I regard it as a very fortunate occurrence, inasmuch as about the beginning of October, 1639, it induced me, in expectation of so grand a spectacle, to

[1] Astronomical almanacs, giving the position of celestial bodies, particularly the planets, at various times.
[2] Philip Lansberg (1561-1632), a Dutch astronomer and pastor of a church at Ter-Goes.

observe with increased attention. I pardon, in the meantime, the miserable arrogance of the Belgian astronomer, who has overloaded his useless tables with such unmerited praise, and cease to lament the misapplication of my own time, deeming it a sufficient reward that I was thereby led to consider and to foresee the appearance of Venus in the Sun.

But on the other hand, may Lansberg forgive me that I hesitated to trust him in an observation of such importance; and, from having been so often deceived by his pretension to universal accuracy, that I disregarded the general reception of his tables. Besides, I thought it my duty to consult other calculations, especially those of Rudolph,[3] which Hortensius [4] has vainly labored to depreciate. Daily experience indeed convinces me that what Lansberg says (whether with less modesty or truth I know not) of his own tables may be affirmed with propriety of Kepler's, namely, that they are superior to all others,

"Quantum lenta solent inter viburna cupressi."

[As cypresses are among the pliant viburnums.]

The more accurate calculations of Rudolph very much confirmed my expectations; and I rejoiced exceedingly in the hope of seeing Venus, the rarity of whose appearance in conjunction with the Sun had induced me to pay less attention to the more common phenomena of the same kind visible in the planet Mercury; for though hitherto these phenomena have been observed on one occasion only, the science of astronomy holds out to us the assurance that they will, even in our time, frequently appear.

But lest a vain exultation should deceive me, and to prevent the chance of disappointment, I not only determined diligently to watch the important spectacle myself, but exhorted others whom I knew

3 Kepler's tables, published in 1627, and named for his imperial patron, the Emperor Rudolph.
4 A contemporary Dutch astronomer.

to be fond of astronomy to follow my example; in order that the testimony of several persons, if it should so happen, might the more effectually promote the attainment of truth; and because by observing in different places, our purpose would be less likely to be defeated by the accidental interposition of the clouds or any fortuitous impediment.

The chance of a clouded atmosphere caused me much anxiety; for Jupiter and Mercury were in conjunction with the Sun almost at the same time as Venus. This remarkable assemblage of the planets (as if they were desirous of beholding, in common with ourselves, the wonders of the heavens, and of adding to the splendour of the scene), seemed to forebode great severity of weather. Mercury, whose conjunction with the Sun is invariably attended with storm and tempest, was especially to be feared. In this apprehension I coincide with the opinion of the astrologers, because it is confirmed by experience; but in other respects I cannot help despising their more than puerile vanities. . . .

Having attentively examined Venus with my instrument, I described on a sheet of paper a circle whose diameter was nearly equal to six inches, the narrowness of the apartment not permitting me conveniently to use a larger size. This however admitted of a sufficiently accurate division; nor could the arc of a quadrant be apportioned more exactly, even with a radius of fifty feet, which is as great a one as any astronomer has divided; and it is in my opinion far more convenient than a larger, for although it represents the sun's image less, yet it depicts it more clearly and steadily. I divided the circumference of this circle into 360 degrees in the usual manner, and its diameter into thirty equal parts, which gives about as many minutes as are equivalent to the sun's apparent diameter: each of these thirty parts was again divided into four equal portions, making in all one hundred and twenty; and these, if necessary, may be more minutely subdivided; the rest I left to ocular computation, which, in such small sections, is quite as certain as any mechanical division. Suppose then each of these thirty parts to be divided into 60 seconds, according to the practice of astronomers.

When the time of the observation approached, I retired to my apartment, and having closed the windows against the light, I di-

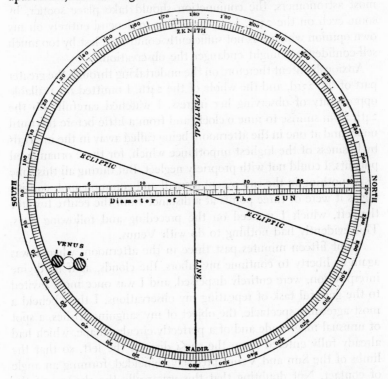

Venus on the sun's disk.

rected my telescope, previously adjusted to a focus, through the aperture towards the sun and received his rays at right angles upon the paper already mentioned. The sun's image exactly filled the circle, and I watched carefully and unceasingly for any dark body that might enter upon the disc of light.

Although the corrected computation of Venus' motions which I had before prepared, and on the accuracy of which I implicitly relied, forbad me to expect anything before three o'clock in the afternoon of the 24th; yet since, according to the calculations of most astronomers, the conjunction should take place sooner, by some even on the 23rd, I was unwilling to depend entirely on my own opinion which was not sufficiently confirmed, lest by too much self-confidence I might endanger the observation.

Anxiously intent therefore on the undertaking through the greater part of the 23rd, and the whole of the 24th, I omitted no available opportunity of observing her ingress. I watched carefully on the 24th from sunrise to nine o'clock, and from a little before ten until noon, and at one in the afternoon, being called away in the intervals by business of the highest importance which, for these ornamental pursuits, I could not with propriety neglect. But during all this time I saw nothing in the sun except a small and common spot, consisting as it were of three points at a distance from the centre towards the left, which I noticed on the preceding and following days. This evidently had nothing to do with Venus.

About fifteen minutes past three in the afternoon, when I was again at liberty to continue my labors, the clouds, as if by divine interposition, were entirely dispersed, and I was once more invited to the grateful task of repeating my observations. I then beheld a most agreeable spectacle, the object of my sanguine wishes, a spot of unusual magnitude and of a perfectly circular shape, which had already fully entered upon the sun's disc on the left, so that the limbs of the Sun and Venus precisely coincided, forming an angle of contact. Not doubting that this was really the shadow of the planet, I immediately applied myself sedulously to observe it.

In the first place, with respect to the inclination, the line of the diameter of the circle being perpendicular to the horizon, although its plane was somewhat inclined on account of the sun's altitude, I found that the shadow of Venus at the aforesaid hour, namely fifteen minutes past three, had entered the sun's disc about 62 degrees 30 minutes, certainly between 60 degrees and 65 degrees, from the top towards the right. This was the appearance in the dark apartment; therefore out of doors beneath the open sky, according to the law of optics, the contrary would be the case, and Venus would be below the centre of the sun, distant 62 degrees 30 minutes from the lower limb, or the nadir, as the Arabians term it. The inclination remained to all appearance the same until sunset, when the observation was concluded.

In the second place, the distance between the centres of Venus and the Sun I found, by three observations, to be as follows:—

The Hour.	Distance of the Centres.	
At 3.15 by the clock	14′	24″
— 3.35 —	13′	30″
— 3.45 —	13′	0″
— 3.50 the apparent sunset.		

The true setting being 3.45, and the apparent about 5 minutes later, the difference being caused by refraction. The clock therefore was sufficiently correct.

In the third place, I found after careful and repeated observation, that the diameter of Venus, as her shadow was depicted on the paper, was larger indeed than the thirtieth part of the solar diameter, though not more so than the sixth, or at the utmost the fifth, of such a part. . . .

This observation was made in an obscure village where I have long been in the habit of observing, about fifteen miles to the north of Liverpool, the latitude of which I believe to be 53 degrees 20 minutes, although by the common maps it is stated at 54 degrees 12 minutes, therefore the latitude of the village will be 53 degrees 35 minutes, and the longitude of both 22 degrees 30 minutes from the Fortunate Islands, now called the Canaries. This is 14 degrees 15 minutes to the west of Uraniburg in Denmark, the longitude of which is stated by Brahe, a native of the place, to be 36 degrees 45 minutes from these Islands.

This is all I could observe respecting this celebrated conjunction, during the short time the Sun remained in the horizon; for although Venus continued on his disc for several hours, she was not visible to me longer than half-an-hour, on account of his so quickly setting. Nevertheless, all the observations which could possibly be made in so short a time, I was enabled, by Divine Providence, to complete so effectually that I could scarcely have wished for a more extended period. The inclination was the only point upon which I failed to attain the utmost precision; for, owing to the rapid motion of the Sun, it was difficult to observe with certainty to a single degree, and I frankly confess that I neither did nor could ascertain it. But all the rest is sufficiently accurate, and as exact as I could desire.

ISAAC NEWTON [1]

1 6 4 2 · 1 7 2 7

From his youth, Newton was an experimenter and investigator. He made mechanical toys that worked and a clock that ran; his early notebooks are full of investigations into alchemy, and he showed more than a passing interest in astrology. After studying with Barrow at Cambridge, he returned home during the plague years (1664-1666) and at the age of twenty-one to twenty-three laid down the basis of his later work in science and mechanics.

It occurred to him that the gravity of the earth, which Galileo had demonstrated in his experiments on falling bodies, might extend far beyond the top of an apple tree, even to the moon and the sun; but that the attractive force would be less for far objects. The attraction between two bodies, according to Galileo's findings, would be reduced to one-fourth, if the distance doubled, and to one-ninth, if the distance tripled.

This was the clue to the law of universal gravitation. By calculation Newton found that the gravitational attraction was exactly the force needed at the moon's distance to supply the necessary centripetal force to keep it in its orbit about the earth. Gravity was the string, the "centripetal force," which bound the moon to the earth and kept it from flying off into space.

The development of this first intuition into a soundly based, self-consistent system, was the labor of twenty years. First, Newton had to clarify the current ideas (Galileo's) on motion, acceleration, and momentum, for which he developed some of the methods of the differential calculus. Then, the need of calculating the distance a

[1] For other work of Newton, see pp. 148 and 604.

61

body travels in a given time, when its velocity is continually changing, led him to invent the integral calculus, by which he also proved that any body acts as if its gravitational force was concentrated at the center.

Edmund Halley (1656-1742), the astronomer for whom a famous comet is named, induced Newton to write down his discoveries and paid for publication of the 250,000 word Philosophiae Naturalis Principia Mathematica (Mathematical Principles of Natural Philosophy). The following excerpts are from the translation made in 1729 by Andrew Motte, revised by Florian Cajori (University of California Press, 1934). The whole work will repay study. The selections given here start with the introduction to the Principia, followed by a necessary group of definitions of mass, momentum, inertia, force, acceleration, etc., and an informal discussion of absolute and relative time, space and motion, which are at the basis of Newton's system of mechanics. Immediately following is his discussion of his three famous laws of motion, then his statement of the law of universal gravitation, with its application to tides on the earth, ending up with his concluding speculations as to the way in which this force can be exerted.

MATHEMATICAL PRINCIPLES
OF NATURAL PHILOSOPHY

ॐ

Preface to the First Edition

SINCE the Ancients (as we are told by *Pappus*) esteemed the science
of mechanics of greatest importance in the investigation of natural
things, and the moderns, rejecting substantial forms and occult
qualities, have endeavored to subject the phenomena of nature to
the laws of mathematics, I have in this treatise cultivated mathematics as far as it relates to philosophy. The ancients considered
mechanics in a twofold respect; as rational, which proceeds accurately by demonstration, and practical. To practical mechanics all
the manual arts belong, from which mechanics took its name. But
as artificers do not work with perfect accuracy, it comes to pass that
mechanics is so distinguished from geometry that what is perfectly
accurate is called geometrical; what is less so, is called mechanical.
However, the errors are not in the art, but in the artificers. He that
works with less accuracy is an imperfect mechanic; and if any could
work with perfect accuracy, he would be the most perfect mechanic
of all, for the description of right lines and circles, upon which
geometry is founded, belongs to mechanics.

Geometry does not teach us to draw these lines, but requires
them to be drawn, for it requires that the learner should first be
taught to describe these accurately before he enters upon geometry,
then it shows how by these operations problems may be solved.
To describe right lines and circles are problems, but not geometrical
problems. The solution of these problems is required from mechanics, and by geometry the use of them, when so solved, is shown;

63

and it is the glory of geometry that from those few principles, brought from without, it is able to produce so many things. Therefore geometry is founded on mechanical practice, and is nothing but that part of universal mechanics which accurately proposes and demonstrates the art of measuring. But since the manual arts are chiefly employed in the moving of bodies, it happens that geometry is commonly referred to their magnitude, and mechanics to their motion. In this sense rational mechanics will be the science of motions resulting from any forces whatsoever, and of the forces required to produce any motions, accurately proposed and demonstrated.

This part of mechanics, as far as it extended to the five powers which relate to manual arts, was cultivated by the ancients, who considered gravity (it not being a manual power) no otherwise than in moving weights by those powers. But I consider philosophy rather than arts and write not concerning manual but natural powers, and consider chiefly those things which relate to gravity, levity, elastic force, the resistance of fluids, and the like forces, whether attractive or repulsive; and therefore I offer this work as the mathematical principles of philosophy, for the whole burden of philosophy seems to consist in this—from the phenomena of motions to investigate the forces of nature, and then from these forces to demonstrate the other phenomena; and to this end the general propositions in the first and second Books are directed. In the third Book, I give an example of this in the explication of the System of the World; for by the propositions mathematically demonstrated in the former Books, in the third I derive from the celestial phenomena the forces of gravity with which bodies tend to the sun and the several planets. Then from these forces, by other propositions which are also mathematical, I deduce the motions of the planets, the comets, the moon, and the sea.

I wish we could derive the rest of the phenomena of Nature by the same kind of reasoning from mechanical principles, for I am induced by many reasons to suspect that they may all depend upon certain forces by which the particles of bodies, by some causes hitherto unknown, are either mutually impelled towards one another, and cohere in regular figures or are repelled and recede from one another. These forces being unknown, philosophers have hitherto attempted the search of Nature in vain; but I hope the principles here laid down will afford some light either to this or some truer method of philosophy.

In the publication of this work the most acute and universally learned Mr. *Edmund Halley*[1] not only assisted me in correcting the errors of the press and preparing the geometrical figures, but it was through his solicitations that it came to be published; for when he had obtained of me my demonstrations of the figure of the celestial orbits, he continually pressed me to communicate the same to the *Royal Society*, who afterwards, by their kind encourage- ment and entreaties, engaged me to think of publishing them. But after I had begun to consider the inequalities of the lunar motions, and had entered upon some other things relating to the laws and measures of gravity and other forces; and the figures that would be described by bodies attracted according to given laws; and the motion of several bodies moving among themselves; the motion of bodies in resisting mediums; the forces, densities, and motions, of mediums; the orbits of the comets, and such like, I deferred that publication till I had made a search into those matters, and could put forth the whole together.

What relates to the lunar motions (being imperfect), I have put all together in the corollaries of Prop. LXVI, to avoid being obliged to propose and distinctly demonstrate the several things there con- tained in a method more prolix than the subject deserved and inter- rupt the series of the other propositions. Some things, found out

[1] Edmund Halley (1656-1742), Astronomer Royal and Secretary of the Royal Society of London, predicted the time of the next appearance of the comet which bears his name.

after the rest, I chose to insert in places less suitable, rather than change the number of the propositions and the citations. I heartily beg that what I have here done may be read with forbearance; and that my labors in a subject so difficult may be examined, not so much with the view to censure, as to remedy their defects.

Is. Newton.

Cambridge, Trinity College, May 8, 1686.

DEFINITIONS

DEFINITION I

The quantity of matter is the measure of the same, arising from its density and bulk conjointly.

Thus air of a double density, in a double space, is quadruple in quantity; in a triple space, sextuple in quantity. The same thing is to be understood of snow, and fine dust or powders that are condensed by compression or liquefaction, and of all bodies that are by any causes whatever differently condensed. I have no regard in this place to a medium, if any such there is, that freely pervades the interstices between the parts of bodies. It is this quantity that I mean hereafter everywhere under the name of body or mass. And the same is known by the weight of each body, for it is proportional to the weight, as I have found by experiments on pendulums, very accurately made, which shall be shown hereafter.

DEFINITION II

The quantity of motion is the measure of the same, arising from the velocity and quantity of matter conjointly.

The motion of the whole is the sum of the motions of all the parts; and therefore in a body double in quantity, with equal velocity. the motion is double; with twice the velocity, it is quadruple.

DEFINITION III

The vis insita, *or innate force of matter, is a power of resisting, by which every body, as much as in it lies, continues in its present state, whether it be of rest, or of moving uniformly forwards in a right line.*

This force is always proportional to the body whose force it is and differs nothing from the inactivity of the mass but in our manner of conceiving it. A body, from the inert nature of matter, is not without difficulty put out of its state of rest or motion. Upon which account, this *vis insita* may, by a most significant name, be called inertia (*vis inertiae*) or force of inactivity. But a body only exerts this force when another force, impressed upon it, endeavors to change its condition; and the exercise of this force may be considered as both resistance and impulse; it is resistance so far as the body, for maintaining its present state, opposes the force impressed; it is impulse so far as the body, by not easily giving way to the impressed force of another, endeavors to change the state of that other. Resistance is usually ascribed to bodies at rest, and impulse to those in motion; but motion and rest, as commonly conceived, are only relatively distinguished; nor are those bodies always truly at rest, which commonly are taken to be so.

DEFINITION IV

An impressed force is an action exerted upon a body, in order to change its state, either of rest, or of uniform motion in a right line.

This force consists in the action only, and remains no longer in the body when the action is over. For a body maintains every new state it acquires, by its inertia only. But impressed forces are of different origins, as from percussion, from pressure, from centripetal force.

DEFINITION V

A centripetal force is that by which bodies are drawn or impelled, or any way tend, towards a point as to a centre.

Of this sort is gravity, by which bodies tend to the centre of the earth; magnetism, by which iron tends to the loadstone; and that force, whatever it is, by which the planets are continually drawn aside from the rectilinear motions, which otherwise they would pursue, and made to revolve in curvilinear orbits. A stone, whirled about in a sling, endeavors to recede from the hand that turns it; and by that endeavor distends the sling, and that with so much the greater force as it is revolved with the greater velocity, and as soon as it is let go, flies away. That force which opposes itself to this endeavor, and by which the sling continually draws back the stone towards the hand, and retains it in its orbit, because it is directed to the hand as the centre of the orbit, I call the centripetal force.

And the same thing is to be understood of all bodies, revolved in any orbits. They all endeavor to recede from the centres of their orbits; and were it not for the opposition of a contrary force which restrains them to, and detains them in their orbits, which I therefore call centripetal, would fly off in right lines, with an uniform motion. A projectile, if it was not for the force of gravity, would not deviate towards the earth, but would go off from it in a right line, and that with an uniform motion, if the resistance of the air was taken away. It is by its gravity that it is drawn aside continually from its rectilinear course, and made to deviate towards the earth, more or less, according to the force of its gravity, and the velocity of its motion. The less its gravity is, or the quantity of its matter, or the greater the velocity with which it is projected, the less will it deviate from a rectilinear course, and the farther it will go.

If a leaden ball, projected from the top of a mountain by the force of gunpowder, with a given velocity, and in a direction parallel to

the horizon, is carried in a curved line to the distance of two miles
before it falls to the ground; the same, if the resistance of the air were
taken away, with a double or decuple velocity, would fly twice or ten
times as far. And by increasing the velocity, we may at pleasure
increase the distance to which it might be projected, and diminish
the curvature of the line which it might describe, till at last it should
fall at the distance of 10, 30 or 90 degrees, or even might go quite
round the whole earth before it falls; or lastly, so that it might never
fall to the earth, but go forwards into the celestial spaces, and proceed in its motion *in infinitum*.

And after the same manner that a projectile, by the force of gravity, may be made to revolve in an orbit, and go round the whole
earth, the moon also, either by the force of gravity, if it is endued
with gravity, or by any other force that impels it towards the earth,
may be continually drawn aside towards the earth, out of the rectilinear way which by its innate force it would pursue; and would be
made to revolve in the orbit which it now describes; nor could the
moon without some such force be retained in its orbit. If this force
was too small, it would not sufficiently turn the moon out of a rectilinear course; if it was too great, it would turn it too much, and
draw down the moon from its orbit towards the earth. It is necessary
that the force be of a just quantity, and it belongs to the mathematicians to find the force that may serve exactly to retain a body in a
given orbit with a given velocity; and *vice versa*, to determine the
curvilinear way into which a body projected from a given place, with
a given velocity, may be made to deviate from its natural rectilinear
way, by means of a given force.

The quantity of any centripetal force may be considered as of
three kinds; absolute, accelerative, and motive.

DEFINITION VI

The absolute quantity of a centripetal force is the measure
of the same, proportional to the efficacy of the cause that

propagates it from the centre, through the spaces round about.

Thus the magnetic force is greater in one loadstone and less in another, according to their sizes and strength of intensity.

DEFINITION VII

The accelerative quantity of a centripetal force is the measure of the same, proportional to the velocity which it generates in a given time.

Thus the force of the same loadstone is greater at a less distance, and less at a greater; also the force of gravity is greater in valleys, less on tops of exceeding high mountains; and yet less (as shall hereafter be shown) at greater distances from the body of the earth; but at equal distances, it is the same everywhere; because (taking away, or allowing for, the resistance of the air) it equally accelerates all falling bodies, whether heavy or light, great or small.

DEFINITION VIII

The motive quantity of a centripetal force is the measure of the same, proportional to the motion which it generates in a given time.

Thus the weight is greater in a greater body, less in a less body; and, in the same body, it is greater near to the earth and less at remoter distances. This sort of quantity is the centripetency, or propension of the whole body towards the center, or, as I may say, its weight; and it is always known by the quantity of an equal and contrary force just sufficient to hinder the descent of the body. . . .

The reader is not to imagine that by those words I anywhere take upon me to define the kind, or the manner of any action, the causes or the physical reason thereof, or that I attribute forces, in a true and physical sense, to certain centres (which are only mathematical points); when at any time I happen to speak of centres as attracting, or as endued with attractive powers.

Hitherto I have laid down the definitions of such words as are less known, and explained the sense in which I would have them to be understood in the following discourse. I do not define time, space, place, and motion, as being well known to all. Only I must observe, that the common people conceive those quantities under no other notions but from the relation they bear to sensible objects. And thence arise certain prejudices, for the removing of which it will be convenient to distinguish them into absolute and relative, true and apparent, mathematical and common.

I. Absolute, true, and mathematical time, of itself, and from its own nature, flows equably without relation to anything external, and by another name is called duration: relative, apparent, and common time, is some sensible and external (whether accurate or unequable) measure of duration by the means of motion, which is commonly used instead of true time; such as an hour, a day, a month, a year.

II. Absolute space, in its own nature, without relation to anything external, remains always similar and immovable. Relative space is some movable dimension or measure of the absolute spaces; which our senses determine by its position to bodies; and which is commonly taken for immovable space; such is the dimension of a subterraneous, an aerial, or celestial space, determined by its position in respect of the earth. Absolute and relative space are the same in figure and magnitude; but they do not remain always numerically the same. For if the earth, for instance, moves, a space of our air, which relatively and in respect of the earth remains always the same, will at one time be one part of the absolute space into which the air passes; at another time it will be another part of the same, and so, absolutely understood, it will be continually changed.

III. Place is a part of space which a body takes up, and is according to the space, either absolute or relative. I say, a part of space; not the situation, nor the external surface of the body. For the places of equal solids are always equal; but their surfaces, by reason of their dissimilar figures, are often unequal. Positions properly have no quantity, nor are they so much the places themselves, as the properties of places. The motion of the whole is the same with the sum of the motions of the parts; that is, the translation of the whole out of its place is the same thing with the sum of the translations of the parts out of their places; and therefore the place of the whole is the same as the sum of the places of the parts, and for that reason, it is internal, and in the whole body.

IV. Absolute motion is the translation of a body from one absolute place into another; and relative motion, the translation from one relative place into another. Thus in a ship under sail, the relative place of a body is that part of the ship which the body possesses; or that part of the cavity which the body fills, and which therefore moves together with the ship: and relative rest is the continuance of the body in the same part of the ship, or of its cavity. But real, absolute rest, is the continuance of the body in the same part of that immovable space, in which the ship itself, its cavity, and all that it contains, is moved.

Wherefore, if the earth is really at rest, the body, which relatively rests in the ship, will really and absolutely move with the same velocity which the ship has on the earth. But if the earth also moves, the true and absolute motion of the body will arise, partly from the true motion of the earth in immovable space, partly from the relative motion of the ship on the earth; and if the body moves also relatively in the ship, its true motion will arise, partly from the true motion of the earth in immovable space, and partly from the relative motions as well of the ship on the earth, as of the body in the ship; and from these relative motions will arise the relative motion of the body on the earth. As if that part of the earth, where the ship is, was truly moved towards the east, with a velocity of 10010 parts; while the ship itself, with a fresh gale, and full sails, is carried towards the west, with a velocity expressed by 10 of those parts; but a sailor walks in the ship towards the east, with 1 part of the said velocity; then the sailor will be moved truly in immovable space towards the east, with a velocity of 10001 parts, and relatively on the earth towards the west, with a velocity of 9 of those parts.

Absolute time, in astronomy, is distinguished from relative, by the equation or correction of the apparent time. For the natural days are truly unequal, though they are commonly considered as equal, and used for a measure of time; astronomers correct this inequality that they may measure the celestial motions by a more accurate time. It may be, that there is no such thing as an equable motion, whereby time may be accurately measured. All motions may be accelerated and retarded, but the flowing of absolute time is not liable to any change. The duration or perseverance of the existence of things remains the same, whether the motions are swift or slow, or none at all; and therefore this duration ought to be distinguished from what are only sensible measures thereof. . . .

But because the parts of space cannot be seen, or distinguished from one another by our senses, therefore in their stead we use sensible measures of them. For from the positions and distances of things from any body considered as immovable, we define all places; and then with respect to such places, we estimate all motions, considering bodies as transferred from some of those places into others. And so, instead of absolute places and motions, we use relative ones; and that without any inconvenience in common affairs; but in philosophical disquisitions, we ought to abstract from our senses, and consider things themselves, distinct from what are only sensible measures of them. For it may be that there is no body really at rest, to which the places and motions of others may be referred.

But we may distinguish rest and motion, absolute and relative, one from the other by their properties, causes, and effects. It is a property of rest, that bodies really at rest do rest in respect to one another. And therefore as it is possible, that in the remote regions of the fixed stars, or perhaps far beyond them, there may be some body absolutely at rest; but impossible to know, from the position of bodies to one another in our regions, whether any of these do keep the same position to that remote body, it follows that absolute rest cannot be determined from the position of bodies in our regions. . . .

The effects which distinguish absolute from relative motion are the forces of receding from the axis of a circular motion. For there are no such forces in a circular motion purely relative, but in a true and absolute circular motion they are greater or less, according to the quantity of the motion. If a vessel, hung by a long cord, is so often turned about that the cord is strongly twisted, then filled with water, and held at rest together with the water; thereupon, by the sudden action of another force, it is whirled about the contrary way, and while the cord is untwisting itself, the vessel continues for some time in this motion, the surface of the water will at first be plain, as before the vessel began to move; but after that, the vessel, by gradually communicating its motion to the water, will make it begin sensibly to revolve, and recede by little and little from the middle, and ascend to the sides of the vessel, forming itself into a concave figure (as I have experienced); and the swifter the motion becomes, the higher will the water rise, till at last, performing its revolutions in the same times with the vessel, it becomes relatively at rest in it. This ascent of the water shows its endeavor to recede from the axis of its motion; and the true and absolute circular motion of the water, which is here directly contrary to the relative, becomes known, and may be measured by this endeavor.

At first, when the relative motion of the water in the vessel was greatest, it produced no endeavor to recede from the axis; the water showed no tendency to the circumference, nor any ascent towards the sides of the vessel, but remained of a plain surface, and therefore its true circular motion had not yet begun. But afterwards, when the relative motion of the water had decreased, the ascent thereof towards the sides of the vessel proved its endeavor to recede from the axis; and this endeavor showed the real circular motion of the water continually increasing, till it had acquired its greatest quantity, when the water rested relatively in the vessel. And therefore this endeavor does not depend upon any translation of the water in respect of the ambient bodies, nor can true circular motion be defined by such translation. There is only one real circular motion of any one revolving body, corresponding to only one power of endeavoring to recede from its axis of motion, as its proper and adequate effect; but relative motions, in one and the same body, are innumerable, according to the various relations it bears to external bodies, and, like other relations, are altogether destitute of any real effect, any otherwise than they may perhaps partake of that one only true motion. . . .

It is indeed a matter of great difficulty to discover, and effectually to distinguish, the true motions of particular bodies from the apparent; because the parts of that immovable space, in which those motions are performed, do by no means come under the observation of our senses. Yet the thing is not altogether desperate; for we have some arguments to guide us, partly from the apparent motions, which are the differences of the true motions; partly from the forces, which are the causes and effects of the true motions. . . . But how we are to obtain the true motions from their causes, effects, and apparent difference, and the converse, shall be explained more at large in the following treatise. For to this end it was that I composed it.

AXIOMS, OR LAWS OF MOTION

LAW I

Every body continues in its state of rest, or of uniform motion in a right line, unless it is compelled to change that state by forces impressed upon it.

Projectiles continue in their motions, so far as they are not retarded by the resistance of the air, or impelled downwards by the force of gravity. A top, whose parts by their cohesion are continually drawn aside from rectilinear motions, does not cease its rotation, otherwise than as it is retarded by the air. The greater bodies of the planets and comets, meeting with less resistance in freer spaces, preserve their motions both progressive and circular for a much longer time.

LAW II

The change of motion is proportional to the motive force impressed; and is made in the direction of the right line in which that force is impressed.

If any force generates a motion, a double force will generate double the motion, a triple force triple the motion, whether that force be impressed altogether and at once, or gradually and successively. And this motion (being always directed the same way with the generating force), if the body moved before, is added to or subtracted from the former motion, according as they directly conspire with or are directly contrary to each other; or obliquely joined, when they are oblique, so as to produce a new motion compounded from the determination of both.

LAW III

To every action there is always opposed an equal reaction: or, the mutual actions of two bodies upon each other are always equal, and directed to contrary parts.

Whatever draws or presses another is as much drawn or pressed by that other. If you press a stone with your finger, the finger is also pressed by the stone. If a horse draws a stone tied to a rope, the horse (if I may so say) will be equally drawn back towards the stone; for the distended rope, by the same endeavor to relax or unbend itself, will draw the horse as much towards the stone as it does the stone towards the horse, and will obstruct the progress of the one as much as it advances that of the other. If a body impinge upon another, and by its force change the motion of the other, that body also (because of the equality of the mutual pressure) will undergo an equal change, in its own motion, towards the contrary part. The changes made by these actions are equal, not in the velocities but in the motions of bodies; that is to say, if the bodies are not hindered by any other impediments. For, because the motions are equally changed, the changes of the velocities made towards contrary parts are inversely proportional to the bodies. This law takes place also in attractions, as will be proved in the next Scholium.

COROLLARY I

A body, acted on by two forces simultaneously, will describe the diagonal of a parallelogram in the same time as it would describe the sides by those forces separately.

If a body in a given time, by the force M impressed apart in the place A, should with an uniform motion be carried from A to B, and by the force N impressed apart in the same place, should be carried from A to C, let the parallelogram ABCD be completed, and, by both forces acting together, it will in the same time be carried in the diagonal from A to D. For since the force N acts in the direction of the line AC, parallel to BD, this force

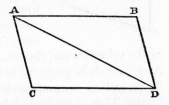

(by the second Law), will not at all alter the velocity generated by the other force M, by which the body is carried towards the line BD. The body therefore will arrive at the line BD in the same time, whether the force N be impressed or not; and therefore at the end of that time it will be found somewhere in the line BD. By the same argument, at the end of the same time it will be found somewhere in the line CD. Therefore it will be found in the point D, where both lines meet. But it will move in a right line from A to D, by Law I....

SCHOLIUM

Hitherto I have laid down such principles as have been received by mathematicians, and are confirmed by abundance of experiments. By the first two Laws and the first two Corollaries, *Galileo* discovered that the descent of bodies varied as the square of the time and that the motion of projectiles was in the curve of a parabola; experience agreeing with both, unless so far as these motions are a little retarded by the resistance of the air. When a body is falling, the uniform force of its gravity acting equally, impresses, in equal intervals of time, equal forces upon that body, and therefore generates equal velocities; and in the whole time impresses a whole force, and

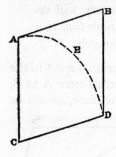

generates a whole velocity proportional to the time. And the spaces described in proportional times are as the product of the velocities and the times; that is, as the squares of the times. And when a body is thrown upwards, its uniform gravity impresses forces and reduces velocities proportional to the times; and the times of ascending to the greatest heights are as the velocities to be taken away, and those heights are as the product of the velocities and the times, or as the squares of the velocities. And if a body be projected in any direction, the motion arising from its projection is compounded with the motion arising from its gravity. Thus, if the body A by its motion of projection alone could describe in a given time the right line AB, and with its motion of falling alone could describe in the same time the altitude AC; complete the parallelogram ABCD, and the body by that compounded motion will at the end of the time be found in the place D; and the curved line AED, which that body describes, will be a parabola, to which the right line AB will be a tangent at A; and whose ordinate BD will be as the square of the line AB. On the same Laws and Corollaries depend those things which have been demonstrated concerning the times of the vibration of pendulums, and are confirmed by the daily experiments of pendulum clocks. By the same, together with Law III, Sir Christopher Wren, Dr. Wallis, and Mr. Huygens, the greatest geometers of our times, did severally determine the rules of the impact and reflection of hard bodies, and about the same time communicated their discoveries to the Royal Society, exactly agreeing among themselves as to those rules. . . .

The power and use of machines consist only in this, that by diminishing the velocity we may augment the force, and the contrary; from whence, in all sorts of proper machines, we have the solution of this problem: *To move a given weight with a given power*, or with a given force to overcome any other given resistance. For if machines are so contrived that the velocities of the agent and resistant are inversely as their forces, the agent will just sustain the resistant, but with a greater disparity of velocity will overcome it. So that if the disparity of velocities is so great as to overcome all that resistance which commonly arises either from the friction of contiguous bodies as they slide by one another, or from the cohesion of continuous bodies that are to be separated, or from the weights of bodies to be raised, the excess of the force remaining, after all those resistances are overcome, will produce an acceleration of motion proportional thereto, as well in the parts of the machine as in the resisting body. But to treat of mechanics is not my present business. I was aiming only to show by those examples the great extent and certainty of the third Law of Motion. For if we estimate the action of the agent from the product of its force and velocity, and likewise the reaction of the impediment from the product of the velocities of its several parts, and the forces of resistance arising from the friction, cohesion, weight, and acceleration of those parts, the action and reaction in the use of all sorts of machines will be found always equal to one another. And so far as the action is propagated by the intervening instruments, and at last impressed upon the resisting body, the ultimate action will be always contrary to the reaction. . . .

SYSTEM OF THE WORLD

PROPOSITION 6. THEOREM 6

Gravitational Forces Are Universal

Corollary I. Hence the weights of bodies do not depend upon their forms and textures; for if the weights could be altered with the forms, they would be greater or less, according to the variety of forms, in equal matter; altogether against experience.

Corollary II. Universally, all bodies about the earth gravitate towards the earth; and the weights of all, at equal distances from the earth's center, are as the quantities of matter which they severally contain. This is the quality of all bodies within the reach of our experiments; and therefore (by Rule 3) to be affirmed of all bodies whatsoever. If the ether, or any other body, were either altogether void of gravity, or were to gravitate less in proportion to its quantity of matter, then, because (according to Aristotle, Descartes, and others) there is no difference between that and other bodies but in mere form of matter, by a successive change from form to form, it might be changed at last into a body of the same condition with those which gravitate most in proportion to their quantity of matter; and, on the other hand, the heaviest bodies, acquiring the first form of that body, might by degrees quite lose their gravity. And therefore the weights would depend upon the forms of bodies, and with those forms, might be changed: contrary to what was proved in the preceding Corollary.

Corollary III. All spaces are not equally full; for if all spaces were equally full, then the specific gravity of the fluid which fills the region of the air, on account of the extreme density of the matter, would fall nothing short of the specific gravity of quicksilver, or gold, or any other most dense body; and, therefore, neither gold, nor any other body, could descend in air; for bodies do not descend in fluids, unless they are specifically heavier than the fluids. And if the quantity of matter in a given space can, by any rarefaction, be diminished, what should hinder a diminution to infinity?

Corollary IV. If all the solid particles of all bodies are of the same density, and cannot be rarefied without pores, then a void, space, or vacuum must be granted. By bodies of the same density, I mean those whose inertias are in the proportion of their bulks.

Corollary V. The power of gravity is of a different nature from the power of magnetism; for the magnetic attraction is not as the matter attracted. Some bodies are attracted more by the magnet, others less; most bodies not at all. The power of magnetism in one and the same body may be increased and diminished; and is sometimes far stronger, for the quantity of matter, than the power of gravity; and in receding from the magnet decreases not as the square but almost as the cube of the distance, as nearly as I could judge from some rude observations.

PROPOSITION 7. THEOREM 7

That There Is a Power of Gravity Pertaining to All Bodies, Proportional to the Several Quantities of Matter Which They Contain

That all the planets gravitate one towards another, we have proved before; as well as that the force of gravity towards every one of them, considered apart, is inversely as the square of the distance of places from the center of the planet. And thence (by Prop. LXIX, Book I, and its Corollaries) it follows, that the gravity tending towards all the planets is proportional to the matter which they contain.

Moreover, since all the parts of any planet A gravitate towards any other planet B; and the gravity of every part is to the gravity of the whole as the matter of the part to the matter of the whole; and (by Law III) to every action corresponds an equal reaction; therefore the planet B will, on the other hand, gravitate towards all the parts of the planet A; and its gravity towards any one part will be to the gravity towards the whole as the matter of the part to the matter of the whole. Q.E.D.

Corollary I. Therefore the force of gravity towards any whole planet arises from, and is compounded of, the forces of gravity towards all its parts. Magnetic and electric attractions afford us examples of this; for all attraction towards the whole arises from the attractions towards the several parts. The thing may be easily understood in gravity, if we consider a greater planet, as formed of a number of lesser planets, meeting together in one globe; for hence it would appear that the force of the whole must arise from the forces of the component parts. If it is objected, that, according to this law, all bodies with us must gravitate one towards another, whereas no such gravitation anywhere appears, I answer, that since the gravitation towards these bodies is to the gravitation towards the whole earth as these bodies are to the whole earth, the gravitation towards them must be far less than to fall under the observation of our senses.

Corollary II. The force of gravity towards the several equal particles of any body is inversely as the square of the distance of places from the particles.

PROPOSITION 10. THEOREM 10

That the Motions of the Planets in the Heavens May Subsist an Exceedingly Long Time

It is shown in the Scholium of Prop. XXII, Book II, that at the height of 200 miles above the earth the air is more rare than it is at the surface of the earth in the ratio of 30 to 0.0000000000003998, or as 75,000,000,000,000 to 1, nearly. And hence the planet Jupiter, revolving in a medium of the same density with that superior air, would not lose by the resistance of the medium the 1,000,000th part of its motion in 1,000,000 years. In the spaces near the earth the resistance is produced only by the air, exhalations, and vapors. When these are carefully exhausted by the air pump from under the receiver, heavy bodies fall within the receiver with perfect freedom, and without the least sensible resistance: gold itself, and the lightest down, let fall together, will descend with equal velocity; and though they fall through a space of four, six, and eight feet, they will come to the bottom at the same time; as appears from experiments. And therefore, the celestial regions being perfectly void of air and exhalations, the planets and comets meeting no sensible resistance in those spaces will continue their motions through them for an immense tract of time.

PROPOSITION 37. PROBLEM 18

To Find the Force of the Moon to Move the Sea

Corollary I. Since the waters attracted by the sun's force rise to the height of 1 foot and 11 1/30 inches, the moon's force will raise the same to the height of 8 feet and 7 5/22 inches; and the joint forces of both will raise the same to the height of 10½ feet; and when the moon is in its perigee[1] to the height of 12½ feet, and more, especially when the wind sets the same way as the tide. And a force of that amount is abundantly sufficient to produce all the motions of the sea, and agrees well with the ratio of those motions; for in such seas as lie free and open from east to west, as in the Pacific sea, and in those tracts of the Atlantic and Ethiopic seas which lie without the tropics, the waters commonly rise to 6, 9, 12, or 15 feet; but in the Pacific sea, which is of a greater depth, as well as of a larger extent, the tides are said to be greater than in the Atlantic and Ethiopic seas; for, to have a full tide raised, an extent of sea from east to west is required of no less than 90 degrees. In the Ethiopic sea, the waters rise to a less height within the tropics than in the temperate zones: because of the narrowness of the sea between Africa and the southern parts of America. In the middle of the open sea the waters cannot rise without falling together, and at the same time, upon both the eastern and western shores, when, notwithstanding, in our narrow seas, they ought to fall on those shores by alternate turns; upon this account there is commonly but a small flood and ebb in such islands as lie far distant from the continent. On the contrary, in some ports, where to fill and empty the bays alternately the waters are with great violence forced in and out through shallow channels, the flood and ebb must be greater than ordinary; as at Plymouth and Chepstow Bridge in England, at the mountains of St. Michael, and the town of Avranches, in Normandy, and at Cambaia and Pegu in the East Indies. In these places the sea is hurried in and out

[1] The point in the orbit of the moon nearest to the earth.

with such violence as sometimes to lay the shores under water, some-times to leave them dry for many miles. Nor is this force of the influx and efflux to be stopped till it has raised and depressed the waters to 30, 40, or 50 feet and above. And a like account is to be given of long and shallow channels or straits, such as the Magellanic straits, and those channels which environ England. The tide in such ports and straits, by the violence of the influx and efflux, is aug-mented greatly. But on such shores as lie towards the deep and open sea with a steep descent, where the waters may freely rise and fall without that precipitation of influx and efflux, the ratio of the tides agrees with the forces of the sun and moon.

Corollary II. Since the moon's force to move the sea is to the force of gravity as 1 to 2,871,400, it is evident that this force is inappreci-able in statical or hydrostatical experiments, or even in those of pendulums. It is in the tides only that this force shows itself by any sensible effect.

GENERAL SCHOLIUM

Bodies projected in our air suffer no resistance but from the air. Withdraw the air, as is done in Mr. Boyle's vacuum,[2] and the re-sistance ceases, for in this void a bit of fine down and a piece of solid gold descend with equal velocity. And the same argument must apply to the celestial spaces above the earth's atmosphere; in these spaces, where there is no air to resist their motions, all bodies will move with the greatest freedom; and the planets and comets will constantly pursue their revolutions in orbits given in kind and posi-tion, according to the laws above explained; but though these bodies may, indeed, continue in their orbits by the mere laws of gravity, yet they could by no means have at first derived the regular position of the orbits themselves from those laws.

The six primary planets are revolved about the sun in circles con-centric with the sun, and with motions directed towards the same parts, and almost in the same plane. Ten moons are revolved about

2 See below, p. 244 ff.

the earth, Jupiter, and Saturn, in circles concentric with them, with the same direction of motion, and nearly in the planes of the orbits of those planets; but it is not to be conceived that mere mechanical causes could give birth to so many regular motions, since the comets range over all parts of the heavens in very eccentric orbits; for by that kind of motion they pass easily through the orbs of the planets, and with great rapidity; and in their aphelions, where they move the slowest, and are detained the longest, they recede to the greatest distances from each other, and hence suffer the least disturbance from their mutual attractions.

This most beautiful system of the sun, planets, and comets, could only proceed from the counsel and dominion of an intelligent and powerful Being. And if the fixed stars are the centers of other like systems, these, being formed by the like wise counsel, must be all subject to the dominion of One; especially since the light of the fixed stars is of the same nature with the light of the sun, and from every system light passes into all the other systems: and lest the systems of the fixed stars should, by their gravity, fall on each other, he hath placed those systems at immense distances from one another. . . .

Hitherto we have explained the phenomena of the heavens and of our sea by the power of gravity, but have not yet assigned the cause of this power. This is certain, that it must proceed from a cause that penetrates to the very centers of the sun and planets, without suffering the least diminution of its force; that it operates not according to the quantity of the surfaces of the particles upon which it acts (as mechanical causes used to do), but according to the quantity of the solid matter which they contain, and propagates its virtue on all sides to immense distances, decreasing always as the inverse square of the distances. Gravitation towards the sun is made up out of the gravitations towards the several particles of which the body of the sun is composed; and in receding from the sun decreases accurately as the inverse square of the distances as far as the orbit of Saturn, as evidently appears from the quiescence of the aphelion of the planets; nay, and even to the remotest aphelion of the comets, if those aphelions are also quiescent.

But hitherto I have not been able to discover the cause of those properties of gravity from phenomena, and I frame no hypotheses; for whatever is not deduced from the phenomena is to be called an hypothesis; and hypotheses, whether metaphysical or physical, whether of occult qualities or mechanical, have no place in experimental philosophy. In this philosophy particular propositions are inferred from the phenomena, and afterwards rendered general by induction. Thus it was that the impenetrability, the mobility, and the impulsive force of bodies, and the laws of motion and of gravitation, were discovered. And to us it is enough that gravity does really exist, and act according to the laws which we have explained, and abundantly serves to account for all the motions of the celestial bodies, and of our sea.

And now we might add something concerning a certain most subtle spirit which pervades and lies hid in all gross bodies; by the force and action of which spirit the particles of bodies attract one another at near distances, and cohere, if contiguous; and electric bodies operate to greater distances, as well repelling as attracting the neighboring corpuscles; and light is emitted, reflected, refracted, inflected, and heats bodies; and all sensation is excited, and the members of animal bodies move at the command of the will, namely, by the vibrations of this spirit, mutually propagated along the solid filaments of the nerves, from the outward organs of sense to the brain, and from the brain into the muscles. But these are things that cannot be explained in few words, nor are we furnished with that sufficiency of experiments which is required to an accurate determination and demonstration of the laws by which this electric and elastic spirit operates.

ROBERT HOOKE[1]

1 6 3 5 · 1 7 0 3

SHORTLY AFTER the Royal Society of London was given its charter
in 1662, Robert Hooke, formerly assistant to Robert Boyle,[2] was
appointed Curator of Experiments for the Society, with the responsi-
bility of preparing three or four demonstrations for each meeting.
During the next forty years he examined organisms through the
microscope, measured the refractive index of transparent liquids,
performed biological experiments and dissections, worked with
barometers, thermometers, pendulums and springs, and generally
contributed greatly to the work of the members of the Society. He
however lacked the power to generalize his results; his name is remembered chiefly as the author of the law of elasticity.

The spring balance now used everywhere for rough weighing is
based on the fact that if one pound will stretch a spring one inch,
two pounds will stretch it two inches, and so on. The first statement of this principle is found in Hooke's De potentia restitutiva,
1678, which was reprinted in Early Science in Oxford, by R. T.
Gunther, 1931.

[1] For an account of another of Hooke's inventions, see below, p. 133.
[2] On Boyle, see below, p. 242.

87

THE THEORY OF SPRINGS

꙳

THE THEORY OF SPRINGS, though attempted by divers eminent Mathematicians of this Age, has hitherto not been Published by any. It is now about eighteen years since I first found it out, but designing to apply it to some particular use, I omitted the publishing thereof.

About three years since, His Majesty was pleased to see the Experiment that made out this Theory tried at White-Hall, as also my Spring Watch.

About two years since, I printed this Theory in an Anagram at the end of my Book of the Descriptions of Helioscopes, viz, ceiiino sssttuv,[1] *id est, Ut tensio sic vis*; That is, The Power of any Spring is in the same proportion with the Tension thereof; That is, if one power stretch or bend it one space, two will bend it two, and three will bend it three, and so forward. Now as the Theory is very short, so the way of trying it is very easie.

Take then a quantity of even-drawn wire, either Steel, Iron, or Brass, and coyl it on an even Cylinder into a Helix of what length or number of turns you please, then turn the ends of the Wire into Loops, by one of which suspend this coyl upon a nail, and by the other sustain the weight that you would have to extend it, and hanging on several Weights observe exactly to what length each of the weights do extend it beyond the length that its own weight doth stretch it to, and shall find that if one ounce, or one pound, or one certain weight doth lengthen it one line, or one inch, or one certain length, then two ounces, two pounds, or two weights will extend it two lines, two inches, or two lengths; and three ounces, pounds, or

---

[1] This "anagram" consists simply of the letters of the following Latin formula, "Ut tensio sic vis," which in English is literally, "As the tension, so the force."

weights, three lines, inches, or lengths; and so forward. And this is the Rule or Law of Nature, upon which all manner of Restituent of Springing motion doth proceed, whether it be of Rarefaction, or Extension, or Condensation and Compression.

Or take a Watch Spring, and coyl it into a Spiral, so as no part thereof may touch another, then provide a very light wheel of Brass, or the like, and fix it on an arbor that hath two small Pivots of Steel, upon which Pivot turn the edge of the said Wheel very even and smooth, so that a small silk may be coyled upon it; then put this Wheel into a Frame, so that the Wheel may move very freely on its Pivots; fasten the central end of the aforesaid Spring close to the Pivot hole or center of the frame in which the Arbor of the Wheel doth move, and the other end thereof to the Rim of the Wheel, then coyling a fine limber thread of Silk upon the edge of the Wheel hang a small light scale at the end thereof fit to receive the weight that shall be put thereinto; then suffering the Wheel to stand in its own position by a little index

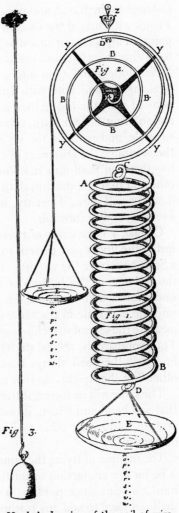

Hooke's drawing of the coil of wire, watch spring, and straight wire, with which he experimented.

fastened to the frame, and pointing to the Rim of the Wheel, make a mark with Ink, or the like, on that part of the Rim that the Index pointeth at; then put in a drachm weight into the scale, and suffer the Wheel to settle, and make another mark on the Rim where the Index doth point; then add a drachm more, and let the Wheel settle again, and note with Ink, as before, the place of the Rim pointed at by the Index; then add a third drachm, and do as before, and so a fourth, fifth, sixth, seventh, eighth, etc. suffering the Wheel to settle, and marking the several places pointed at by the Index, then examine the Distances of all those marks, and comparing them together you shall find that they will all be equal the one to the other, so that if a drachm doth move the Wheel ten degrees, two drachms will move it twenty, and three thirty, and four forty, and five fifty, and so forwards.

Or take a Wire string of twenty, or thirty, or forty foot long, and fasten the upper part thereof to a nail, and to the other end fasten a Scale to receive the weights: Then with a pair of Compasses take the distance of the bottom of the scale from the ground or floor underneath, and set down the said distance, then put in weights into the said scale in the same manner as in the former trials, and measure the several stretchings of the said string, and set them down. Then compare the several stretchings of the said string, and you will find that they will always bear the same proportions one to the other that the weights do that made them.

The same will be found, if trial be made, with a piece of dry wood that will bend and return, if one end thereof be fixt in a horizontal posture, and to the other end be hanged weights to make it bend downwards.

The manner of trying the same thing upon a body of Air, whether it be for the rarefaction or for the compression thereof I did about fourteen years since publish in my *Micrographia*, and therefore I shall not need to add any further description thereof.

From all which it is very evident that the Rule or Law of Nature in every springing body is, that the force or power thereof to restore itself to its natural position is always proportionate to the Distance or space it is removed therefrom, whether it be by rarefaction, or separation of its parts the one from the other, or by a Condensation, or crowding of those parts nearer together. Nor is it observable in these bodies only, but in all other springy bodies whatsoever, whether Metal, Wood, Stones, baked Earths, Hair, Horns, Silk, Bones, Sinews, Glass, and the like. Respect being had to the particular figures of the bodies bended, and the advantagious or disadvantagious ways of bending them.

From this principle it will be easie to calculate the several strength of Bows, as of Long Bows or Cross-Bows, whether they be made of Wood, Steel, Horns, Sinews, or the like. As also of the *Balistae* or *Catapultae* used by the Ancients, which being once found, and Tables thereof calculated, I shall anon shew a way how to calculate the power they have in shooting or casting Arrows, Bullets, Stones, Granadoes, or the like.

From these principles also it will be easie to calculate the proportionate strength of the spring of a Watch upon the Fusey thereof, and consequently of adjusting the Fusey to the Spring so as to make it draw or move the Watch always with an equal force.

From the same also it will be easie to give the reason of the *Isochrone* motion of a Spring or extended string, and of the uniform sound produced by those whose Vibrations are quick enough to produce an audible sound, and likewise the reason of the sounds, and their variations in all manner of sonorous or springing Bodies, of which more on another occasion.

From this appears the reason, as I shall shew by and by, why a Spring applied to the balance of a Watch doth make the vibrations thereof equal, whether they be greater or smaller, one of which kind I shewed to the right Honourable Robert Boyle Esq.; and Sir Robert Morey in the year 1660, in order to have gotten Letters Patents for the use and benefit thereof.

From this it will be easy to make a Philosophical Scale to examine the weight of any body without putting in weights . . .

This Scale I contrived in order to examine the gravitation of bodies towards the Center of the Earth, viz, to examine whether bodies at a further distance from the Center of the Earth did not lose somewhat of their power or tendency towards it. And pro pounded it as one of the Experiments to be tried at the top of the Pike of *Teneriff*, and attempted the same at the top of the Tower of St. *Paul's* before the burning of it in the late great Fire; [2] as also at the top and bottom of the Abbey of St. *Peter's* in *Westminster*, though these being by but small distances removed from the Surface, I was not able certainly to perceive any manifest difference. I propounded the same also to be tried at the bottom and several stations of deep Mines; and D. *Power* did make some trials to that end, but his Instruments not being good, nothing could be certainly concluded from them.

These are the Phenomena of Springs and springy bodies, which as they have not hitherto been by any that I know reduced to Rules, so have all the attempts for the explications of the reason of their power, and of springiness in general, been very insufficient. . . .

2 The great London fire of 1660, in which the medieval cathedral of St. Paul's was destroyed.

NEVIL MASKELYNE

1 7 3 2 · 1 8 1 1

NINETY YEARS after Newton's Principia, the actual density of the earth had not yet been measured, though this knowledge was needed in order to compute the mass of the earth, moon, sun, and other stellar bodies.

In 1772 the Reverend Nevil Maskelyne, Astronomer Royal, read before the Royal Society of London a proposal, part of which is here quoted, for following up a suggestion of Newton's for making this measurement, which already had been roughly tried in Chile by Bouguer in 1740. The proposal, briefly, was this: A large and steep mountain ought, by the law of universal gravitation, to pull a pendulum towards itself. By measuring the distance a suspended weight (plumb line) was pulled towards the mountain whose mass was known, and comparing it to the downward pull of the earth, the mass, or "weight," of the whole earth might be computed. The sideways pull on the weight could be found by astronomy; for if the string was pulled to one side it would make the apparent zenith or overhead point different from the actual zenith, which was mathematically equivalent to the latitude of the place.

What actually happened was that the mountain pulled the weight toward itself through an arc of about 6 seconds [1] at each of two observation posts, one north, one south of the mountain. The correct distance between these two places was found by surveying to be about 43 seconds of an arc (around three quarters of a mile). The apparent distance between the stations, computed from their apparent latitudes, as indicated in the experiment, was 55 seconds of

[1] A six-foot pendulum would have been pulled two thousandths of an inch to the side.

an arc, or almost a mile. After suitable calculation, this figure indicated that the average density of the earth was 4½ times that of water.

For his brilliant success in this experiment, Maskelyne was awarded great honors. The report of his plans and later observations was printed in the Philosophical Transactions of the Royal Society of London, vol. 65, 1775.

MEASURING THE ATTRACTION
OF SOME HILL BY
ASTRONOMICAL OBSERVATIONS

Redde in the year 1772.

IF THE ATTRACTION of gravity be exerted, as Sir Isaac Newton supposes, not only between the large bodies of the universe, but between the minutest particles of which these bodies are composed, or into which the mind can imagine them to be divided, acting universally according to that law by which the force which carries on the celestial motions is regulated; namely, that the accelerative force of each particle of matter towards every other particle decreases as the squares of the distances increase, it will necessarily follow, that every hill must, by its attraction, alter the direction of gravitation in heavy bodies in its neighbourhood from what it would have been from the attraction of the earth alone, considered as bounded by a smooth and even surface. For, as the tendency of heavy bodies downwards perpendicular to the earth's surface is owing to the combined attraction of all the parts of the earth upon it, so a neighbouring mountain ought, though in a far less degree, to attract the heavy body towards its centre of attraction, which cannot be placed far from the middle of the mountain. Hence the plumb-line of a quadrant, or any other astronomical instrument, must be deflected from its proper situation by a small quantity towards the mountain; and the apparent altitudes of the stars, taken with the instrument, will be altered accordingly.

It will easily be acknowledged that to find a sensible attraction of any hill from undoubted experiment would be a matter of no small curiosity, would greatly illustrate the general theory of gravity, and would make the universal gravitation of matter palpable, if I may so express myself, to every person, and fit to convince those who will yield their assent to nothing but downright experiment. Nor would its uses end here; as it would serve to give us a better idea of the total mass of the earth, and the proportional density of the matter near the surface compared with the mean density of the whole earth. The result of such an uncommon experiment, which I should hope would prove successful, would doubtless do honour to the nation where it was made, and the society which executed it.

Sir Isaac Newton gives us the first hint of such an attempt, in his popular Treatise of the System of the World, where he remarks, "That a mountain of an hemispherical figure, three miles high and six broad, will not, by its attraction, draw the plumb-line two minutes out of the perpendicular." It will appear, by a very easy calculation, that such a mountain would attract the plumb-line 1 minute 18 seconds from the perpendicular . . .

An Account of Observations Made on the Mountain Schehallien for Measuring its Attraction

Redde July 6, 1775.

IN THE YEAR 1772, I presented the foregoing proposal, for measuring the attraction of some hill in this kingdom by astronomical observations, to the Royal Society; who, ever inclined to promote useful observations which may enlarge our views of nature, honoured it with their approbation. A committee was in consequence appointed, of which number I was one, to consider of a proper hill whereon to try the experiment, and to prepare every thing necessary for carrying the design into execution. The Society was already provided with a ten-feet zenith sector made by Mr. Sisson, furnished with an achromatic object glass, the principal instrument requisite for this experiment, the same which I took with me to St. Helena in the year 1761. . . .

Perthshire afforded us a remarkable hill, nearly in the centre of

Scotland, of sufficient height, tolerably detached from other hills, and considerably larger from East to West than from North to South, called by the people of the low country Maiden-pap, but by the neighbouring inhabitants, Schehallien; which, I have since been informed, signifies in the Erse language, Constant Storm; a name well adapted to the appearance which it so frequently exhibits to those who live near it, by the clouds and mists which usually crown its summit. It had, moreover, the advantage, by its steepness, of having but a small base from North to South; which circumstance, at the same time that it increases the effect of attraction, brings the two stations on the North and South sides of the hill, at which the sum of the two contrary attractions is to be found by the experiment, nearer together; so that the necessary allowance of the number of seconds for the difference of latitude, due to the measured horizontal distance of the two stations in the direction of the meridian, would be very small, and consequently not subject to sensible error from any probable uncertainty of the length of a degree of latitude in this parallel. For these reasons the mountain Schehallien was chosen, in preference to all others, for the scene of the intended operations; and it was concluded to make the experiment in the summer of the year 1774. . . .

The quantity of attraction of the hill, the grand point to be determined, is measured by the deviation of the plumb-line from the perpendicular, occasioned by the attraction of the hill, or by the angle contained between the actual perpendicular and that which would have obtained if the hill had been away. The meridian zenith distances of fixed stars, near the zenith, taken with a zenith sector, being of all observations hitherto devised capable of the greatest accuracy, ought by all means to be made use of on this occasion: and it is evident, that the zenith instrument should be placed directly to the North or South of the centre of the hill, or nearly so. In observations taken in this manner, the zenith distances of the stars, or the apparent latitude of the station, will be found as they are affected by the attraction of the hill. If then we could by any means know what the zenith distances of the same stars, or what the latitude, of the place would have been, if the hill had been away, we should be able to decide upon the effect of attraction. This will be found, by repeating the observations of the stars at the East or West end of the hill, where the attraction of the hill, acting in the direction of the prime vertical, hath no effect on the plumb-line in the direction of the meridian, nor consequently on the apparent zenith distances of the stars; the differences of the zenith distances of the stars taken on the North or South side of the hill, and those observed at the East or West end of it, after allowing for the difference of latitude answering to the distance of the parallels of latitude passing through the two stations, will shew the quantity of the attraction at the North or South station.

But the experiment may be made to more advantage on a hill like Schehallien, which is steep both on the North and South sides, by making the two observations of the stars on both sides; for the plumb-line being attracted contrary ways at the two stations, the apparent zenith distances of stars will be affected contrary ways; those which were increased at the one station being diminished at the other, and consequently their difference will be affected by the sum of the two contrary attractions of the hill. On the South side of the hill, the plumb-line being carried Northward at its lower extremity, will occasion the apparent zenith, which is in the direction of the plumb-line continued backwards, to be carried Southward, and consequently to approach the equator; and therefore, the latitude of the place will appear too small by the quantity of the attraction; the distance of the equator from the zenith being equal to the latitude of the place. The contrary happens on the North side of the hill; the lower extremity of the plumb-line being there carried Southward will occasion the apparent zenith to be carried Northward or from the equator; and the latitude of the place will appear too great by the quantity of the attraction. Thus the lesser latitude appearing too small by the attraction on the South side, and the greater latitude appearing too great by the attraction on the

North side, the difference of the latitudes will appear too great by the sum of the two contrary attractions; if therefore there is an attraction of the hill, the difference of latitude by the celestial observations ought to come out greater than what answers to the distance of the two stations measured trigonometrically according to the length of a degree of latitude in that parallel, and the observed difference of latitude subtracted from the difference of latitude inferred from the terrestrial operations, will give the sum of the two contrary attractions of the hill. To ascertain the distance between the parallels of latitude passing through the two stations on contrary sides of the hill, a base must be measured in some level spot near the hill, and connected with the two stations by a chain of triangles, the direction of whose sides, with respect to the meridian, should be settled by astronomical observations.

If it be required, as it ought to be, not only to know the attraction of the hill, but also from thence the proportion of the density of the matter of the hill to the mean density of the earth; then a survey must be made of the hill to ascertain its dimensions and figure, from whence a calculation may be made, how much the hill ought to attract, if its density was equal to the mean density of the earth; it is evident, that the proportion of the actual attraction of the hill to that computed in this manner will be the proportion of the density of the hill to the mean density of the earth.

Thus there were three principal operations requisite to be performed. 1. To find by celestial observations the apparent difference of latitude between the two stations chosen on the North and South sides of the hill. 2. To find the distance between the parallels of latitude. 3. To determine the figure and dimensions of the hill. . . .

And thus I compleated my whole series of observations with the sector, having observed 43 different stars in all, on both sides of the hill, and taken 337 observations.

As a few observations, taken with so excellent an instrument as this zenith sector, would have been sufficient to determine the apparent difference of latitude of the two stations of the observatory,

to a second or two; I am apprehensive I may be thought by many
to have multiplied observations unnecessarily. However that may
be, I apprehend, that doubling the observations in each station of
the observatory, by taking them with the plane of the instrument
alternately facing the East and West, will be allowed to be a proper
step, as the line of collimation of the instrument is hereby separately determined at each station, and thereby all danger of any
alteration happening in the same, in its removal from one side of
the hill to the other, is entirely obviated. I had, indeed, all the
reason in the world to think that the sector was carried from one
station to the other without the least accident; but still it was proper
to guard against what was possible to happen.

But I had reasons also for multiplying the observations made in
the same position of the instrument. It was important to demonstrate the exactness of the instrument from the near agreement of
a number of observations taken with it, as its excellence was not
to be entirely presumed, unless this proof could be shewn in its
favour. Besides, it might be expected that some unsteadiness or
warping of the wooden stand on which it was supported might affect
the accuracy of the observations; or there might be variable and
discordant refractions, even near the zenith, on the side of so steep
a hill, more than are found in lower situations. . . .

Thus the difference of latitude found by the astronomical observations, comes out greater than the difference of latitude answering
to the distance of the parallels, the former being 54.6 seconds, the
later only 42.94 seconds. The difference 11.6 seconds is to be attributed to the sum of the two contrary attractions of the hill.

The attraction of the hill, computed in a rough manner, on supposition of its density being equal to the mean density of the earth,
and the force of attraction being inversely as the squares of the distances, comes out about double this. Whence it should follow, that
the density of the hill is about half the mean density of the earth.
But this point cannot be properly settled till the figure and dimen-

sions of the hill have been calculated from the survey, and thence the attraction of the hill, found from the calculation of several separate parts of it, into which it is to be divided, which will be a work of much time and labour; the result of which will be communicated at some future opportunity.

Having thus come to a happy end of this experiment, we may now consider several consequences flowing from it, tending to illustrate some important questions in natural philosophy.

1. It appears from this experiment, that the mountain Schehallien exerts a sensible attraction; therefore, from the rules of philosophising, we are to conclude that every mountain, and indeed every particle of the earth, is endued with the same property, in proportion to its quantity of matter.

2. The law of the variation of this force, in the inverse *ratio* of the squares of the distances, as laid down by Sir Isaac Newton, is also confirmed by this experiment. For, if the force of attraction of the hill had been only to that of the earth as the matter in the hill to that of the earth, and had not been greatly increased by the near approach to its centre, the attraction thereof must have been wholly insensible. But now, by only supposing the mean density of the earth to be double to that of the hill, which seems very probable from other considerations, the attraction of the hill will be reconciled to the general law of the variation of attraction in the inverse duplicate *ratio* of the distances, as deduced by Sir Isaac Newton from the comparison of the motion of the heavenly bodies with the force of gravity at the surface of the earth; and the analogy of nature will be preserved.

3. We may now, therefore, be allowed to admit this law; and to acknowledge, that the mean density of the earth is at least double of that at the surface, and consequently, that the density of the internal parts of the earth is much greater than near the surface. Hence also, the whole quantity of matter in the earth will be at least as great again as if it had been all composed of matter of the same

density with that at the surface; or will be about four or five times as great as if it were all composed of water. The idea thus afforded us, from this experiment, of the great density of the internal parts of the earth, is totally contrary to the hypothesis of some naturalists, who suppose the earth to be only a great hollow shell of matter; supporting itself from the property of an arch, with an immense vacuity in the midst of it. But, were that the case, the attraction of mountains, and even smaller inequalities in the earth's surface, would be very great, contrary to experiment, and would affect the measures of the degrees of the meridian much more than we find they do; and the variation of gravity in different latitudes in going from the equator to the poles, as found by pendulums, would not be near so regular as it has been found by experiment to be.

4. The density of the superficial parts of the earth, being, however, sufficient to produce sensible deflections in the plumb-lines of astronomical instruments, will thereby cause apparent inequalities in the mensurations of degrees in the meridian; and therefore it becomes a matter of great importance to chuse those places for measuring degrees, where the irregular attractions of the elevated parts may be small, or in some measure compensate one another; or else it will be necessary to make allowance for their effects, which cannot but be a work of great difficulty, and perhaps liable to great uncertainty.

After all, it is to be wished, that other experiments of the like kind with this were made in various places, attended with different circumstances. We seldom acquire full satisfaction from a single experiment on any subject. Some may doubt, whether the density of the matter near the surface of the earth may not be subject to considerable variation; though perhaps, taking large masses together, the density may be more uniform than is commonly imagined, except in hills that have been volcanos. The mountain Schehallien, however, bears not any appearance of having ever been in that state; it being extremely solid and dense, and seemingly composed of an entire rock. New observations on the attraction of other hills, would tend to procure us satisfaction in these points. But whatever experiments of this kind be made hereafter, let it be always gratefully remembered, that the world is indebted for the first satisfactory one to the learned zeal of the Royal Society, supported by the munificence of George the Third.

HENRY CAVENDISH[1]

1 7 3 1 - 1 8 1 0

HAD THE BRILLIANT and eccentric recluse, Henry Cavendish, published more of his findings, instead of leaving them to gather dust until at last, years after his death, they were discovered, his name would today be as well known in electricity as it is in chemistry and mechanics. He was the elder son of Lord Charles Cavendish, himself an experimenter of great ability, and a nephew of the Duke of Devonshire. Through inheritance he became one of the wealthiest men in England, and spent his entire life in independent scientific research over a wide range of fields. Many of his papers were read at the meetings of the Royal Society, but his important electrical researches—anticipating the discoveries of later men—remained unknown, in possession of the Devonshire family until, late in the nineteenth century, they were edited by James Clerk-Maxwell.

Cavendish's greatest achievement in mechanics was the execution of a new experiment, the results of which made possible a more precise computation of the density of the earth than Maskelyne's. The experiment consisted of careful measurement of the almost inconceivably small gravitational attraction between lead balls.

The following account of a part of this experiment is taken from the Philosophical Transactions of the Royal Society, vol. 88, 1798. The complete account details the exact precautions taken to overcome the influence of any air currents created by the warmth of the weights, and to eliminate all possibility of the magnetism of the earth affecting the experiment.

[1] For Cavendish's most notable work in chemistry, see below, p. 259.

EXPERIMENTS TO DETERMINE
THE DENSITY OF THE EARTH

Read June 21, 1778.

MANY YEARS AGO, the late Rev. John Michell, of this Society, contrived a method of determining the density of the earth, by rendering sensible the attraction of small quantities of matter; but, as he was engaged in other pursuits, he did not complete the apparatus till a short time before his death, and did not live to make any experiments with it. After his death, the apparatus came to the Rev. Francis John Hyde Wollaston, Jacksonian Professor at Cambridge, who, not having conveniences for making experiments with it, in the manner he could wish, was so good as to give it to me.

The apparatus is very simple; it consists of a wooden arm, 6 feet long, made so as to unite great strength with little weight. This arm is suspended in an horizontal position, by a slender wire 40 inches long, and to each extremity is hung a leaden ball, about 2 inches in diameter; and the whole is inclosed in a narrow wooden case, to defend it from the wind.

As no more force is required to make this arm turn round on its centre, than what is necessary to twist the suspending wire, it is plain, that if the wire is sufficiently slender, the most minute force, such as the attraction of a leaden weight a few inches in diameter, will be sufficient to draw the arm sensibly aside. The weights which Mr. Michell intended to use, were 8 inches in diameter. One of these was to be placed on one side the case, opposite to one of the balls, and as near it as could conveniently be done, and the other on the other side, opposite to the other ball, so that the attraction of both these weights would conspire in drawing the arm aside;

and when its position, as affected by these weights, was ascertained, the weights were to be removed to the other side of the case, so as to draw the arm the contrary way, and the position of the arm was to be again determined; consequently, half the difference of these positions would show how much the arm was drawn aside by the attraction of the weights.

In order to determine from hence the density of the earth, it is necessary to ascertain what force is required to draw the arm aside through a given space. This Mr. Michell intended to do, by putting the arm in motion, and observing the time of its vibrations, from which it may easily be computed.[1]

Mr. Michell had prepared 2 wooden stands, on which the leaden weights were to be supported, and pushed forwards, till they came almost in contact with the case; but he seems to have intended to move them by hand.

As the force with which the balls are attracted by these weights is excessively minute, not more than 1/50,000,000 of their weight, it is plain that a very minute disturbing force will be sufficient to destroy the success of the experiment; and from the following experiments it will appear, that the disturbing force most difficult to guard against, is that arising from the variations of heat and cold; for if one side of the case be warmer than the other, the air in contact with it will be rarefied, and in consequence will ascend, while that on the other side will descend, and produce a current which will draw the arm sensibly aside.

As I was convinced of the necessity of guarding against this source of error, I resolved to place the apparatus in a room which should remain constantly shut, and to observe the motion of the arm from without, by means of a telescope; and to suspend the leaden weights in such manner, that I could move them without entering into the

---

[1] Mr. Coulomb has, in a variety of cases, used a contrivance of this kind for trying small attractions; but Mr. Michell informed me of his intention of making this experiment, and of the method he intended to use, before the publication of any of Mr. Coulomb's experiments.

room. This difference in the manner of observing, rendered it necessary to make some alteration in Mr. Michell's apparatus; and as
there were some parts of it which I thought not so convenient as
could be wished, I chose to make the greatest part of it anew. . . .

. . . . [Now] the position of the arm may be observed with ease
to 100ths of an inch, and may be estimated to less. These divisions

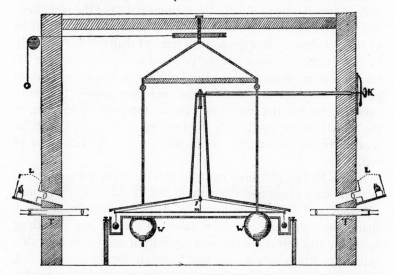

are viewed, by means of the short telescopes T and T [see fig.],
through slits cut in the end of the case, and stopped with glass;
they are enlightened by the lamps . . . placed so as to throw the
light on the divisions; no other light being admitted to the room. . . .

K [see fig.] is a wooden rod, which, by means of an endless screw
. . . enables the observer to turn round the wire, till the arm settles
in the middle of the case, without danger of touching either side.
The wire g is fastened to its support at top, and to the centre of
the arm at bottom, by brass clips, in which it is pinched by screws.
In these 2 figures, the different parts are drawn nearly in the proper
proportion to each other. . . .

Before I proceed to the account of the experiments, it will be proper to say something of the manner of observing. Suppose the arm to be at rest, and its position to be observed, let the weights be then moved, the arm will not only be drawn aside thereby, but it will be made to vibrate, and its vibrations will continue a great while; so that, in order to determine how much the arm is drawn aside, it is necessary to observe the extreme points of the vibrations, and from thence to determine the point which it would rest at if its motion was destroyed, or the point of rest, as I shall call it. To do this, I observe three successive extreme points of a vibration, and take the mean between the first and the third of these points, as the extreme point of vibration in one direction, and then assume the mean between this and the second extreme, as the point of rest; for, as the vibrations are continually diminishing, it is evident that the mean between two extreme points will not give the true point of rest.

It may be thought more exact to observe many extreme points of vibration, so as to find the point of rest by different sets of three extremes, and to take the mean result; but it must be observed, that notwithstanding the pains taken to prevent any disturbing force, the arm will seldom remain perfectly at rest for an hour altogether; for which reason, it is best to determine the point of rest, from observations made as soon after the motion of the weights as possible.

The next thing to be determined is the time of vibration, which I find in this manner: I observe the two extreme points of a vibration, and also the times at which the arm arrives at two given divisions between these extremes, taking care, as well as I can guess, that these divisions shall be on different sides of the middle point, and not very far from it. I then compute the middle point of the vibration, and, by proportion, find the time at which the arm comes to this middle point. I then, after a number of vibrations, repeat this operation, and divide the interval of time, between the coming of the arm to these two middle points, by the number of vibrations, which gives the time of one vibration. . . .

[A detailed account of seventeen experiments is omitted.]

From this table it appears, that though the experiments agree pretty well together, yet the difference between them, both in the quantity of motion of the arm and in the time of vibration, is greater than can proceed merely from the error of observation. As to the difference in the motion of the arm, it may very well be accounted for, from the current of air produced by the difference of temperature; but whether this can account for the difference the density of the earth is 4½ times that of water; which differs rather more from the preceding determination than I should have expected. But I forbear entering into any consideration of which determination is most to be depended on, till I have examined more carefully how much of the preceding determination is affected by irregularities whose quantity I cannot measure.

WILLIAM HERSCHEL[1]

1 7 3 8 · 1 8 2 2

AIDED BY superb new telescopes of his own making, which brought thousands of previously unseen stellar bodies to his eyes, William Herschel undertook to determine the patterns in which the stars are distributed in space. It had always been obvious that the stars visible to the naked eye seemed closer together in some areas, such as the Milky Way, than in the rest of the heavens. Herschel found this to be true of the fainter and more distant bodies, which he was the first to see. He directed his telescope systematically to a thousand positions across the heavens, and found that in some directions as many as five hundred stars could be seen at once, while in others only one or two were visible. Herschel concluded that our earth is part of an island universe or galaxy, shaped like a thick pancake or grindstone, with our solar system somewhat displaced from the center.

In addition to distinct stars, Herschel saw a great number of cloudy nebulae of various shapes, as well as many star clusters which he thought to be great galaxies like our own, in outer space. The essay quoted below describes his new method of mapping the heavens, and some of his conclusions.

Like many other famous astronomers, Herschel started as an amateur. He was born in Germany; served in the band of the Hanoverian Guards from the age of fourteen to nineteen; resigned after seeing severe fighting in the Seven Years' War; became church organist in Bath, England, and then took up astronomy as a hobby. He made the finest telescopes of his day, and, in 1781, discovered the

[1] For Herschel's experiments with light, see below, p. 200.

planet Uranus, a feat which brought him fame and a position as "Astronomer to the King," with a small stipend. The article here quoted was read in June, 1784, before a meeting of the Royal Society of London, and appears in the Philosophical Transactions for that year.

OBSERVATIONS ON THE
CONSTRUCTION OF THE HEAVENS

IN A FORMER paper I mentioned that a more powerful instrument was preparing for continuing my reviews of the heavens. The telescope I have lately completed, though far inferior in size to the one I had undertaken to construct when that paper was written, is of the Newtonian form, the object speculum being 20 feet focal length, and its aperture 18 7/10 inches. . . .

It would, perhaps, have been more eligible to have waited longer, in order to complete the discoveries that seem to lie within the reach of this instrument, and are already, in some respects, pointed out to me by it. By taking more time I would undoubtedly be enabled to speak more confidently of the interior construction of the heavens, and its various nebulous and sidereal strata (to borrow a term from the natural historian) of which this paper can as yet only give a few outlines, or rather hints. As an apology, however, for this pre-maturity, it may be said, that the end of all discoveries being communication, we can never be too ready in giving facts and observations, whatever we may be in reasoning upon them.

Hitherto the sidereal heavens have, not inadequately for the purpose designed, been represented by the concave surface of a sphere, in the center of which the eye of an observer might be supposed to be placed. It is true, the various magnitudes of the fixed stars even then plainly suggested to us and would have better suited the idea of an expanded firmament of three dimensions; but the observations upon which I am now going to enter still farther illustrate and enforce the necessity of considering the heavens in this point of view. In future, therefore, we shall look upon those regions into which we may now penetrate by means of such large telescopes, as a naturalist regards a rich extent of ground or chain of mountains, containing strata variously inclined and directed, as well as consisting of very different materials. A surface of a globe or map, therefore, will but ill delineate the interior parts of the heavens.

It may well be expected that the great advantage of a large aperture would be most sensibly perceived with all those objects that require much light, such as the very small and immensely distant fixed stars, the very faint nebulae and close and compressed clusters of stars, and the remote planets.

On applying the telescope to a part of the Milky Way, I found that it completely resolved the whole whitish appearance into small stars, which my former telescopes had not light enough to effect. The portion of this extensive tract which it has hitherto been convenient for me to observe is that immediately about the hand and club of Orion. The glorious multitude of stars of all possible sizes that presented themselves here to my view was truly astonishing; but, as the dazzling brightness of glittering stars may easily mislead us so far as to estimate their number greater than it really is, I endeavored to ascertain this point by counting many fields, and computing, from a mean of them, what a certain given portion of the Milky Way might contain. Among many trials of this sort I found, last January the 18th, that six fields, promiscuously taken, contained 110, 60, 70, 90, 70, and 74 stars each. I then tried to pick out the most vacant place that was to be found in that neighborhood, and counted 63 stars. A mean of the first six gives 79 stars for each field. Hence, by allowing 15 minutes of a great circle for the diameter of my field of view, we gather that a belt of 15 degrees long and two broad, or the quantity which I have often seen pass through the field of my telescope in one hour's time, could not well contain less than fifty thousand stars, that were large enough to be distinctly numbered. But, besides these, I suspected at least twice as many more, which, for want of light, I could only see now and then by faint glittering and interrupted glimpses.

The excellent collection of nebulae and clusters of stars which has lately been given in the *Connaissance des Temps* for 1783 and 1784, leads me next to a subject which, indeed, must open a new view of the heavens. As soon as the first of these volumes came to my hands, I applied my former 20-feet reflector of 12 inches aperture to them; and saw, with the greatest pleasure, that most of the nebulae, which I had an opportunity of examining in proper situations, yielded to the force of my light and power, and were resolved into stars; and many which are said to be nebulae without stars, have either plainly appeared to be nothing but stars, or at least to contain stars, and to shew every other indication of consisting of them entirely. . . . I expect my present telescope will, perhaps, render the stars visible of which I suppose them to be composed. Here I might point out many precautions necessary to be taken with the very best instruments, in order to succeed in the resolution of the most difficult of them; but reserving this at present too extensive subject for a future opportunity, I proceed to speak of the effects of my last instrument with regard to nebulae. . . .

When I began my present series of observations, I surmised that several nebulae might yet remain undiscovered, for want of sufficient light to detect them; and was, therefore, in hopes of making a valuable addition to the clusters of stars and nebulae already collected and given us in the work before referred to, which amount to 103. The event has plainly proved that my expectations were well founded; for I have already found 466 new nebulae and clusters of stars, none of which, to my present knowledge, have been seen before by any person; most of them, indeed, are not within the reach of the best common telescopes now in use. In all probability many more are still in reserve; and as I am pursuing this track, I shall make them up into separate catalogues, of about two or three hundred at a time, and have the honor of presenting them in that form to the Royal Society.

A very remarkable circumstance attending the nebulae and clusters of stars is that they are arranged into strata, which seem to run on to a great length; and some of them I have already been able to pursue, so as to guess pretty well at their form and direction. It is probable enough that they may surround the whole apparent sphere of the heavens, not unlike the Milky Way, which undoubtedly is nothing but a stratum of fixed stars. And as this latter immense starry bed is not of equal breadth or lustre in every part, nor runs on in one straight direction, but is curved and even divided into two streams along a very considerable portion of it, we may likewise expect the greatest variety in the strata of the clusters of stars and nebulae. One of these nebulous beds is so rich that, in passing through a section of it, in the time of only 36 minutes, I detected no less than 31 nebulae, all distinctly visible upon a fine blue sky. Their situation and shape, as well as condition, seems to denote the greatest variety imaginable. In another stratum, or perhaps a different branch of the former, I have seen double and treble nebulae, variously arranged; large ones with small, seeming attendants; narrow but much extended, lucid nebulae or bright dashes; some of the shape of a fan, resembling an electric brush, issuing from a lucid point; others of the cometic shape, with a seeming nucleus in the center; or like cloudy stars, surrounded with a nebulous atmosphere; a different sort again contain a nebulosity of the milky kind, like that wonderful inexplicable phaenomenon about Orion; while others shine with a fainter, mottled kind of light, which denotes their being resolvable into stars. But it should be too extensive at present to enter more minutely into such circumstances; therefore I proceed with the subject of nebulous and sidereal strata.

It is very probable that the great stratum, called the Milky Way, is that in which the sun is placed, though perhaps not in the very center of its thickness. We gather this from the appearance of the Galaxy, which seems to encompass the whole heavens, as it certainly must do if the sun is within the same. For, suppose a number of stars arranged between two parallel planes, indefinitely extended every way, but at a given considerable distance from each other; and, calling this a sidereal stratum, an eye placed somewhere within it will see all the stars in the direction of the planes of the stratum projected into a great circle, which will appear lucid on account of the accumulation of the stars; while the rest of the heavens, at the sides, will only seem to be scattered over with constellations, more or less crowded, according to the distance of the planes or number of stars contained in the thickness or sides of the stratum. . . .

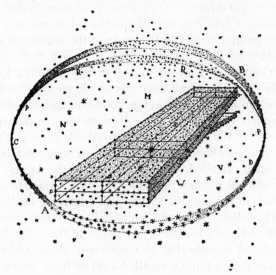

Herschel's picture of the Milky Way.

If the eye were placed somewhere without the stratum, at no very great distance, the appearance of the stars within it would assume the form of one of the less circles of the sphere, which would be more or less contracted to the distance of the eye; and if this distance were exceedingly increased, the whole stratum might at last be drawn together into a lucid spot of any shape, according to the position, length, and height of the stratum. . . .

From appearances then, as I observed before, we may infer that the sun is most likely placed in one of the great strata of the fixed stars, and very probably not far from the place where some smaller stratum branches out from it. Such a supposition will satisfactorily, and with great simplicity, account for all the phaenomena of the Milky Way, which, according to this hypothesis, is no other than the appearance of the projection of the stars contained in this stratum and its secondary branch. As a farther inducement to look at the Galaxy in this point of view, let it be considered that we can no longer doubt of its whitish appearance arising from the mixed lustre of the numberless stars that compose it. Now, should we imagine it to be an irregular ring of stars, in the center nearly of which we must then suppose the sun to be placed, it will appear not a little extraordinary that the sun, being a fixed star like those which compose this imagined ring, should just be in the center of such a multitude of celestial bodies, without any apparent reason for this singular distinction; whereas, on our supposition, every star in this stratum, not very near the termination of its length or height, will be so placed as also to have its own Galaxy, with only such variations in the form and lustre of it as may arise from the particular situation of each star.

Various methods may be pursued to come to a full knowledge of the sun's place in the sidereal stratum, of which I shall only mention one as the most general and most proper for determining this important point, and which I have already begun to put in practice. I call it *Gaging the Heavens,* or the *Star-Gage.* It consists in repeatedly taking the number of stars in ten fields of view of my reflector very near each other, and by adding their sums, and cutting off one decimal on the right, a mean of the contents of the heavens, in all the parts which are thus gaged, is obtained. By way of example, I have joined a short table, extracted from the gages contained in my journal, by which it appears that the number of stars increases very fast as we approach the Milky Way.

PIERRE SIMON,
MARQUIS DE LAPLACE [1]

1 7 4 9 · 1 8 2 7

WHILE OTHER MEN were concerned with outer space, the French mathematical astronomer, Laplace, remained primarily interested in the structure and origin of our solar system. He did extensive work in the theory of tides; he proved analytically that the solar system is essentially stable. Finally, he assembled and codified all existing data on dynamic astronomy, publishing his work, in 1796, in five large volumes, under the title, La Mécanique Céleste (The System of the Heavens). The selection which follows is the sixth chapter of Book V, Volume II, translated from the French by J. Pond in 1809. It summarizes astronomical discoveries to the end of the eighteenth century, and includes Laplace's own "nebular hypothesis," a view of world origins which was to be popularly accepted for the next hundred years.

[1] For another selection from Laplace, see below, p. 620.

CONSIDERATIONS ON THE SYSTEM
OF THE UNIVERSE

LET US NOW direct our attention to the arrangement of the solar system, and its relation with the stars. The immense globe of the Sun, the focus of these motions, revolves upon its axis in twenty-five days and a half. Its surface is covered with an ocean of luminous matter, whose active effervescence forms variable spots, often very numerous, and sometimes larger than the Earth. Above this ocean exists an immense atmosphere, in which the planets, with their satellites, move, in orbits nearly circular, and in planes a little inclined to the ecliptic. Innumerable comets, after having approached the Sun, remove to distances, which evince that his empire extends beyond the known limits of the planetary system.

This luminary not only acts by its attraction upon all these globes, and compels them to move around him, but imparts to them both light and heat; his benign influence gives birth to the animals and plants which cover the surface of the Earth, and analogy induces us to believe, that it produces similar effects on the planets; for it is not natural to suppose that matter, of which we see the fecundity develope itself in such various ways, should be sterile upon a planet so large as Jupiter, which, like the Earth, has its days, its nights, and its years, and on which observation discovers changes that indicate very active forces. Man, formed for the temperature which he enjoys upon the Earth, could not, according to all appearance, live upon the other planets; but ought there not to be a diversity of organization suited to the various temperatures of the globes of this universe? If the difference of elements and climates alone causes such variety in the productions of the Earth, how infinitely diversified must be the productions of the planets and their satellites? The most active imagination cannot form any just idea of them, but still their existence is extremely probable.

However arbitrary the system of the planets may be, there exists between them some very remarkable relations, which may throw light on their origin; considering them with attention, we are astonished to see all the planets move round the Sun from west to east, and nearly in the same plane, all the satellites moving round their respective planets in the same direction and nearly in the same plane with the planets. Lastly, the Sun, the planets, and those satellites in which a motion of rotation has been observed, turn on their own axis, in the same direction, and nearly in the same plane as their motion of projection.

A phenomenon so extraordinary is not the effect of chance; it indicates an universal cause, which has determined all these motions. To approximate somewhat to the probable explanation of this cause, we should observe that the planetary system, such as we now consider it, is composed of seven planets, and fourteen satellites. We have observed the rotation of the Sun, of five planets, of the Moon, of Saturn's ring, and of his farthest satellite; these motions with those of revolution, form together thirty direct movements, in the same direction. If we conceive the plane of any direct motion whatever coinciding at first with that of the ecliptic, afterwards inclining itself towards this last plane, and passing over all the degrees of inclination, from zero to half the circumference; it is clear that the motion will be direct in all its inferior inclinations to a hundred degrees, and that it will be retrograde in its inclination beyond that; so that, by the change of inclination alone, the direct and retrograde motions of the solar system can be represented. Beheld in this point of view, we may reckon twenty-nine motions, of which the planes are inclined to that of the Earth, at most one-fourth of the circumference; but supposing their inclinations had been the effect of chance, they would have extended to half the circumference, and the probability that one of them would have exceeded the quarter, would be 1—1/29, or $\frac{536870911}{536870912}$. It is then extremely probable that the direction of the planetary motion is not the effect of chance, and this becomes still more probable, if we consider that the inclination of the greatest number of these motions to the ecliptic is very small, and much less than a quarter of the circumference.

Another phenomenon of the solar system equally remarkable, is the small excentricity of the orbits of the planets and their satellites, while those of comets are much extended. The orbits of the system offer no intermediate shades between a great and small excentricity. We are here again compelled to acknowledge the effect of a regular cause; chance alone could not have given a form nearly circular to the orbits of all the planets. This cause then must also have influenced the great excentricity of the orbits of comets, and, what is very extraordinary, without having any influence on the direction of their motion; for, in observing the orbits of retrograde comets, as being inclined more than 100 degrees to the ecliptic, we find that the mean inclination of the orbits of all the observed comets approaches near to 100 degrees, which would not be the case if the bodies had been projected at random.

Thus, to investigate the cause of the primitive motions of the planets, we have given the five following phenomena: 1st, The motions of planets in the same direction, and nearly in the same plane. 2d, The motion of their satellites in the same direction, and nearly in the same plane with those of the planets. 3d, The motion of rotation of these different bodies, and of the Sun in the same direction as their motion of projection, and in planes but little different. 4th, The small excentricity of the orbits of the planets, and of their satellites. 5th, The great excentricity of the orbits of comets, although their inclinations may have been left to chance.

Buffon [1] is the only one whom I have known, who, since the dis-

---

[1] For Buffon's theory of the origin of the earth, see below, p. 366.

covery of the true system of the world, has endeavoured to investigate the origin of the planets, and of their satellites. He supposes that a comet, in falling from the Sun, may have driven off a torrent of matter, which united itself at a distance into various globes, greater or smaller, and more or less distant from this luminary. These globes are the planets and satellites, which, by their cooling, are become opaque and solid.

This hypothesis accounts for the first of the five preceding phenomena; for, it is clear that all bodies thus formed must move nearly in the plane which passes through the centre of the Sun, and in the direction of the torrent of matter which produces them. The four other phenomena appear to me inexplicable by his theory. In fact, the absolute motion of the particles of a planet would then be in the same direction as the motion of its centre of gravity; but it does not follow that the rotation of the planet would be in the same direction. Thus, the Earth may turn from west to east, and yet the absolute direction of each of its particles may be from east to west. What I say of the rotatory motion of the planets is equally applicable to the motion of their satellites in their orbits, of which the direction in the hypothesis he adopts is not necessarily the same with the projectile motion of the planets.

The small excentricity of the motion of the planetary orbits is not only very difficult to explain on this hypothesis, but the phenomenon contradicts it. We know by the theory of central forces, that if a body moving in an orbit round the Sun touched the surface of this luminary, it would uniformly return to it at the completion of each revolution, from whence it follows, that if the planets had originally been detached from the Sun, they would have touched it at every revolution, and their orbits, far from being circular, would be very excentric. It is true that a torrent of matter, sent off from the Sun, cannot correctly be compared to a globe which touches its surface. The impulse which the particles of this torrent receive from one another, and the reciprocal attraction exercised among them may change the direction of their motion, and increase their perihelion distances; but their orbits would uniformly become very excentric, or at least it must be a very extraordinary chance that would give them excentricities so small as those of the planets. In a word, we do not see, in this hypothesis of Buffon, why the orbits of about eighty comets, already observed, are all very elliptical. This hypothesis, then, is far from accounting for the preceding phenomena. Let us see if it is possible to arrive at their true cause.

Whatever be its nature, since it has produced or directed the motion of the planets and their satellites, it must have embraced all these bodies, and considering the prodigious distance which separates them, it can only be a fluid of immense extent. To have given in the same direction, a motion nearly circular round the Sun, this fluid must have surrounded the luminary like an atmosphere. This view, therefore, of planetary motion leads us to think that, in consequence of excessive heat, the atmosphere of the Sun originally extended beyond the orbits of all the planets, and that it has gradually contracted itself to its present limits, which may have taken place from causes similar to those which caused the famous star that suddenly appeared in 1572, in the constellation Cassiopaea, to shine with the most brilliant splendour during many months. . . .

But how has it determined the motions of revolution and rotation of the planets? If these bodies had penetrated this fluid, its resistance would have caused them to fall into the Sun. We may then conjecture that they have been formed at the successive bounds of this atmosphere, by the condensation of zones, which it must have abandoned in the plane of its equator, and which in becoming cold have condensed themselves towards the surface of this luminary, as we have seen in the preceding Book. One may likewise conjecture that the satellites have been formed in a similar way by the atmosphere of the planets. The five phenomena, explained above, naturally result from this hypothesis, to which the rings of Saturn add an additional degree of probability.

Whatever may have been the origin of this arrangement of the planetary system, which I offer with that distrust which every thing ought to inspire that is not the result of observation or calculation, it is certain that its elements are so arranged that it must possess the greatest stability, if foreign observations do not disturb it. Through this cause alone, that the motions of planets and satellites are nearly circular, and impelled in the same direction, and in planes differing but little from each other, it arises that this system can only oscillate to a certain extent, from which its deviation must be extremely limited; the mean motions of rotation and revolution of these different bodies are uniform, and their mean distances to the foci of the principal forces which animate them are uniform. It seems that nature has disposed every thing in the heavens to insure the duration of the system, by views similar to those which she appears to us admirably to follow upon Earth, to preserve the individual and insure the perpetuity of the species.

Let us now look beyond the solar system. Innumerable suns, which may be the foci of as many planetary systems, are spread out in the immensity of space, and at such a distance from the Earth, that the entire diameter of it, seen from the center, is insensible. Many stars experience both in their colour and splendour, periodical variations very remarkable; there are some which have appeared all at once, and disappeared after having some time spread a brilliant light. What prodigious change must have operated on the surface of these great bodies, to be thus sensible at the distance which separates them from us, and how much they must exceed those which we observe on the surface of the Sun? All these bodies which are become invisible remain in the same place where they were observed, since there was no change during the time of their appearance; there exist then in space obscure bodies as considerable, and perhaps as numerous, as the stars. A luminous star, of the same density as the Earth, and whose diameter should be two hundred and fifty times larger than that of the Sun, would not, in consequence of its attraction, allow any of its rays to arrive at us; it is therefore possible that the largest luminous bodies in the universe may, through this cause, be invisible. A star, which, without being of this magnitude, should yet considerably surpass the Sun, would perceptibly weaken the velocity of its light, and thus augment the extent of its aberration. This difference in the aberration of stars and their situation, observed at the moment of their transient splendour, the determination of all the changeable stars, and the periodical variations of their light—in a word, the motions peculiar to all those great bodies, which, influenced by their mutual attraction, and probably by their primitive impulses, describe immense orbits, should, relatively to the stars, be the principal objects of future astronomy.

It appears that these stars, far from being disseminated at distances nearly equal in space, are united in various groups, each consisting of many millions of stars. Our Sun and the most brilliant stars probably make part of one of these groups, which, seen from the point where we are, seems to encircle the heavens, and forms the Milky Way. The great number of stars which are seen at once in the field of a large telescope directed towards this Way, proves its immense depth, which surpasses a thousand times the distance of Sirius from the Earth; as it recedes, it terminates, by presenting the appearance of a white and continued light of small diameter, for then the irradiation which exists even in the most powerful telescopes covers and obscures the intervals between the stars. It is then probable that those nebulae without distinct stars are groups of stars seen from a distance, and which, if approached, would present appearances similar to the Milky Way.

The relative distances of the stars which form each group are at least a hundred thousand times greater than the distance of the Sun from the Earth. Thus, we may judge of the prodigious extent of these groups by the number of stars which are perceived in the Milky Way, if we afterwards reflect on the small extent and infinite number of nebulae which are separated from one another by an interval incomparably greater than the relative distance of the stars of which they are formed. The imagination, lost in the immensity of the universe, will have difficulty to conceive its bounds.

From these considerations, founded on telescopic observations, it follows that nebulae, which appear so well defined that their centres can be precisely determined, are, with regard to us, the celestial objects most fixed, and those to which it is best to refer the situation of all the stars. It follows, then, that the motions of the bodies of our solar system are very complicated. The Moon describes an orbit nearly circular around the Earth; but, seen from the Sun, she describes a series of epicycloids, of which the centres are on the circumference of the terrestrial orbit. In like manner, the Earth describes a series of epicycloids, of which the centres are on the arc which the Sun describes around the centre of gravity of our nebulae; finally, the Sun himself describes a series of epicycloids, of which the centres are on the arc described by the centre of gravity of our nebulae around that of the universe.

Astronomy has already made one great step in making us acquainted with the motion of the Earth, and the series of epicycles which the Moon and the satellites describe upon the orbits of the planets. It remains to determine the orbit of the Sun, and the centre of gravity of its nebulae; but, if ages are necessary to become acquainted with the motions of the planetary system, what a prodigious duration of time will it require to determine the motions of the Sun and stars? Observation begins to render them perceptible; an attempt has been made to explain them by a change of position in the Sun, indicated by its rotatory motion. Many observations are sufficiently well explained by supposing the solar system carried towards the constellation Hercules. Other observations seem to prove that these apparent motions of the stars are a combination of their real motion with that of the Sun. Upon this subject, time will discover curious and important facts.

There still remain numerous discoveries to be made in our own system. The planet Uranus and its satellites, but lately known to us, leaves room to suspect the existence of other planets, hitherto unobserved. We cannot yet determine the rotatory motion, or the flattening of many of the planets, and the greatest part of their satellites. We know not, with sufficient precision, the density of all these bodies. The theory of their motions is a series of approximations, whose convergence depends, at the same time, on the perfection of our instruments and the progress of analysis, and which must, by these means, daily acquire new degrees of correctness. By accurate and repeated measurement, the inequalities in the figure of the Earth and the variation of weight on its surface will be determined. The return of comets already observed, new comets which will appear, the appearance of those which, moving in hyperbolic orbits, can wander from system to system, the disturbance all those stars experience, and which, at the approach of a large planet, may entirely change their orbits, as is conjectured happened by the action of Jupiter on the comet of 1770; the accidents that the proximity, and even the shock of these bodies may occasion in the planets and in the satellites; in a word, the changes which the motions of the solar system experience with respect to the stars, such are the principal objects which the system presents to astronomical researches, and future geometricians.

Contemplated as one grand whole, astronomy is the most beautiful monument of the human mind, the noblest record of its intelligence. Seduced by the illusions of the senses and of self-love, man considered himself, for a long time, as the centre of the motion of the celestial bodies, and his pride was justly punished by the vain terrors they inspired. The labour of many ages has at length withdrawn the veil which covered the system. Man appears upon a small planet, almost imperceptible in the vast extent of the solar system, itself only an insensible point in the immensity of space. The sublime results to which this discovery has led may console him for the limited place assigned him in the universe. Let us carefully preserve, and even augment the number of these sublime discoveries, which form the delight of thinking beings.

They have rendered important services to navigation and astronomy; but their great benefit has been that they have dissipated the alarms occasioned by extraordinary celestial phenomena, and destroyed the errors springing from the ignorance of our true relation with nature; errors so much the more fatal as social order can only rest in the basis of these relations. TRUTH, JUSTICE, these are its immutable laws. Far from us be the dangerous maxim that it is sometimes useful to mislead, to deceive, and enslave men, to insure their happiness. Cruel experience has at all times proved that with impunity these sacred laws can never be infringed.

II

Light, Heat, and Fire

WHEN THE EARLY philosophers developed the theory that matter consisted of a mixture of just four elements—namely, earth, air, water, and fire—a view which everyone held for many centuries, they grouped all the phenomena of light, heat, and flame under fire. It was apparent to them that when anything burned, all these three aspects were present, and the conclusion that they were necessarily connected aspects of a single element seemed obvious.

Little by little, however, they had to admit exceptions to this rule. The glow of phosphorus and of decaying wood—that strange phosphorescence without heat—the warmth of frictional heat, which was not invariably accompanied by light and flame, and similar inconsistencies brought about many fanciful explanations, none of which led closer to the truth.

With the advent of the scientific age, the problems of heat, light, and fire, although still held to be closely related to each other, began to be considered each by itself. Fire, as one of the four classical elements, still might stand for light, flame, or heat, as best suited the meaning of the speaker. But in order to simplify the description of the processes that take place in the burning of materials and in the calcination of metals,[1] Georg Ernst Stahl (1660-1734), a German court physician and professor, asserted the existence of a fluid which he called *phlogiston*. This fluid existed, he said, in metals and in combustible materials of every kind, and disappeared from metals when they were calcined and from

[1] Metals when subjected for a long time to intense heat in the presence of air or oxygen turn to powder; this process is known as calcination.

the other materials when they burned. On the other hand, he said, when the powder of calcined metals (now called oxides) was heated together with a material containing phlogiston, such as carbon, the metal was restored by the reintroduction of the needful amount of phlogiston. Although entirely false, the phlogiston theory did permit simpler explanations than before of many natural processes. It was still the approved theory at the time of Priestley, Cavendish, Scheele, Black, and the young Lavoisier. In his later work, Lavoisier showed by careful measurements that the theory was erroneous and that both the calcination of metals and the combustion of other substances were examples of oxidation.

Heat too was supposed by eighteenth century chemists (in spite of previous guesses in the right direction) to be an intangible fluid, which they called *caloric*. Vestiges of this belief linger in our present-day vocabulary, as when we speak of the "flow" of heat. But already primitive thermometers had been invented to attempt the measurement of heat as it had never been done before. Fahrenheit's invention of the closed mercury thermometer now eliminated the effects of barometric pressure from temperature readings, and Black's more careful quantitative studies led to a distinction between the intensity of heat (degrees of temperature) and the quantity of heat (now measured in calories).

Scheele's studies of the transmission of radiant heat, which could be reflected like light, combined with Count Rumford's discovery that air, water, flame, and steam were all non-conductors of heat, led to a greater strain on the caloric theory. Finally, in 1798, Rumford reported his classic experiments with gun castings, which proved beyond question that heat was not a substance; that limitless quantities of it could be created by friction. Two years later Herschel demonstrated the continuity of heat and light rays from the sun, thus showing that the long association of heat with light was neither a human error nor a trivial coincidence, and that the transmission of radiant heat and light could be explained by the same laws.

During these years light was explained by two theories. The selections presented here include Huygens' early discussion of light as a motion of waves in a medium rarer than air, which he called *ether*. It is followed by

Newton's report of his remarkable experiments proving that light of different colors is bent differently by a prism of glass, and his conclusion that sensations of light are produced by streams of material particles moving swiftly through the air. The authority of the great Newton relegated Huygens' theory to the background for a hundred and fifty years. Herschel, in his discussion of the subject, spoke of "particles of light of certain momenta." But not long afterwards Thomas Young (1773-1829), in a study of the interference of light rays, revived Huygens' theory of light as wave motion in ether, and it then became the accepted theory of the nineteenth century. Today both theories, though seemingly so incompatible, are admitted. The propagation of light is usually explained as wave motion, but in other ways light is observed to act as if composed of Newtonian particles.

ROBERT HOOKE[1]

1 6 3 5 - 1 7 0 3

THE FOLLOWING account of the invention of the magic lantern, written about fifty years after Galileo first looked through his telescope, was duly printed in the Philosophical Transactions of the newiy formed Royal Society of London for August 1668, with the testimony of the editor that the contrivance had actually been constructed. It is typical of the less technical material which interested the leading scientists at the threshold of modern science.

[1] For other work of Robert Hooke, see above, p. 88.

A MAGIC LANTERN

§

A Contrivance to make the Picture of anything appear on a
Wall, Cub-board, or within a Picture-frame, &c. in the
midst of a Light room in the Day-time; or in the Night-
time, in any room that is enlightened with a considerable
number of Candles; devised and communicated by the
Ingenious Mr. Hook, as follows;

THIS OPTICAL Experiment, here to be described, is New, though
easy and obvious; and hath not, that I know, been ever made by any
other person this way. It produces Effects not onely very delightful,
but to such as know not the contrivance, very wonderful; so that
Spectators, not well versed in *Opticks*, that should see the various
Apparitions and Disappearances, the Motions, Changes, and
Actions, that may this way be represented, would readily believe
them to be super-natural and miraculous, and would as easily be
affected with all those passions of Love, Fear, Reverence, Honour,
and Astonishment, that are the natural consequences of such belief.
And had the *Heathen* Priests of old been acquainted with it, their
Oracles and Temples would have been much more famous for the
Miracles of their Imaginary Deities. For by such an Art as this,
what could they not have represented in their Temples? Apparitions
of Angels, or Devils, Inscriptions and Oracles on Walls; the Prospect
of Countryes, Cities, Houses, Navies, Armies; the Actions and Motions of Men, Beasts, Birds, &c. the vanishing of them in a cloud,
and their appearing no more after the cloud is vanisht: And indeed
almost any thing, that may be seen, may by this contrivance be very
vividly and distinctly represented, in such a manner, that, unless to
very curious and sagacious persons, the means how such Appari-

tions are made, shall not be discoverable. The way in short is this:

Opposite to the place or wall where the Apparition is to be, let a Hole be made of about a foot in diameter, or bigger; if there be a high Window that hath a Casement in it, 'twill be so much the better. Without this hole or Casement, open'd at a convenient distance (that it may not be perceived by the Company in the room), place the Picture or Object which you will represent, inverted, and by means of Looking-glasses placed behind, if the picture be *transparent*, reflect the rayes of the Sun so as that they may pass through it towards the place where it is to be represented; and to the end that no rayes may pass besides it, let the Picture be encompass'd on every side with a board or cloath. If the Object be a *Statue*, or some living Creature, then it must be very much enlightn'd by casting the Sunbeams on it by Refraction, Reflexion, or both. Between this Object, and the Place where 'tis to be represented, there is to be placed a broad Convex-glass, ground of such a convexity as that it may represent the Object distinct on the said place; which any one that hath any insight in the *Opticks*, may easily direct. The nearer it is placed to the object, the more is the Object magnified on the Wall, and the further off, the less; which diversity is effected by Glasses of several spheres. If the Object cannot be *inverted* (as 'tis pretty difficult to do with Living Animals, Candles, &c), then there must be *two* large Glasses of convenient Spheres, and they plac'd at their appropriated distances (which are very easily found by tryals), so as to make the representation *erect* as well as the Object.

These Objects, Reflecting and Refracting Glasses, and the whole Apparatus; as also the Persons employ'd to order, change, and make use of them, must be placed without the said high Window or Hole, so that they may not be perceived by the Spectators in the room; and the whole Operation will be easily perform'd.

The particular manner of preparing the Objects, adapting the Glasses, collecting the Rayes of the Sun, varying the Object, making the representations of the Sky (by the help of other Glasses) and of

Clouds (by the help of Smoak) &c. I intend hereafter, when I have leisure and opportunity, more particularly to describe; as also the way of making a natural *Landskip*, &c. to appear upon the walls of a *light* room; which will not only be very pleasant but of great use in painting. Whatsoever may be done by means of the Sun beams in the Day-time, the same may be done with much more ease in the night, by the help of torches, lamps, or other bright lights, plac'd about the Objects, according to the several sorts of them.

So far our Inventor; who hath not contented himself with the bare speculation, but put the same in practice some years since, in the presence of several members of the R. *Society,* among whom the *Publisher* had the good fortune to see the successful performance of what is here delivered.

CHRISTIAN HUYGENS

1 6 2 9 - 1 6 9 5

SEVENTEENTH CENTURY astronomers had to make their own telescopes. And because telescopes are essentially light-gathering instruments, the best minds were led to consider afresh what light is and
how it acts.

Christian Huygens, son of a distinguished Dutch poet, inventor of
the first good pendulum clock and discoverer of the rings of Saturn,
was the first to propound a "wave theory" of light. At the time that
Newton was teaching optics at Cambridge, Huygens in France was
developing a comprehensive theory of the way that light waves travel
through space. This view was not, however, generally accepted until
after 1800, up to which time Newton's "corpuscular" theory held
sway. Today we know that the two are not mutually exclusive; they
are now in fact both considered "right."

Huygens was a member of the Royal Society of London, but it was
to the French Academy of Sciences, in 1678, that he first presented
his ideas on the subject of light. The excerpt here presented is from
the beginning of his treatise on light, published in 1690. The section
recounts the sensational experiment of the celebrated Danish astronomer, Olaus Römer (1644-1710), performed at Paris between
1672 and 1676 to ascertain the speed of light. Having shown that
light takes time to travel, Huygens assumes that light must travel
through something, and discusses the characteristics that the medium must have in order to conduct waves of light. He names the
medium ether.

The translation used is by Henry Crew from The Wave Theory
of Light (American Book Co., New York, 1900).

THE WAVE THEORY OF LIGHT

DEMONSTRATIONS IN optics, as in every science where geometry is applied to matter, are based upon experimental facts; as, for instance, that light travels in straight lines, that the angles of incidence and reflection are equal, and that rays of light are refracted according to the law of sines. For this last fact is now as widely and as certainly known as either of the preceding.

Most writers upon optical subjects have been satisfied to assume these facts. But others, of a more investigating turn of mind, have tried to find the origin and the cause of these facts, considering them in themselves interesting natural phenomena. And although they have advanced some ingenious ideas, these are not such that the more intelligent readers do not still want further explanation in order to be thoroughly satisfied.

Accordingly, I here submit some considerations on this subject with the hope of elucidating, as best I may, this department of natural science, which not undeservedly has gained the reputation of being exceedingly difficult. I feel myself especially indebted to those who first began to make clear these deeply obscure matters, and to lead us to hope that they were capable of simple explanations.

But, on the other hand, I have been astonished to find these same writers accepting arguments which are far from evident as if they were conclusive and demonstrative. No one has yet given even a probable explanation of the fundamental and remarkable phenomena of light, viz: why it travels in straight lines and how rays coming from an infinitude of different directions cross one another without disturbing one another. I shall attempt in this volume to present in accordance with the principles of modern philosophy, some clearer and more probable reasons. . . .

We cannot help believing that light consists in the motion of a certain material. For when we consider its production we find that here on the earth it is generally produced by fire and flame, which, beyond doubt, contain bodies in a state of rapid motion, since they are able to dissolve and melt numerous other more solid bodies. And if we consider its effects, we see that when light is converged, as, for instance, by concave mirrors, it is able to produce combustion just as fire does; i.e.: it is able to tear bodies apart; a property that surely indicates motion, at least in the true philosophy where one believes all natural phenomena to be mechanical effects. And, in my opinion, we must admit this, or else give up all hope of ever understanding anything in physics.

Since, according to this philosophy, it is considered certain that the sensation of sight is caused only by the impulse of some form of matter upon the nerves at the base of the eye, we have here still another reason for thinking that light consists in a motion of the matter situated between us and the luminous body.

When we consider, further, the very great speed with which light is propagated in all directions, and the fact that when rays come from different directions, even those directly opposite, they cross without disturbing each other, it must be evident that we do not see luminous objects by means of matter translated from the object to us, as a shot or an arrow travels through the air. For certainly this would be in contradiction to the two properties of light which we have just mentioned, and especially to the latter. Light is then propagated in some other manner, an understanding of which we may obtain from our knowledge of the manner in which sound travels through the air.

We know that through the medium of the air, an invisible and impalpable body, sound is propagated in all directions from the point where it is produced, by means of a motion which is communicated successively from one part of the air to another; and since this motion travels with the same speed in all directions, it must form spherical surfaces which continually enlarge until finally they strike our ear. Now there can be no doubt that light also comes from the luminous body to us by means of some motion impressed upon the matter which lies in the intervening space; for we have already seen that this cannot occur through the translation of matter from one point to the other.

If, in addition, light requires time for its passage—a point we shall presently consider—it will then follow that this motion is impressed upon the matter gradually, and hence is propagated, as that of sound, by surfaces and spherical waves. I call these *waves* because of their resemblance to those which are formed when one throws a pebble into water and which represent gradual propagation in circles, although produced by a different cause and confined to a plane surface.

As to the question of light requiring time for its propagation, let us consider first whether there is any experimental evidence to the contrary. What we can do here on the earth with sources of light placed at great distances (although showing that light does not occupy a sensible time in passing over these distances) may be objected to on the ground that these distances are still too small, and that, therefore, we can conclude only that the propagation of light is exceedingly rapid. M. Descartes thought it instantaneous, and based his opinion upon much better evidence, furnished by the eclipse of the moon. Nevertheless . . . even this evidence is not conclusive. . . .

It is somewhat unusual, we must confess, to assume a speed one hundred thousand times as great as that of sound, which, according to my observations, travels about 180 toises [1150 feet][1] in a second, or during a pulse-beat; but this supposition appears by no means impossible, for it is not a question of carrying a body with such speed, but of a motion passing successively from one point to another.

I do not, therefore, in thinking of these matters, hesitate to sup-

[1] This is the correct figure for the speed of sound at about 86° F.

pose that the propagation of light occupies time, for on this view all
the phenomena can be explained, while on the contrary view none
of them can be explained. Indeed, it seems to me, and to many
others also, that M. Descartes, whose object has been to discuss all
physical subjects in a clear way, and who has certainly succeeded
better than anyone before him, has writ-
ten nothing on light and its properties
which is not either full of difficulty or
even inconceivable.

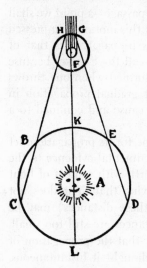

But this idea which I have advanced
only as a hypothesis has recently been
almost established as a fact by the ingenious method of Römer, whose work
I propose here to describe, expecting that
he himself will later give a complete confirmation of this view.

His method is . . . astronomical. He
proves not only that light requires time
for its propagation, but shows also how
much time it requires and that its speed
must be at least six times greater than
the estimate which I have just given.

For this demonstration, he uses the eclipses of the small planets
which revolve about Jupiter, and which very often pass into its
shadow. His reasoning is as follows: Let A denote the sun; BCDE,
the annual orbit of the earth; F, Jupiter; and GH, the orbit of the
innermost satellite, for this one, on account of its short period, is
better adapted to this investigation than is any of the other three.
Let G represent the point of the satellite's entrance into, and H the
point of its emergence from, Jupiter's shadow.

Let us suppose that an emergence of this satellite has been observed while the earth occupies the position B, at some time before
the last quarter. If the earth remained in this position, 42½ hours
would elapse before the next emergence would occur. For this is the

time required for the satellite to make one revolution in its orbit and return to opposition with the sun. If, for instance, the earth remained at the point B during 30 revolutions, then, after an interval of 30 times 42½ hours, the satellite would again be observed to emerge. But if meanwhile the earth has moved to a point C, more distant from Jupiter, it is evident that, provided light requires time for its propagation, the emergence of the little planet will be recorded later at C than it would have been at B. For it will be necessary to add to this interval, of 30 times 42½ hours, the time occupied by light in passing over a distance BC, the difference of the distances CH and BH. In like manner, in the other quarter, while the earth travels from D to E, approaching Jupiter, the eclipses will [appear to] occur earlier when the earth is at E than if it had remained at D.

Now by means of a large number of these eclipse observations, covering a period of ten years, it is shown that these inequalities are very considerable, amounting to as much as ten minutes or more; whence it is concluded that, for traversing the whole diameter of the earth's orbit KL, twice the distance from here to the sun, light requires about 22 minutes.

The motion of Jupiter in its orbit, while the earth passes from B to C or from D to E, has been taken into account in the computation, where it is also shown that these inequalities cannot be due either to an irregularity in the motion of the satellite or to its eccentricity.

If we consider the enormous size of this diameter, KL, which I have found to be about 24 thousand times that of the earth, we get some idea of the extraordinary speed of light. Even if we suppose that KL were only 22 thousand diameters of the earth, a speed covering this distance in 22 minutes would be equivalent to the rate of one thousand diameters per minute, i.e., 16⅔ diameters a second (or a pulse-beat), which makes more than eleven hundred times one hundred thousand toises [133,000 miles] per second.[2] . . .

[2] Michelson, in 1927, found the speed of light to be 186,284 miles per second.

But, as I have said above, sound travels at the rate of only 180 toises per second. Accordingly, the speed of light is more than 600,000 times as great as that of sound, which, however, is a very different thing from being instantaneous, the difference being exactly that between a finite quantity and infinity. The idea that luminous disturbances are handed on from point to point in a gradual manner being thus confirmed, it follows, as I have already said, that light is propagated by spherical waves, as is the case with sound.

But if they resemble each other in this respect, they differ in several others—viz: in the original production of the motion which causes them, in the medium through which they travel, and in the manner in which they are transmitted in this medium.

Sound, we know, is produced by the rapid disturbance of some body (either as a whole or in part); this disturbance setting in motion the contiguous air. But luminous disturbances must arise at each point of the luminous object, else all the different parts of this object would not be visible. This fact will be more evident in what follows.

In my opinion, this motion of luminous bodies cannot be better explained than by supposing that those which are fluid, such as a flame, and apparently the sun and stars, are composed of particles that float about in a much more subtle medium, which sets them in rapid motion, causing them to strike against the still smaller particles of the surrounding ether. But in the case of luminous solids, such as red-hot metal or carbon, we may suppose this motion to be caused by the violent disturbance of the particles of the metal or of the wood, those which lie on the surface exciting the ether. Thus the motion which produces light must also be more sudden and more rapid than that which causes sound, since we do not observe that sonorous disturbances give rise to light any more than that the motion of the hand through the air gives rise to sound.

The question next arises as to the nature of the medium in which is propagated this motion produced by luminous bodies. I have called it ether; but it is evidently something different from the medium through which sound travels. For this matter is simply the air which we feel and breathe, and which, when removed from any region, leaves behind the luminiferous medium. This fact is shown by enclosing a sounding body in a glass vessel and removing the atmosphere by means of the air-pump which Mr. Boyle has devised,[3] and with which he has performed so many beautiful experiments. But in trying this it is well to place the sounding body on cotton or feathers in such a way that it cannot communicate its vibrations either to the glass receiver or to the air-pump, a point which has hitherto been neglected. Then, when all the air has been removed, one hears no sound from the metal even when it is struck.

From this we infer not only that our atmosphere, which is unable to penetrate glass, is the medium through which sound travels, but also that it is different from that which carries luminous disturbances; for when the vessel is exhausted of air, light traverses it as freely as before.

This last point is demonstrated even more clearly by the celebrated experiment of Torricelli.[4] That part of the glass tube which the mercury does not fill contains a high vacuum, but transmits light the same as when filled with air. This shows that there is within the tube some form of matter which is different from air, and which penetrates either glass or mercury, or both, although both the glass and the mercury are impervious to air. And if the same experiment is repeated, except that a little water be placed on top of the mercury, it becomes equally evident that the form of matter in question passes either through the glass or through the water or through both.

As to the different modes of transmission of sound and light, it is easy to understand what happens in the case of sound when one recalls that air can be compressed and reduced to a much smaller volume than it ordinarily occupies, and that just in proportion as its volume is diminished it tends to regain its original size. This property, taken in conjunction with its penetrability, which it retains in

[3] See p. 244.
[4] See p. 226.

spite of compression, appears to show that it is composed of small particles which float about, in rapid motion, in an ether composed of still finer particles. Sound, then, is propagated by the effort of these air particles to escape when at any point in the path of the wave they are more compressed than at some other point.

But the enormous speed of light, together with its other properties, hardly allows us to believe that it is propagated in the same way. Accordingly, I propose to explain the manner in which I think it must occur. It will be necessary first, however, to describe that property of hard bodies, in virtue of which they transmit motion from one to another.

If one takes a large number of spheres of equal size, made of any hard material, and arranges them in contact in a straight line, he will find that, on allowing a sphere of the same size to roll against one end of the line, the motion is transmitted in an instant to the other end of the line. The last sphere in the row flies off while the intermediate ones are apparently undisturbed; the sphere which originally produced the disturbance also remains at rest. Here we have a motion which is transmitted with high speed, which varies directly as the hardness of the spheres.

Nevertheless, it is certain that this motion is not instantaneous, but is gradual, requiring time. For if the motion, or, if you please, the tendency to motion, did not pass successively from one sphere to another, they would all be affected at the same instant, and would all move forward together. So far from this being the case, it is the last one only which leaves the row, and it acquires the speed of the sphere which gave the blow. Besides this experiment, there are others which show that all bodies, even those which are considered hardest, such as tempered steel, glass, and agate, are really elastic, and bend to some extent, whether they are made into rods, spheres, or bodies of any other shape; that is, they yield slightly at the point where they are struck, and immediately regain their original figure. For I have found that in allowing a glass or agate sphere to strike upon a large, thick, flat piece of the same material, whose surface has been dulled by the breath, the point of contact is marked by a circular disc which varies in size directly as the strength of the blow. This shows that during the encounter these materials yield and then fly back, a process which must require time.

Now to apply this kind of motion to the explanation of light nothing prevents our imagining the particles of the ether as endowed with a hardness almost perfect and with an elasticity as great as we please. It is not necessary here to discuss the cause either of this hardness or of this elasticity, for such a consideration would lead us too far from the subject. I will, however, remark in passing that these ether particles, in spite of their small size, are in turn composed of parts, and that their elasticity consists in a very rapid motion of a subtle material which traverses them in all directions and compels them to assume a structure which offers an easy and open passage to this fluid. This accords with the theory of M. Descartes, except that I do not agree with him in assigning to the pores the form of hollow circular canals. So far from there being anything absurd or impossible in all this, it is quite credible that nature employs an infinite series of different-sized molecules, endowed with different velocities, to produce her marvelous effects.

But although we do not understand the cause of elasticity, we cannot fail to observe that most bodies possess this property; it is not unnatural, therefore, to suppose that it is a characteristic also of the small, invisible particles of the ether. If, indeed, one looks for some other mode of accounting for the gradual propagation of light, he will have difficulty in finding one better adapted than elasticity to explain the fact of uniform speed. And this appears to be necessary; for if the motion slowed up as it became distributed through a larger mass of matter, and receded farther from the source of light, then its high speed would be lost at great distances. But we suppose the elasticity to be a property of the ether so that its particles regain their shape with equal rapidity whether they are struck with a hard or a gentle blow; and thus the rate at which the light moves remains the same [at all distances from the source]. . . .

I have now shown how we may consider light as propagated, in time, by spherical waves, and how it is possible that the speed of propagation should be as great as that demanded by experiment and by astronomical observation.

ISAAC NEWTON [1]

1 6 4 2 · 1 7 2 7

NEWTON'S FIRST public paper tells of a series of experiments he
started at the age of twenty-four, the results of which would have
made him famous had he accomplished nothing more. A New
Theory of Light and Colors shows his power to make a few simple
experiments reveal long-hidden secrets of nature. He reports how he
set up a prism to see the "celebrated phenomena of colors," perhaps
for amusement; how he noticed that the patch of colors thrown on
the wall was not shaped like the round spot of light in the prism, but
very much longer; how he compared this appearance with the known
laws of light, and found, finally, that the red light was always refracted less than the yellow, the yellow than the green, the green
than the blue or violet, and that the original white light was actually
a combination of all the colored lights in the spectrum.

The paper was read in 1672 before the Royal Society of London
and published in English in that year in the Philosophical Transactions. During the next few years that journal devoted much space to
articles in support and rebuttal of the new theory. But it stands today
still correct, save that we now know that light exhibits properties of
waves as well as those of corpuscles.

[1] For other selections from Newton's works, see p. 63 and p. 604.

A NEW THEORY OF
LIGHT AND COLORS

Sir:

To perform my late promise to you, I shall without further cere-
mony acquaint you that in the beginning of the year 1666 (at which
time I applied myself to the grinding of optick glasses of other figures than spherical), I procured me a triangular glass prism, to try
therewith the celebrated phenomena of colors. And in order thereto,
having darkened my chamber, and made a small hole in my window-
shuts, to let in a convenient quantity of the sun's light, I placed my
prism at its entrance, that it might thereby be refracted to the opposite wall. It was at first a very pleasing divertisement to view the vivid
and intense colors [1] produced thereby; but after a while applying
myself to consider them more circumspectly, I became surprised to
see them in an oblong form; which, according to the received laws
of Refraction, I expected should have been circular.

They were terminated at the sides with straight lines, but at the
ends the decay of light was so gradual that it was difficult to determine justly what was their figure; yet they seemed semicircular.

Comparing the length of this colored spectrum with its breadth, I
found it about five times greater; a disproportion so extravagant
that it excited me to a more than ordinary curiosity of examining
from whence it might proceed. I could scarce think that the various
thicknesses of the glass, or the termination with shadow or darkness could have any influence on light to produce such an effect;
yet I thought it not amiss, first to examine those circumstances, and
so tried what would happen by transmitting light through parts of

[1] See the diagram of the colors of a spectrum produced by a prism on p. 150.

the glass of divers thicknesses, or through holes in the window of divers bignesses, or by setting the prism without so that the light might pass through it, and be refracted before it was terminated by the hole. But I found none of those circumstances material. The fashion of the colors was in all these cases the same.

Then I suspected, whether by any unevenness in the glass or other contingent irregularity, these colors might be thus dilated. And to try this, I took another prism like the former, and so placed it that the light, passing through them both, might be refracted contrary ways, and so by the latter returned into that course from which the former had diverted it. For by this means I thought the regular effects of the first prism would be destroyed by the second prism, but the irregular ones more augmented by the multiplicity of the refractions. The event was that the light, which by the first prism was diffused into an oblong form, was by the second reduced into an orbicular one with as much regularity as when it did not at all pass through them. So that, whatever was the cause of that length, 'twas not any contingent irregularity. . . .

[Newton then attempted to explain the oblong shape of the colored light spectrum by the fact that light is bent when it enters or leaves a dense medium. But he found the length of the oblong to be far greater than could be explained in this way.]

Then I began to suspect whether the rays, after their trajection through the prism did not move in curve lines, and according to their more or less curvity tend to divers parts of the wall. And it increased my suspicion when I remembered that I had often seen a tennis ball, struck with an oblique racket, describe such a curve line. For, a circular as well as a progressive motion being communicated to it by that stroke, its parts on that side where the motions conspire must press and beat the contiguous air more violently than on the other, and there excite a reluctancy and reaction of the air proportionately greater. And for the same reason, if the rays of light should possibly be globular bodies, and by their oblique passage out of one medium into another acquire a circulating motion, they ought to feel the greater resistance from the ambient ether, on that side, where the motions conspire, and thence be continually bowed to the other. But notwithstanding this plausible ground of suspicion, when I came to examine it, I could observe no such curvity in them. And besides (which was enough for my purpose) I observed that the difference 'twixt the length of the image and diameter of the hole, through which the light was transmitted, was proportionable to their distance.

The gradual removal of these suspicions at length led me to the

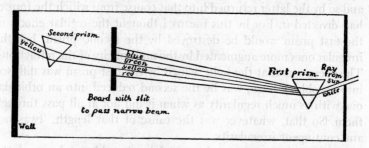

Newton's experiment on bending colored light. When Newton turned the first prism, light of each color came to the slit in the board. The second prism caused no further color change, but red light was bent least far up the wall. Green light was bent more than yellow, and extreme blue was bent most of all.

Experimentum Crucis, which was this: I took two boards and placed one of them close behind the prism at the window, so that the light might pass through a small hole made in it for the purpose and fall on the other board, which I placed at about 12 feet distance, having first made a small hole in it also, for some of that incident light to pass through. Then I placed another prism behind this second board, so that the light, trajected through both the boards might pass through that also, and be again refracted before it arrived at the wall. This done, I took the first prism in my hand and turned it to and fro slowly about its axis, so much as to make the several parts of the image cast on the second board successively pass through the hole in it, that I might observe what places on the wall the second prism would refract them. And I saw by the variation of those places that the light, tending to that end of the image, towards which the refraction of the first prism was made, did in the second prism suffer a refraction considerably greater than the light tending to the other end. And so the true cause of the length of that image was detected to be no other than that light consists of rays differently refrangible, which, without any respect to a difference in their incidence, were, according to their degrees of refrangibility, transmitted towards divers parts of the wall.

When I understood this, I left off my aforesaid glass works, for I saw that the perfection of telescopes was hitherto limited, not so much for want of glasses truly figured according to the prescriptions of optick authors (which all men have hitherto imagined) as because that light itself is a heterogeneous mixture of differently refrangible rays. So that, were a glass so exactly figured as to collect any one sort of rays into one point, it could not collect those also into the same point, which having the same incidence upon the same medium are apt to suffer a different refraction. Nay, I wondered that, seeing the difference of refrangibility was so great as I have it, telescopes should arrive to that perfection they are now at. . . .

But to return from this digression, I told you that light is not similar or homogeneal, but consists of difform rays, some of which are more refrangible than others: so that of those which are alike incident on the same medium, some shall be more refracted than others, and that not by any virtue of the glass, or other external cause, but from a predisposition, which every particular ray hath to suffer a particular degree of refraction.

I shall now proceed to acquaint you with another more notable difformity in its rays, wherein the origin of colors is unfolded; concerning which I shall lay down the doctrine first, and then, for its examination, give you an instance or two of the experiments as a specimen of the rest.

The doctrine you will find comprehended and illustrated in the following propositions.

1. As the rays of light differ in degrees of refrangibility so they also differ in their disposition to exhibit this or that particular color. Colors are not qualifications of light, derived from refractions, or reflections of natural bodies (as 'tis generally believed), but original and connate properties, which in divers rays are diverse. Some rays are disposed to exhibit a red color and no other; some a yellow and no other, some a green and no other, and so of the rest. Nor are there only rays proper and particular to the more eminent colors, but even to all their intermediate gradations.

2. To the same degree of refrangibility ever belongs the same color, and to the same color ever belongs the same degree of refrangibility. The least refrangible rays are all disposed to exhibit a red color, and contrarily those rays which are disposed to exhibit a red color, are all the least refrangible. So the most refrangible rays are disposed to exhibit a deep violet color, and contrarily those which are apt to exhibit such a color are the most refrangible. And so to all the intermediate colors in a continued series belong intermediate degrees of refrangibility. And this analogy 'twixt colors and refrangibility is very precise and strict; the rays always either exactly agreeing in both, or proportionally disagreeing in both.

3. The species of color and degree of refrangibility proper to any particular sort of rays is not mutable by refraction, nor by reflection from natural bodies, nor by any other cause that I could yet observe. When any one sort of rays hath been well parted from those of other kinds, it hath afterwards obstinately retained its color, notwithstanding my utmost endeavors to change it. I have refracted it with prisms, and reflected it with bodies, which in daylight were of other colors; I have intercepted it with the colored film of air interceding two compressed plates of glass; transmitted it through colored mediums, and through mediums irradiated with other sorts of rays, and diversely terminated it; and yet could never produce any new color out of it. It would by contracting or dilating become

more brisk, or faint, and by the loss of many rays, in some cases very obscure and dark; but I could never see it changed *in specie* [in kind].

4. Yet seeming transmutations of colors may be made, where there is any mixture of divers sorts of rays. For in such mixtures, the component colors appear not, but, by their mutual allaying each other, constitute a middling color. And therefore, if by refraction, or any other of the aforesaid causes, the difform rays, latent in such a mixture, be separated, there shall emerge colors different from the color of the composition. Which colors are not new generated, but only made apparent by being parted; for if they be again entirely mixt and blended together, they will again compose that color which they did before separation. And for the same reason, transmutations made by the convening of divers colors are not real; for when the difform rays are again severed, they will exhibit the very same colors which they did before they entered the composition; as you see, blue and yellow powders, when finely mixed, appear to the naked eye green, and yet the colors of the component corpuscles are not thereby really transmuted, but only blended. For, when viewed with a good microscope, they still appear blue and yellow interspersedly.

5. There are therefore two sorts of colors. The one original and simple, the other compounded of these. The original or primary colors are red, yellow, green, blue, and a violet-purple, together with orange, indigo, and an indefinite variety of intermediate gradations.

6. The same colors *in specie* with these primary ones may be also produced by composition: for a mixture of yellow and blue makes green; of red and yellow makes orange; of orange and yellowish green makes yellow. And in general, if any two colors be mixed which in the series of those generated by the prism are not too far distant one from another, they by their mutual alloy compound that color which in the said series appeareth in the midway between them. But those which are situated at too great a distance do not

so. Orange and indigo produce not the intermediate green, nor scarlet and green the intermediate yellow.

7. But the most surprising and wonderful composition was that of whiteness. There is no one sort of rays which alone can exhibit this. 'Tis ever compounded; and to its composition are requisite all the aforesaid primary colors, mixed in a due proportion. I have often with admiration beheld that all the colors of the prism being made to converge, and thereby to be again mixed as they were in the light before it was incident upon the prism, reproduced light, entirely and perfectly white, and not at all sensibly differing from a direct light of the sun, unless when the glasses I used were not sufficiently clear; for then they would a little incline it to their color.

8. Hence, therefore, it comes to pass that whiteness is the usual color of light; for light is a confused aggregate of rays indued with all sorts of colors, as they are promiscuously darted from the various parts of luminous bodies. And of such a confused aggregate, as I said, is generated whiteness, if there be a due proportion of the ingredients; but if any one predominate the light must incline to that color; as it happens in the blue flame of brimstone, the yellow flame of candle, and the various colors of the fixed stars.

9. These things considered, the manner how colors are produced by the prism is evident. For of the rays constituting the incident light, since those which differ in color proportionally differ in refrangibility, they by their unequal refractions must be severed and dispersed into an oblong form in an orderly succession from the least refracted scarlet to the most refracted violet. And for the same reason it is that objects, when looked upon through a prism, appear colored. For the difform rays, by their unequal refractions, are made to diverge toward several parts of the retina, and these express the images of things colored, as in the former case they did the sun's image upon a wall. And by this inequality of refractions they become not only colored, but also very confused and indistinct.

10. Why the colors of the rainbow appear in falling drops of

rain, is also from hence evident. For those drops which refract the rays disposed to appear purple, in greatest quantity to the spectator's eye, refract the rays of other sorts so much less, as to make them pass beside it; and such are the drops on the inside of the primary bow, and on the outside of the secondary or exterior one. So those drops which refract in greatest plenty the rays apt to appear red, toward the spectator's eye, refract those of other sorts so much more as to make them pass beside it; and such are the drops on the exterior part of the primary, and interior part of the secondary bow.

11. The odd phenomena of an infusion of *Lignum Nephriticum,* leaf gold, fragments of colored glass, and some other transparently colored bodies, appearing in one position of one color, and of another in another, are on these grounds no longer riddles. For those are substances apt to reflect one sort of light and transmit another; as may be seen in a dark room, by illuminating them with similar or uncompounded light. For then they appear of that color only, accordingly as they are disposed more or less to reflect or transmit the incident color.

12. From hence also is manifest the reason of an unexpected experiment, which Mr. Hook somewhere in his *Micrography* relates to have made with two wedge-like transparent vessels, filled the one with a red, the other with a blue liquor: namely, that though they were severally transparent enough, yet both together became opaque. For, if one transmitted only red, and the other only blue, no rays could pass through both.

13. I might add more instances of this nature, but I shall conclude with this general one, that the colors of all natural bodies have no other origin than this, that they are variously qualified to reflect one sort of light in greater plenty than another. And this I have experimented in a dark room by illuminating those bodies with uncompounded light of divers colors. For by that means any body may be made to appear of any color. . . .

This, I conceive, is enough for an introduction to experiments of this kind; which if any of the Royal Society shall be so curious as to prosecute, I should be very glad to be informed with what success; that if anything seem to be defective or to thwart this relation, I may have an opportunity of giving further direction about it, or of acknowledging my errors, if I have committed any.

DANIEL GABRIEL FAHRENHEIT

1 6 8 6 · 1 7 3 6

A DOZEN MEN had been working on methods to measure the intensity of heat when Fahrenheit, the scientific son of a wealthy Danzig merchant, invented the mercury thermometer as we know it. Galileo had constructed an air thermometer, in which the expansion of air by heat drove water out of a glass tube with an air bulb at the end. Galileo's friend Sanctorius (1561-1636) seems to have used such a thermometer to measure body heat about 1610. Von Guericke (1602-1686) made an open-ended alcohol thermometer, which he marked to register seven degrees of heat, from great heat to great cold. Amontons (1663-1705) again used air pressure, and corrected it for barometric variation. Huygens suggested that either the boiling point or the freezing point should be used as the basis for scale markings. Halley (1656-1742) compared mercury, water, and alcohol as expanding agents, but decided on air as the best. Newton used linseed oil for low temperatures.

Fahrenheit for the most part lived in England and Holland, devoting himself to the study of physics, and to the invention and manufacture of meterological instruments. Among his inventions was an improved form of hygrometer, a description of which appears with that of his thermometer in the Philosophical Transactions of the Royal Society of London, vol. 33, 1724. Fahrenheit's thermometer was open-ended, but later he sealed both ends and the instrument assumed its present form, unfortunately preserving the inconvenient method of scale marking of the original model, which he explains below. The selection from his report given here was translated from the Latin of the original by W. F. Magie for his Source Book in Physics (McGraw-Hill Book Co., N. Y., 1935).

THE FAHRENHEIT SCALE

ABOUT TEN YEARS ago I read in the *History of the Sciences* issued by the Royal Academy of Paris, that the celebrated Amontons, using a thermometer of his own invention, had discovered that water boils at a fixed degree of heat. I was at once inflamed with a great desire to make for myself a thermometer of the same sort, so that I might with my own eyes perceive this beautiful phenomenon of nature, and be convinced of the truth of the experiment.

I therefore attempted to construct a thermometer, but because of my lack of experience in its construction, my efforts were in vain, though they were often repeated; and since other matters prevented my going on with the development of the thermometer, I postponed any further repetition of my attempts to some more fitting time. Though my powers and my time failed me, yet my zeal did not slacken, and I was always desirous of seeing the outcome of the experiment. It then came into my mind what that most careful observer of natural phenomena had written about the correction of the barometer; for he had observed that the height of the column of mercury in the barometer was a little (though sensibly enough) altered by the varying temperature of the mercury. From this I gathered that a thermometer might perhaps be constructed with mercury, which would not be so hard to construct, and by the use of which it might be possible to carry out the experiment which I so greatly desired to try.

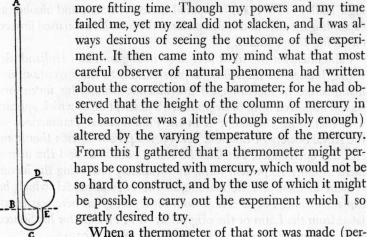

When a thermometer of that sort was made (perhaps imperfect in many ways) the result answered to my prayer; and with great pleasure of mind I observed the truth of the thing.

Three years then passed, in which I was occupied with optical and other work, when I became anxious to try by experiment whether other liquids boiled at fixed degrees of heat.

The results of my experiments are contained in the following table, of which the first column contains the liquids used, the second, their specific gravity, the third, the degree of heat which each liquid attains when boiling.

Liquids	Specific Gravity of Liquids at 48° of Heat	Degree Attained by Boiling
Spirits of Wine or Alcohol.............	8260	176
Rain Water	10000	212
Spirits of Niter.....................	12935	242
Lye prepared from wine lees...........	15634	240
Oil of Vitriol	18775	546

I thought it best to give the specific gravity of each liquid, so that, if the experiments of others already tried, or which may be tried, give different results, it might be determined whether the difference should be looked for as resulting from differences in the specific gravities or from other causes. The experiments were not made at the same time, and hence the liquids were affected by different degrees of temperature or heat, but since their gravity is altered in a different way and unequally, I reduced it by calculation to the degree 48, which in my thermometers holds the middle place between the limit of the most intense cold obtained artificially in a mixture of water, of ice and of sal-ammoniac or even of sea-salt, and the limit of the heat which is found in the blood of a healthy man

BENJAMIN FRANKLIN

1 7 0 6 · 1 7 9 0

Were Franklin not so famed as a diplomat, statesman, printer, publisher and diarist, he would be better known as the first American scientific genius. The quality of his thought on scientific subjects is the more remarkable, because he was so far removed from constant association with other scientists, and because he was able to devote but a few years to scientific pursuits. His first experiments on electricity were performed about 1745. From 1757 on, the political unrest preceding the American Revolutionary War took up most of his attention, and the remainder of his life was devoted principally to statesmanship.

The letter to Dr. Lining, an amateur of science, is reprinted from Franklin's Experiments and Observations on Electricity, London 1774. It is a fine example of the way Franklin tested existing theory by a few well-chosen experiments, and then brought his gift for organization and simplification to clarify and partly solve the problem. It may be contrasted with the vague and doubtful list of categories in the fragment of Bacon's essay on heat included in Section IX.[1]

Hooke had suggested that heat and cold were not separate entities, as Bacon had thought, but that cold was merely absence of heat. Newton had stated the laws of cooling; Fahrenheit had developed a reliable thermometer. But the central problem—what heat was—had not hitherto been satisfactorily attacked. There was only a general tendency to associate it with motion.

In the first few pages Franklin describes some illuminating experiments of his own and attempts to explain them by existing theory,

[1] See below, p. 588.

but in the end finds that facts and theory do not agree. Dr. Black's work on latent heat and heat of vaporization was needed before the first and the last of these experiments could be explained. Lavoisier and Priestley, however, soon after proved that Franklin was right in assuming that body heat comes from the "burning" of food in the body.

It is interesting to speculate how far Franklin might have gone had he not been called away from science. The great European scientists of his day lamented that he was wasting his time on something as transitory as diplomacy. We may note, however, that his work was always limited to study of qualities. He would have had to learn the necessity of measuring quantities before he could have duplicated the work of Black.

THE NATURE OF HEAT

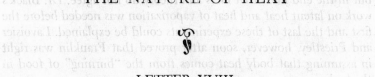

LETTER XVIII.

FROM

BENJ. FRANKLIN, *Esq*; of *Philadelphia,*

TO

Dr. L——, at *Charles Town, South-Carolina.*

New-York, April 14, 1757.

SIR,

It is a long time since I had the pleasure of a line from you; and, indeed, the troubles of our country, with the hurry of business I have been engaged in on that account, have made me so bad a correspondent, that I ought not to expect punctuality in others.

But being about to embark for England, I could not quit the Continent without paying my respects to you, and, at the same time, taking leave to introduce to your acquaintance a Gentleman of learning and merit, Colonel Henry Bouquet, who does me the favour to present you this letter, and with whom I am sure you will be much pleased.

Professor Simpson, of Glasgow, lately communicated to me some curious experiments of a physician of his acquaintance, by which it appeared, that an extraordinary degree of cold, even to freezing, might be produced by evaporation. I have not had leisure to repeat and examine more than the first and easiest of them, viz. - - - Wet the ball of a thermometer by a feather dipt in spirit of wine [alcohol], which has been kept in the same room, and has, of course, the same degree of heat or cold. The mercury sinks presently three or four degrees, and the quicker, if, during the evaporation, you blow on the ball with bellows; a second wetting and blowing, when the mercury is down, carries it yet lower. I think I did not get it lower than five or six degrees from where it naturally stood, which was, at that time sixty. But it is said, that a vessel of water being placed in another somewhat larger, containing spirit, in such a manner that the vessel of water is surrounded with the spirit, and both placed under the receiver of an air-pump; on exhausting the air, the spirit, evaporating, leaves such a degree of cold as to freeze the water, though the thermometer, in the open air, stands many degrees above the freezing point.

I know not how this phænomenon is to be accounted for, but it gives me occasion to mention some loose notions relating to heat and cold, which I have for some time entertained, but not yet reduced into my form. Allowing common fire, as well as electrical, to be a fluid capable of permeating other bodies, and seeking an equilibrium, I imagine some bodies are better fitted by nature to be conductors of that fluid than others; and that, generally, those which are the best conductors of the electrical fluid, are also the best conductors of this; and *e contra*.

Thus a body which is a good conductor of fire readily receives it into its substance, and conducts it through the whole to all the parts, as metals and water do; and if two bodies, both good conductors, one heated, the other in its common state, are brought into contact with each other, the body which has most fire, readily communicates of it to that which had least, and that which had least readily receives it, till an equilibrium is produced. Thus if you take a dollar between your fingers with one hand, and a piece of wood, of the same dimensions, with the other, and bring both at the same time to the flame of a candle, you will find yourself obliged to drop the dollar before you drop the wood, because it conducts the heat of the candle sooner to your flesh. Thus if a silver tea-pot had a handle of the same metal, it would conduct the heat from the water to the hand, and become too hot to be used; we therefore give to a metal tea-pot a handle of wood, which is not so good a conductor as metal. But a china or stone tea-pot being in some degree of the nature of glass, which is not a good conductor of heat, may have a handle of the same stuff. Thus, also, a damp moist air shall make a man more sensible of cold, or chill him more than a dry air that is colder, because a moist air is fitter to receive and conduct away the heat of his body. This fluid entering bodies in great quantity, first expands them, by separating their parts a little; afterwards by farther separating their parts, it renders solids fluid, and at length dissipates their parts in air. Take this fluid from melted lead, or from water, the parts cohere again, the first grows solid, the latter becomes ice: And this is sooner done by the means of good conductors. Thus if you take, as I have done, a square bar of lead, four inches long, and one inch thick, together with three pieces of wood planed to the same dimensions, and lay them, as in the margin, on a smooth board, fixt so as not to be easily separated or moved, and pour into the cavity they form, as much melted lead as will fill it, you will see the melted lead chill, and become firm, on the side next the leaden bar, some time before it chills on the other three sides in contact with the wooden bars, though before the lead was poured in, they might all be supposed to have the same degree of heat or coldness, as they had been exposed in the same room to the same air. You will likewise observe, that the leaden bar, as it has cooled the melted lead more than the wooden bars have done, so it is itself more heated by the melted lead.

There is a certain quantity of this fluid called fire, in every living human body, which fluid being in due proportion, keeps the parts of the flesh and blood, at such a just distance from each other, as that the flesh and nerves are supple, and the blood fit for circulation. If part of this due proportion of fire be conducted away by means of a contact with other bodies, as air, water, or metals, the parts of our skin and flesh that come into such contact, first draw more near together than is agreeable, and give that sensation which we call cold; and if too much be conveyed away, the body stiffens, the blood ceases to flow, and death ensues. On the other hand, if too much of this fluid be communicated to the flesh, the parts are separated too far, and pain ensues, as when they are separated by a pin or lancet. The sensation that the separation by fire occasions, we call heat, or burning. My desk on which I now write, and the lock of my desk, are both exposed to the same temperature of the air, and have therefore the same degree of heat or cold; yet if I lay my hand successively on the wood and on the metal, the latter feels much the coldest, not that it is really so, but being a better conductor, it more readily than the wood takes away and draws into itself the fire that was in my skin. Accordingly if I lay one hand, part on the lock, and part on the wood, and after it has lain so some time, I feel both parts with my other hand, I find the part that has been in contact with the lock, very sensibly colder to the touch, than the part that lay on the wood.

How a living animal obtains its quantity of this fluid called fire, is a curious question. I have shewn that some bodies (as metals) have a power of attracting it stronger than others; and I have sometimes suspected that a living body had some power of attracting out of the air, or other bodies, the heat it wanted. Thus metals hammered, or repeatedly bent, grow hot in the bent or hammered part. But when I consider that air, in contact with the body, cools it; that the surrounding air is rather heated by its contact with the body; that every breath of cooler air drawn in, carries off part of the body's heat when it passes out again; that therefore there must be in the body a fund for producing it, or otherwise the animal would soon grow cold; I have been rather inclined to think that the fluid *fire*, as well as the fluid *air*, is attracted by plants in their growth, and becomes consolidated with the other materials of which they are formed, and makes a great part of their substance: That when they come to be digested, and to suffer in the vessels a kind of fermentation, part of the fire, as well as part of the air, recovers its fluid active state again, and diffuses itself in the body digesting and separating it: That the fire so reproduced by digestion and separation, continually leaving the body, its place is supplied by fresh quantities, arising from the continual separation. That whatever quickens the motion of the fluids in an animal, quickens the separation, and reproduces more of the fire; as exercise. That all the fire emitted by wood, and other combustibles, when burning, existed in them before, in a solid state, being only discovered when separating. That some fossils, as sulphur, sea-coal, &c. contain a great deal of solid fire: That some bodies are almost wholly solid fire; and that, in short, what escapes and is dissipated in the burning of bodies, besides water and earth, is generally the air and fire that before made parts of the solid. — Thus I imagine that animal heat arises by or from a kind of fermentation in the juices of the body, in the same manner as heat arises in the liquors preparing for distillation, wherein there is a separation of the spirituous, from the watry and earthy parts. — And it is remarkable, that the liquor in a distiller's vat, when in its highest and best state of fermentation, as I have been informed, has nearly the same degree of heat with the human body; that is, about 94 or 96.

Thus, as by a constant supply of fuel in a chimney, you keep a warm room, so, by a constant supply of food in the stomach, you keep a warm body; only where little exercise is used, the heat may possibly be conducted away too fast; in which case such materials are to be used for cloathing and bedding, against the effects of an immediate contact of the air, as are, in themselves, bad conductors of heat, and, consequently, prevent its being communicated through their substance to the air. Hence what is called *warmth* in wool, and its preference, on that account, to linen; wool not being so good a conductor: And hence all the natural coverings of animals, to keep them warm, are such as retain and confine the natural heat in the body, by being bad conductors, such as wool, hair, feathers, and the silk by which the silk-worm, in its tender embrio state, is first cloathed. Cloathing, thus considered, does not make a man warm by *giving* warmth, but by *preventing* the too quick dissipation of the heat produced in his body, and so occasioning an accumulation.

There is another curious question I will just venture to touch upon, viz. Whence arises the sudden extraordinary degrees of cold, perceptible on mixing some chemical liquors, and even on mixing salt and snow, where the composition appears colder than the coldest of the ingredients? I have never seen the chemical mixtures made, but salt and snow I have often mixed myself, and am fully satisfied that the composition feels much colder to the touch, and lowers the mercury in the thermometer more than either ingredient would do separately. I suppose, with others, that cold is nothing more than the absence of heat or fire. Now if the quantity of fire before contained or diffused in the snow and salt, was expelled in the uniting of the two matters, it must be driven away either through the air or the vessel containing them. If it is driven off through the air, it must warm the air, and a thermometer held over the mixture, without touching it, would discover the heat, by the rising of the mercury, as it must, and always does in warm air.

This, indeed, I have not tried, but I should guess it would rather be driven off through the vessel, especially if the vessel be metal, as being a better conductor than air; and so one should find the bason warmer after such mixture. But, on the contrary, the vessel grows cold, and even water in which the vessel is sometimes placed for the experiment, freezes into hard ice on the bason. Now I know not how to account for this, otherwise than by supposing that the composition is a better conductor of fire than the ingredients separately, and like the lock compared with the wood, has a stronger power of attracting fire, and does accordingly attract it suddenly from the fingers, or a thermometer put into it, from the bason that contains it, and from the water in contact with the outside of the bason; so that the fingers have the sensation of extreme cold, by being deprived of much of their natural fire; the thermometer sinks, by having part of its fire drawn out of the mercury; the bason grows colder to the touch, as by having its fire drawn into the mixture, it is become more capable of drawing and receiving it from the hand; and through the bason, the water loses its fire that kept it fluid; so it becomes ice. - - - One would expect that from all this attracted acquisition of fire to the composition, it should become warmer; and, in fact, the snow and salt dissolve at the same time into water, without freezing. *I am, Sir, &c.*

B. F.

CARL WILHELM SCHEELE

1 7 4 2 · 1 7 8 6

HEAT CAN MOVE in a current of warm air. Heat can also move through cold air without warming it. The latter sort of heat may be reflected in a mirror, as had been noted as early as 1589, by Baptista Porta (1540-1615) in his Magia Naturalis or Natural Magic, a work devoted largely to optics.

In the following excerpt from Scheele's essay on radiant heat, he describes a series of experiments performed in order to distinguish the form of heat which moves out in straight lines from light. In this same essay he shows how radiant heat may be absorbed by glass and other substances, and gives radiant heat its name. We omit his rather shaky theoretical discussions.

Scheele was born in Pomerania, then a part of Sweden, and from the age of fourteen worked in various pharmacies. The year (1775) that he was elected to the Academy of Sciences in Stockholm, he opened a pharmacy of his own. The prodigious amount of experimentation that he carried on in addition to the regular business of his shop led to his death from overwork at the age of forty-four.

The Collected Papers of Carl Wilhelm Scheele were published in an English translation by Leonard Dobbin (G. Bell and Son, London, 1931).

RADIANT HEAT

It is known that a metallic mirror reflects the heat of brightly red-hot charcoal which is placed in its focus, to such an extent that when this is collected by another metallic concave mirror it produces a focal point by means of which inflammable substances can be kindled. I inquire here whether the heat of this red-hot charcoal, or the light alone, or both together, bring about this action? I am indeed familiar with the confused ways of speaking, in which everything is called fire that possesses only a resemblance to it. Here, light is called fire, there, warmth or heat is fire, and elsewhere the phlogiston [1] contained in all substances is fire. Hence there will not be long delay with the answer to my question. It will be said that it is fire which is reflected, collected, and concentrated by these mirrors, consequently just the same action which sunlight brings about. I hold the view that one cannot begin to read until one knows the letters, and therefore I pause a little with the reply, and first take into consideration the following observations.

(a) Let a person seat himself in winter time in a room before the stove, when the wood in the latter is in full flame, since the heat passing through the open door of the stove can then be felt plainly enough at about three ells' [six feet] distance from it. In spite of this, he will be very plainly aware of the air or breath proceeding out of his mouth, which in summer time, however, is not to be seen in much less warm air. (b) If a burning candle be placed in this heat emanating from the stove in straight lines, or if smoke be brought into it, not only will the former burn away quietly but the latter will also ascend in a perpendicular line. (c) As a continuous air current goes out of the room into this stove, in order to replace the air

[1] The "heat principle," which eighteenth-century scientists believed to exist.

expanded by the heat and ascending through the chimney, the natural question at once arises: Why does not this heat emanating from the stove into the room immediately ascend by aid of the air current along with the latter into the chimney of the stove? (d) Let a strong wind be made by any means in front of this stove door from right to left, nevertheless, as with the rays of the sun, it will not be possible to give the emerging heat any other direction; so that when a person holds his face near the stove, at the left, he feels the wind which passes through the heat, but without warmth. (e) It is known that the shadow of a glowing, or merely hot, body, produced by sunlight on a white wall, is surrounded by a vapor which appears to quiver very rapidly and to be derived from nothing else than the air, expanded now more, now less by the heat, whereby the rays of light become broken. Whence does it arise, now, I ask, that if a person sitting before the stove has the window to the right and the white wall to the left, he nevertheless perceives no such quivering shadow on the wall, although the rays of the sun passing through the window panes cross the heat emanating from the stove and fall upon the opposite wall? When, however, there is hung up in this heat a hot iron or stone which was heated in this same heat, the usual quivering will then be observed in the open air as well as on the white wall. (f) When a large sheet of glass is held between the face and the stove, the fire is seen, indeed, but no heat is felt: the glass on the contrary will take up all the heat. (g) In like manner, the light of this fire can be reflected by means of a flat glass mirror without its being possible to observe in this light the slightest heat; but on the other hand, the mirror will retain all the heat falling upon it. (h) A polished plate of metal, however, will reflect the light as well as the heat, according to the same laws as the sunlight, and since here the heat is reflected, it is no wonder that this plate does not become warm. (i) For this same reason, at two ells' [four feet] distance in front of the stove, by means of a small metallic concave mirror, a focal point can be produced which kindles sulphur. Such a mirror can be held for a very long time in this position without its becoming warm; but if it is coated with some soot over a burning candle, it cannot be held for four minutes in the former position before the stove without burning the fingers upon it. (k) When the heat emanating from the stove is thrown upon another spot by means of a polished plate of metal, a sensitive focal point can be made in this case also, but only from two to three ells from the plate: and although a bright focal point is formed with the same concave mirror when light from a glass mirror is thrown upon it, yet there is not felt the slightest warmth. (l) When a person places a sheet of glass between himself and the fire, he can also, by aid of the concave mirror, produce a bright point behind the glass, yet without heat. For this same reason bright points can indeed be produced in front of the fire, by means of a burning glass, which, however, have not the slightest warmth in them. (m) But the metallic concave mirror and the plate of metal rapidly become hot as soon as they touch a hot body, although they do not become the least warm from the heat proceeding from the stove, for example. When the uppermost flue of the stove is closed, the heated air at once mounts upwards out of the open door: if the preceding metallic concave mirror, or the plate of metal, is held in this perpendicularly ascending heat, the heat does not permit of being reflected, but soon heats these metals also.

It follows from these experiments that the heat rising along with the air in the stove and passing through the flue is really different from that proceeding through the stove door into the room: That it travels from the place of its generation in straight lines, and is reflected again by polished metals at the same angle as the angle of incidence. That it does not unite with the air, and consequently cannot acquire from the current of air any other direction than it received at the beginning of its generation. For this same reason the moisture proceeding from the mouth is visible in this very strong heat. For since the air in summer time has entered into an actual union with the heat, while a warm air can always dissolve more water than a cold one, it is to be seen from this, likewise, that this heat is not united with the air and therefore the air is probably not expanded by it; whence it is also comprehensible why such heat causes no quivering in sunlight. These are properties which belong to light; still I shall not believe that these phenomena will on this account be attributed to the light radiating from the flame. For, in the first place, this light, as against the light of the sun, is far too weak, and in the second place, the before-mentioned action of the burning is much stronger when the wood is consumed and converted into brightly red-hot charcoal; for then the light has already diminished considerably; and further, the light can be separated from this heat by means of a glass mirror, since the heat is then retained in the glass and no warmth is perceived in the light radiating from it. Accordingly it follows that the heat issuing from the door of the stove indeed coincides with light in some respects but has not yet become light completely, since it is not reflected from a glass surface as it is from a metallic surface (Remarkable circumstance!). Also it is only active at a much smaller distance from its place of generation, judging by the feel, at least. But it also very shortly becomes changed into the familiar heat as soon as it has united with some substance; this is seen with the glass and with the metallic concave mirror coated with soot, and in several other instances. Then this heat can pass over from one substance into another; consequently it can also unite with the air and bring about the quivering in it. All this holds not only for the heat which proceeds from the stove into the room but also for any fire whatsoever. Let us assume a small heap built up of red-hot pieces of charcoal; the heat given out from round about this heap is exactly that which is capable of being thrown back again by means of a metallic plate; but what goes up aloft and can be driven hither and thither by the wind is that which has united with the air. I shall name the former radiant heat in order to distinguish it.

JOSEPH BLACK

1 7 2 8 · 1 7 9 9

ALTHOUGH HE published little during his lifetime, Joseph Black,
professor of chemistry at Glasgow and Edinburgh, exerted great
influence on the development of physics and chemistry, in the years
just preceding the Industrial Revolution, through the work of his
students and his own many personal contacts. He was one of the
strongest advocates of quantitative methods of investigation in these
fields. In the study of heat, for example, by showing that to raise
the temperature of one pound of mercury one degree took much
less heat than to raise a pound of water one degree, he proved that
each material required its own specific amount of heat to warm a
given mass of it one degree. He showed that it took much greater
quantities of heat to melt ice and transform water to steam than it
did merely to heat ice or water or steam. The extreme cold produced by the evaporation of the alcohol in Franklin's first experiment he could explain as a result of the alcohol's absorption of
"latent" heat from the glass and mercury of the thermometer. Black's
ideas were used, about 1765, by his assistant James Watt (1736-
1817) to improve Newcomen's wasteful steam engine.

The passages here quoted are from Black's Elements of Chemistry,
published in 1803, four years after his death.

SPECIFIC HEAT

TEMPERATURE DOES NOT MEASURE
QUANTITY OF HEAT

I REMARKED formerly, that, even without the help of thermometers, we can perceive a tendency of heat to diffuse itself from any hotter body to the cooler around, until it be distributed among them, in such a manner that none of them are disposed to take any more heat from the rest. The heat is thus brought into a state of equilibrium. This equilibrium is somewhat curious. We find that when all mutual action is ended, a thermometer, applied to any one of the bodies, acquires the same degree of expansion: Therefore the temperature of them all is the same, and the equilibrium is universal. No previous acquaintance with the peculiar relation of each to heat could have assured us of this, and we owe the discovery entirely to the thermometer. We must therefore adopt, as one of the most general laws of heat, that "all bodies communicating freely with each other, and exposed to no inequality of external action, acquire the same temperature, as indicated by a thermometer." All acquire the temperature of the surrounding medium.

By the use of these instruments we have learned, that if we take 1000, or more, different kinds of matter, such as metals, stones, salts, woods, cork, feathers, wool, water and a variety of other fluids, although they be all at first of different heats, let them be placed together in the same room without a fire, and into which the sun does not shine, the heat will be communicated from the hotter of these bodies to the colder, during some hours perhaps, or the course of a day, at the end of which time, if we apply a thermometer to them all in succession, it will point precisely to the same degree. The heat, therefore, distributes itself upon this occasion, until none of these bodies has a greater demand or attraction for heat than every other of them has; in consequence of which, when we apply a thermometer to them all in succession, after the first to which it is applied has reduced the instrument to its own temperature, none of the rest are disposed to increase or diminish the quantity of heat which that first one left in it. This is what has been commonly called an equal heat, or the equality of heat among different bodies; I call it the *equilibrium of heat*. The nature of this equilibrium was not well understood, until I pointed out a method of investigating it. Dr. Boerhaave[1] imagined, that when it obtains, there is an equal quantity of heat in every equal measure of space, however filled up with different bodies; and Professor Muschenbroeck expressed his opinion to the same purpose. . . . The reason they give for this opinion is, that to whichever of those bodies the thermometer be applied, it points to the same degree.

But this is taking a very hasty view of the subject. It is confounding the quantity of heat in different bodies with its general strength or intensity, though it is plain that these are two different things, and should always be distinguished, when we are thinking of the distribution of heat. . . .

It was formerly a common supposition, that the quantities of heat required to increase the heat of different bodies by the same number of degrees, were directly in proportion to the quantity of matter in each; and therefore, when the bodies were of equal size, the quantities of heat were in proportion to their density. But very soon after I began to think on this subject (anno 1760), I perceived that this opinion was a mistake, and that the quantities of heat which different kinds of matter must receive, to reduce them to an equilibrium with one another, or to raise their temperature by an equal number of degrees, are not in proportion to the quantity of matter in each, but in proportions widely different from this, and for which

[1] Dr. Hermann Boerhaave (1668-1738) was a distinguished physician of Leyden and a famous teacher of chemistry, physics, botany, and medicine.

no general principle or reason can yet be assigned. . . . This opinion was first suggested to me by an experiment described by Dr. Boerhaave. After relating the experiment which Fahrenheit made at his desire, by mixing hot and cold water, he also tells us, that Fahrenheit agitated together quicksilver and water unequally heated. From the Doctor's account, it is quite plain, that quicksilver, though it has more than 13 times the density of water, produced less effect in heating or cooling water to which it was applied, than an equal measure of water would have produced. He says expressly, that the quicksilver, whether it was applied hot to cold water, or cold to hot water, never produced more effect in heating or cooling an equal measure of the water than would have been produced by the water equally hot or cold with the quicksilver, and only two-thirds of its bulk. He adds, that it was necessary to take three measures of quicksilver to two of water, in order to produce the same middle temperature that is produced by mixing equal measures of hot and cold water.

To make this plainer by an example in numbers, let us suppose the water to be at the 100th degree of heat, and that an equal measure of warm quicksilver at the 150th degree, is suddenly mixed and agitated with it. We know that the middle temperature between 100 and 150 is 125, and we know that this middle temperature would be produced by mixing the cold water at 100 with an equal measure of warm water at 150; the heat of the warm water being lowered by 25 degrees, while that of the cold is raised just as much. But when warm quicksilver is used in place of warm water, the temperature of the mixture turns out 120 degrees only instead of 125. The quicksilver, therefore, is become less warm by 30 degrees, while the water has become warmer by twenty degrees only; and yet the quantity of heat which the water has gained is the very same quantity which the quicksilver has lost. This shews that the same quantity of the matter of heat has more effect in heating quicksilver than in heating an equal measure of water, and therefore that a smaller *quantity* of it is sufficient for increasing the sensible heat of quicksilver by the same number of degrees. The same thing appears, whatever way we vary the experiment; for, if the water is the warmer mass, and quicksilver the less warm one, by the above difference, the temperature produced is 130. The water, in this case, is become less warm by 20 degrees, while the heat it has lost, being given to the quicksilver, has made this warmer by 30 degrees. And lastly, if we take three measures of quicksilver to two of water, it is no matter which of them be the hotter. The temperature produced is always the middle temperature between the two, or 125 degrees, in the temperatures already mentioned. Here it is manifest that the same quantity of the matter of heat which makes *two* measures of water warmer by 25 degrees, is sufficient for making *three* measures of quicksilver warmer by the same number of degrees. Quicksilver, therefore, has less *capacity* for the matter of heat than water (if I may be allowed to use this expression) has; it requires a smaller quantity of it to raise its temperature by the same number of degrees.

The inference which Dr. Boerhaave drew from this experiment is very surprising. Observing that heat is not distributed among different bodies in proportion to the quantity of matter in each, he concludes that it is distributed in proportion to the space occupied by each body; a conclusion contradicted by this very experiment. Yet Muschenbroeck has followed him in this opinion.

As soon as I understood this experiment in the manner I have now explained it, I found a remarkable agreement between it and some experiments made by Dr. Martin (Essay on the Heating and Cooling of Bodies) which appeared at first very surprising and unaccountable; but, being compared with this one, may be explained by the same principle. Dr. Martin placed before a good fire, and at an equal distance from it, a quantity of water, and an equal bulk or measure of quicksilver, each of them contained in equal and similar glass vessels, and each having a delicate thermometer immersed into it. He then carefully observed the progress, or celerity, with which each of these fluids was heated by the fire, and raised the thermometers. He found, by repeated experiments, that the quicksilver was warmed by the fire much faster than the water, almost twice as fast; and after each experiment, having heated these two fluids to the same degree, he placed them in a stream of cold air, and found that the quicksilver was always cooled much faster than the water. Before these experiments were made, it was supposed that the quicksilver would require to heat or cool it a longer time than an equal bulk of water, in the proportion of 13 or 14 to one.

But, from the view I have given of Fahrenheit's, or Boerhaave's experiment with quicksilver and water, the above of Dr. Martin's is easily explained. We need only to suppose that the matter of heat, communicated by the fire, was communicated equally to the quicksilver and to the water, but that, as less of it was required for heating the quicksilver, than for heating the water, the quicksilver necessarily was warmed fastest of the two. And when both, being equally heated, were exposed to the cold air to cool, the air at first took their heat from them equally fast, but the quicksilver, by losing the same quantity of the matter of heat that the water lost, was necessarily cooled to a greater degree; it therefore became cold much faster than the water. These experiments of Dr. Martin, therefore, agreeing so well with Fahrenheit's experiment, plainly shew that quicksilver, notwithstanding its great density and weight, requires less heat to heat it, than that which is necessary to heat, by the same number of degrees, an equal measure of equally cold water. The quicksilver, therefore, may be said to have less capacity for the matter of heat. And we are thus taught, that, in cases in which we may have occasion to investigate the capacity of different bodies for heat, we can learn it only by making experiments. Some have accordingly been made, both by myself and others. Dr. Crawford has made a great number of very curious ones, and his Theory of the Heat of Animals is founded partly on some experiments made in this manner, the result of which is given in his book on that subject.

It appears, therefore, from the general result of such experiments, that if we had a thousand masses of matter, of the same size and form, but of different materials, and were to place them all in the same room, until they assumed the same temperature; were we then to introduce into that room a great mass of red hot iron, the heat of which, when communicated with all these different bodies at the same time, might be sufficient for raising the temperature of them all, by 20 degrees; the heat thus communicated from the iron, although it produced an equal effect on each of these bodies, in raising its temperature by 20 degrees, would not however be equally divided or distributed among them. Some of them would attract and retain a much greater quantity of this heat, or matter of heat, than others; and the quantity received by each would not be in proportion to their densities, but in proportions totally unconnected with it; and perhaps not any two of them would receive precisely the same quantity, but each, according to its particular capacity, or its particular force of attraction for this matter, would attract and require its own peculiar quantity to raise its temperature by the 20 degrees, or to reduce it to an equilibrium or equality of saturation with the surrounding bodies. We must, therefore, conclude that different bodies, although they be of the same size, or even of the same weight, when they are reduced to the same temperature or degree of heat, whatever that be, may contain very different quantities of the matter of heat; which different quantities are necessary to bring them to this level, or equilibrium, with one another.

It Takes Heat to Melt Solids

. . . Fluidity was universally considered as produced by a small addition to the quantity of heat which a body contains, when it is once heated up to its melting point; and the return of such a body to a solid state, as depending on a very small diminution of the quantity of its heat, after it is cooled to the same degree; that a solid body, when it is changed into a fluid, receives no greater addition to the heat within it than what is measured by the elevation of temperature indicated after fusion by the thermometer; and that, when the melted body is again made to congeal, by a diminution of its heat, it suffers no greater loss of heat than what is indicated also by the simple application to it of the same instrument.

This was the universal opinion on this subject, so far as I know, when I began to read my lectures in the University of Glasgow, in the year 1757. But I soon found reason to object to it, as inconsistent with many remarkable facts, when attentively considered; and I endeavoured to shew, that these facts are convincing proofs that fluidity is produced by heat in a very different manner.

I shall now describe the manner in which fluidity appeared to me to be produced by heat, and we shall then compare the former and my view of the subject with the phenomena.

The opinion I formed from attentive observation of the facts and phenomena, is as follows. When ice, for example, or any other solid substance, is changing into a fluid by heat, I am of opinion that it receives a much greater quantity of heat than what is perceptible in it immediately after by the thermometer. A greater quantity of heat enters into it, on this occasion, without making it apparently warmer, when tried by that instrument. This heat, however, must be thrown into it, in order to give it the form of a fluid; and I affirm, that this great addition of heat is the principal, and most immediate cause of the fluidity induced.

And, on the other hand, when we deprive such a body of its fluidity again, by a diminution of its heat, a very great quantity of heat comes out of it, while it is assuming a solid form, the loss of which heat is not to be perceived by the common manner of using the thermometer. The apparent heat of the body, as measured by that instrument, is not diminished, or not in proportion to the loss of heat which the body actually gives out on this occasion; and it appears from a number of facts, that the state of solidity cannot be induced without the abstraction of this great quantity of heat. And this confirms the opinion, that this quantity of heat, absorbed, and, as it were, concealed in the composition of fluids, is the most necessary and immediate cause of their fluidity.

To perceive the foundation of this opinion, and the inconsistency of the former with many obvious facts, we must consider, in the first place, the appearances observable in the melting of ice, and the freezing of water.

If we attend to the manner in which ice and snow melt, when exposed to the air of a warm room, or when a thaw succeeds to frost, we can easily perceive, that however cold they might be at the first, they are soon heated up to their melting point, or begin soon at their surface to be changed into water. And if the common opinion had been well founded, if the complete change of them into water required only the further addition of a very small quantity of heat, the mass, though of considerable size, ought all to be melted in a very few minutes or seconds more, the heat continuing incessantly to be communicated from the air around. Were this really the case, the consequences of it would be dreadful in many cases; for, even as things are at present, the melting of great quantities of snow and ice occasions violent torrents, and great inundations in the cold countries, or in the rivers that come from them. But, were the ice and snow to melt as suddenly as they must necessarily do, were the former opinion of the action of heat in melting them well founded, the torrents and inundations would be incomparably more irresistible and dreadful. They would tear up and sweep away every thing, and that so suddenly, that mankind should have great difficulty to escape from their ravages. This sudden liquefaction does not actually happen; the masses of ice or snow melt with a very slow progress, and require a long time, especially if they be of a large size, such as are the collections of ice, and wreaths of snow, formed in some places during the winter. These, after they begin to melt, often require many weeks of warm weather, before they are totally dissolved into water. This remarkable slowness with which ice is melted, enables us to preserve it easily during the summer, in the structures called Ice-houses. It begins to melt in these, as soon as it is put into them; but, as the building exposes only a small surface to the air, and has a very thick covering of thatch, and the access of the external air to the inside of it is prevented as much as possible, the heat penetrates the ice-house with a slow progress, and this, added to the slowness with which the ice itself is *disposed* to melt, protracts the total liquefaction of it so long, that some of it remains to the end of summer. In the same manner does snow continue on many mountains during the whole summer, in a melting state, but melting so slowly, that the whole of that season is not a sufficient time for its complete liquefaction.

This remarkable slowness with which ice and snow melt, struck me as quite inconsistent with the common opinion of the modification of heat, in the liquefaction of bodies.

And this very phenomenon is partly the foundation of the opinion I have proposed; for if we examine what happens, we may perceive that a great quantity of heat enters the melting ice, to form the water into which it is changed, and that the length of time necessary for the collection of so much heat from the surrounding bodies, is the reason of the slowness with which the ice is liquefied. If any person entertain doubts of the entrance and absorption of heat in the melting ice, he needs only to touch it; he will instantly feel that it rapidly draws heat from his warm hand. He may also examine the bodies that surround it, or are in contact with it, all of which he will find deprived by it of a great part of their heat; or if he suspend it by a thread, in the air of a warm room, he may perceive with his hand, or by a thermometer, a stream of cold air descending constantly from the ice; for the air in contact is deprived of a part of its heat, and thereby condensed and made heavier than the warmer air of the rest of the room; it therefore falls downwards, and its place round the ice is immediately supplied by some of the warmer air; but this, in turn, is soon deprived of some heat, and prepared to descend in like manner; and thus there is a constant flow of warm air from around, to the sides of the ice, and a descent of the same in a cold state, from the lower part of the mass, during which operation the ice must necessarily receive a great quantity of heat.

It is, therefore, evident, that the melting ice receives heat very fast, but the only effect of this heat is to change it into water, which is not in the least sensibly warmer than the ice was before. A thermometer, applied to the drops or small streams of water, immediately as it comes from the melting ice, will point to the same degree as when it is applied to the ice itself, or if there is any difference, it is too small to deserve notice. A great quantity, therefore, of the heat, or of the matter of heat, which enters into the melting ice, produces no other effect but to give it fluidity, without augmenting its sensible heat; it appears to be absorbed and concealed within the water, so as not to be discoverable by the application of a thermometer. . . .

I have . . . put a lump of ice into an equal quantity of water, heated to the temperature 176, and the result was, that the fluid was no hotter than water just ready to freeze. Nay, if a little sea salt be added to the water, and it be heated only to 166 or 170, we shall produce a fluid sensibly colder than the ice was in the beginning, which has appeared a curious and puzzling thing to those unacquainted with the general fact.

It is, therefore, proved that the phenomena which attended the melting of ice in different circumstances, are inconsistent with the common opinion which was established upon this subject, and that they support the one which I have proposed. . . .

It Takes Heat to Vaporize Liquids

In the ordinary manner of heating water, the heating cause is applied to the lower parts of the fluid. If the pressure on the surface be not increased, the water soon acquires the greatest heat which it can bear, without assuming the form of vapour. Subsequent additions of heat, therefore, in the same instant in which they enter the water, must convert into vapour that part which they thus affect. As these additions of heat all enter at the bottom of the fluid, there is a constant production of elastic vapour there, which, on account of its weighing almost nothing, must rise through the surrounding water, and appear to be thrown up to the surface with violence, and from thence it is diffused through the air. The water is thus gradually wasted, as the boiling continues, but its temperature is never increased, at least in that part which remains after long continued and violent boiling. The parts, indeed, in contact with the bottom of the vessel may be supposed to have received a little more heat, but this is instantly communicated to the surrounding water through which the elastic vapour rises.

This has the appearance of being a simple, plain, and complete account of the production of vapour, and of the boiling of fluids; and it is the only account that was given of this subject before I began to deliver these lectures: But I am persuaded that it is by no means a full account of the matter. According to this account, and the notion that was conceived of the formation of vapour, it was taken for granted that, after a body is heated up to its vaporific point, nothing further is necessary but the addition of a little more heat to change it into vapour. It was also supposed, on the other hand, that when the vapour of water is so far cooled as to be ready for condensation, this condensation, or return into the state of water, will happen at once, or in consequence of its losing only a very small quantity of heat.

But I can easily shew, in the same manner as in the case of fluidity, that a very great quantity of heat is necessary to the production of vapour, although the body be already heated to that temperature which it cannot pass, by the smallest possible degree, without being so converted. The undeniable consequence of this should be, an explosion of the whole water, with a violence equal to that of gunpowder. But I can shew, that this great quantity of heat enters into the vapour gradually, while it is forming, without making it perceptibly hotter to the thermometer. The vapour, if examined with a thermometer, is found to be exactly of the same temperature as the boiling water from which it arose. The water must be raised to a certain temperature, because, at that temperature only, is it disposed to absorb heat; and it is not instantly exploded, because, in that instant, there cannot be had a sufficient supply of heat through the whole mass. On the other hand, I can shew that when the vapour of water is condensed into a liquid, the very same great quantity of heat comes out of it into the colder matter by which it is condensed; and the matter of the vapour, or the water into which it is changed, does not become sensibly colder by the loss of this great quantity of heat. It does not become colder in proportion to the quantity of heat obtainable from it during its condensation.

All this will become evident, when we consider with attention the gradual formation of vapour, in consequence of the continued application of a heating cause, and the like gradual condensation of this vapour, when we continue to apply to it a body that is colder. . . .

I, therefore, set seriously about making experiments, conformable to the suspicion that I entertained concerning the boiling of fluids. My conjecture, when put into form, was to this purpose. I imagined that, during the boiling, heat is absorbed by the water, and enters into the composition of the vapour produced from it, in the same manner as it is absorbed by ice in melting, and enters into the composition of the produced water. And, as the ostensible effect of the heat, in this last case, consists, not in warming the surrounding bodies, but in rendering the ice fluid; so, in the case of boiling, the heat absorbed does not warm surrounding bodies, but converts the water into vapour. In both cases, considered as the cause of warmth, we do not perceive its presence: it is concealed, or latent, and I gave it the name of *latent heat*.

BENJAMIN THOMPSON,
COUNT RUMFORD

1 7 5 3 · 1 8 1 4

BENJAMIN THOMPSON, born in Concord (then called Rumford),
New Hampshire, fought on both sides of the American Revolutionary War. In England, where he went after the war, and again in
Bavaria, where he served under the Elector, he superintended the
manufacture of cannon. His tests of gunpowder and his experiments
with drilling gun bores involved him in a study of heat, a subject
which came to interest him intensely. His interest was given practical expression in a number of inventions, which included lamps,
stoves, chimneys, as well as coffee pots and steam tables for keeping
food warm. For his services to the Elector as Minister of War and of
the Interior, he was created Count Rumford of the Holy Roman
Empire. Eventually he married the widow of the chemist Lavoisier,
and spent his last years in France.

Our first selection, taken from The Complete Works of Count
Rumford (Boston, 1870), describes how he found that gases and
liquids, though they are, strictly speaking, non-conductors of heat,
carry heat by currents within themselves, later called convection
currents. The second selection is part of a report to the Royal
Society of London which was printed in their Philosophical Transactions for 1798. It describes an experiment in which far more heat
was generated by friction from a given amount of material than could
reside in fluid form in that material, if heat were the fluid it was
commonly supposed to be. The argument runs thus: if there is a
fluid or "caloric" contained in the material, it must exist in some

definite and limited amount; but heat can be drawn by friction from the material indefinitely; hence heat cannot be a fluid and the caloric theory is wrong; heat is related to motion.

However, the caloric theory was not generally abandoned until Joule (1818-1889) and Helmholtz (1821-1894) proved that a definite amount of work would always create a definite amount of heat. For example, the work which will lift 780 pounds one foot will also raise the temperature of one pound of water one degree Fahrenheit.

AIR AND WATER
DO NOT CONDUCT HEAT

It is certain that there is nothing more dangerous in philosophical investigation than to take anything for granted, however unquestionable it may appear, till it has been proved by direct and decisive experiment. I have very often, in the course of my philosophical researches, had occasion to lament the consequences of my inattention to this most necessary precaution.

There is not, perhaps, any phenomenon that more frequently falls under our observation than Propagation of Heat. The changes of the temperature of sensible bodies—of solids, liquids, and elastic fluids—are going on perpetually under our eyes; and there is no fact which one would not as soon think of calling in question, as to doubt of the free passage of Heat in all directions, through all kinds of bodies. But, however obviously this conclusion appears to flow from all that we observe and experience in the common course of life, yet it is certainly not true; and to the erroneous opinion respecting this matter, which has been universally entertained by the *learned*, and by the *unlearned*, and which has, I believe, never even been called in question, may be attributed the little progress that has been made in the investigation of the science of Heat:—a science, assuredly, of the utmost importance to mankind!

Under the influence of this opinion, I, many years ago, began my experiments on Heat; and had not an accidental discovery drawn my attention with irresistible force, and fixed it on the subject, I probably never should have entertained a doubt of the free passage of Heat *through air*; and even after I had found reason to conclude, from the results of experiments which to me appeared to be perfectly decisive, that air is a *non-conductor* of Heat; or that Heat cannot pass through it, without being transported by its particles; which, in this process, act individually, or independently of each other; yet, so far from pursuing the subject, and contriving experiments to ascertain the manner in which Heat is communicated in other bodies, I was not sufficiently awakened to suspect it to be even possible, that this quality could extend farther than to elastic Fluids.

With regard to liquids, so entirely persuaded was I, that Heat could pass freely *in them* in all directions, that I was perfectly blinded by this prepossession, and rendered incapable of seeing the most striking and most evident proofs of the fallacy of this opinion.

I have already given an account, in one of my late publications,[1] of the manner in which I was led to discover, that *steam* and *flame* are *non-conductors* of Heat. I shall now lay before the Public an account of a number of experiments I have lately made, which seem to show that *water*, and probably all other liquids, and Fluids of every kind, possess the same property. That is to say, that although the particles of any Fluid, *individually*, can receive heat from other bodies, or communicate it to them; yet, among these particles themselves all *interchange* and *communication* of Heat is absolutely impossible.

It may, perhaps, be thought not altogether uninteresting, to be acquainted with the various steps by which I was led to an experimental investigation of this curious subject of inquiry.

When dining, I had often observed that some particular dishes retained their Heat much longer than others; and that apple pies, and apples and almonds mixed, (a dish in great repute in England) remained hot a surprising length of time. Much struck with this extraordinary quality of retaining Heat, which apples appeared to possess, it frequently occurred to my recollection; and I never burnt my mouth with them, or saw others meet with the same misfortune, without endeavouring, but in vain, to find out some way of accounting, in a satisfactory manner, for this surprising phenomenon.

[1] Essay on "The Management of Fire and the Economy of Fuel."

About four years ago, a similar accident awakened my attention, and excited my curiosity still more; being engaged in an experiment which I could not leave, in a room heated by an iron stove, my dinner, which consisted of a bowl of thick rice soup, was brought into the room; and as I happened to be too much engaged at the time to eat it, in order that it might not grow cold, I ordered it to be set down on the top of the stove; about an hour afterwards, as near as I can remember, beginning to grow hungry, and seeing my dinner standing on the stove, I went up to it, and took a spoonful of the soup, which I found almost cold, and quite thick. Going, by accident, deeper with the spoon the second time, this second spoonful burnt my mouth. (It is probable that the stove happened to be nearly cold when the bowl was set down upon it, and that the soup had grown almost cold; when a fresh quantity of fuel being put into the stove, the Heat had been suddenly increased.) This accident recalled very forcibly to my mind the recollection of the hot apples and almonds with which I had so often burned my mouth, a dozen years before, in England; but even this, though it surprised me very much, was not sufficient to open my eyes, and to remove my prejudices respecting the conducting power of water.

Being at Naples in the beginning of the year 1794, among the many natural curiosities which attracted my attention, I was much struck with several very interesting phenomena which the hot baths of Baia presented to my observation, and among them there was one which quite astonished me: standing on the seashore, near the baths, where the hot steam was issuing out of every crevice of the rocks, and even rising up out of the ground, I had the curiosity to put my hand into the water. As the waves which came in from the sea followed each other without intermission, and broke over the even surface of the beach, I was not surprised to find the water cold; but I was more than surprised, when, on running the ends of my fingers through the cold water into the sand, I found the heat so intolerable that I was obliged instantly to remove my hand. The sand was perfectly wet; and yet, the temperature was so very different at the small distance of two or three inches! I could not reconcile this with the supposed great conducting power of water. I even found that the top of the sand was, to all appearance, quite as cold as the water which flowed over it, and this increased my astonishment still more. I then, for the first time, began to doubt of the conducting power of water, and resolved to set about making experiments to ascertain the fact. I did not however put this resolution into execution till about a month ago; and should perhaps never have done it, had not another unexpected appearance again called my attention to it, and excited afresh all my curiosity.

In the course of a set of experiments on the communication of Heat, in which I had occasion to use thermometers of an uncommon size (their globular bulbs being above four inches in diameter), filled with various kinds of liquids, having exposed one of them, which was filled with spirits of wine [alcohol], in as great a heat as it was capable of supporting, I placed it in a window, where the sun happened to be shining, to cool; when, casting my eye on its tube, which was quite naked (the divisions of its scale being marked in the glass with a diamond), I observed an appearance which surprised me, and at the same time interested me very much indeed. I saw the whole mass of the liquid in the tube in a most rapid motion, running swiftly in two opposite directions, *up*, and *down*, at the same time. The bulb of the thermometer, which is of copper, had been made two years before I found leisure to begin my experiments; and having been left unfilled, without being closed with a stopple, some fine particles of dust had found their way into it, and these particles, which were intimately mixed with the spirits of wine, on their being illuminated by the sun's beams, became perfectly visible (as the dust in the air of a darkened room is illuminated and rendered visible by the sun-beams which come in through a hole), and by their motion discovered the violent motions by which the spirits of wine in the tube of the thermometer was agitated.

This tube, which is 43/100 of an inch in diameter internally, and very thin, is composed of very transparent, colourless glass, which rendered the appearance clear and distinct, and exceedingly beautiful. On examining the motion of the spirits of wine with a lens, I found that the ascending current occupied the *axis of the tube*, and that it descended by the *sides of the tube*.

On inclining the tube a little, the rising current moved out of the axis, and occupied the side of the tube which was uppermost, while the *descending* current occupied the whole of the lower side of it.

When the cooling of the spirits of wine in the tube was hastened by wetting the tube with ice cold water, the velocities of both the ascending and the descending currents were sensibly accelerated.

The velocity of these currents was gradually lessened, as the thermometer was cooled; and when it had acquired nearly the temperature of the air of the room, the motion ceased entirely.

By wrapping up the bulb of the thermometer in furs, or any other warm covering, the motion might be greatly prolonged.

I repeated the experiment with a similar thermometer of equal dimensions, filled with linseed-oil, and the appearances, on setting it in the window to cool, were just the same. The directions of the currents, and the parts they occupied in the tube, were the same; and their motions were to all appearance quite as rapid as those in the thermometer which was filled with spirits of wine.

Having now no longer any doubt with respect to the cause of these appearances, being persuaded that the motion in these liquids was occasioned by their particles *going individually*, and *in succession*, to give off their Heat to the cold side of the tube, in the same manner as I have shown in another place, that the particles of air give off *their* Heat to other bodies, I was led to conclude that these, and probably all other liquids, are in fact *non-conductors* of Heat. . . .

HEAT IS A FORM OF MOTION

§

IT FREQUENTLY HAPPENS that in the ordinary affairs and occupations of life opportunities present themselves of contemplating some of the most curious operations of nature; and very interesting philosophical experiments might often be made, almost without trouble or expense, by means of machinery contrived for the mere mechanical purposes of the arts and manufactures.

I have frequently had occasion to make this observation, and am persuaded that a habit of keeping the eyes open to everything that is going on in the ordinary course of the business of life has oftener led, as it were by accident, or in the playful excursions of the imagination, put into action by contemplating the most common appearances, to useful doubts, and sensible schemes for investigation and improvement, than all the more intense meditations of philosophers, in the hours expressly set apart for study.

It was by accident that I was led to make the experiments of which I am about to give an account; and, though they are not perhaps of sufficient importance to merit so formal an introduction, I cannot help flattering myself that they will be thought curious in several respects, and worthy of the honor of being made known to the Royal Society.

Being engaged, lately, in superintending the boring of cannon, in the workshops of the military arsenal at Munich, I was struck with the very considerable degree of heat which a brass gun acquires, in a short time, in being bored; and with the still more intense heat (much greater than that of boiling water, as I found by experiment) of the metallic chips separated from it by the borer.

The more I meditated on these phenomena the more they appeared to me to be curious and interesting. A thorough investigation of them seemed even to bid fair to give a farther insight into the hidden nature of heat; and to enable us to form some reasonable conjectures respecting the existence, or non-existence, of an igneous fluid: a subject on which the opinions of philosophers have, in all ages, been much divided.

In order that the Society may have clear and distinct ideas of the speculations and reasonings to which these appearances gave rise in my mind, and also of the specific objects of philosophical investigation they suggested to me, I must beg leave to state them at some length and in such manner as I shall think best suited to answer this purpose.

From whence comes the heat actually produced in the mechanical operation above mentioned?

Is it furnished by the metallic chips which are separated by the borer from the solid mass of metal?

If this were the case, then, according to the modern doctrines of latent heat, and of caloric, the capacity for heat of the parts of the metal, so reduced to chips, ought not only to be changed, but the change undergone by them should be sufficiently great to account for all the heat produced.

But no such change had taken place; for I found, upon taking equal quantities, by weight, of these chips, and of thin slips of the same block of metal separated by means of a fine saw, and putting them, at the same temperature (that of boiling water) into equal quantities of cold water (that is to say, at the temperature of $59\frac{1}{2}°F.$), the portion of water into which the chips were put was not, to all appearance, heated either less or more than the other portion, in which the slips of metal were put.

This experiment being repeated several times, the results were always so nearly the same that I could not determine whether any, or what change, had been produced in the metal, in regard to its capacity for heat, by being reduced to chips by the borer.

From hence it is evident that the heat produced could not possibly have been furnished at the expense of the latent heat of the metallic chips. But, not being willing to rest satisfied with these trials, however conclusive they appeared to me to be, I had recourse to the following still more decisive experiment. [Rumford devised an apparatus in which a 130 lb. cylinder of brass was bored with a dull drill in an insulated tank of water.]

The result of this beautiful experiment was very striking, and the pleasure it afforded me amply repaid me for all the trouble I had had in contriving and arranging the complicated machinery used in making it.

The cylinder, revolving at the rate of about thirty-two times in a minute, had been in motion but a short time when I perceived, by putting my hand into the water and touching the outside of the cylinder, that heat was generated; and it was not long before the water which surrounded the cylinder began to be sensibly warm.

At the end of one hour I found, by plunging a thermometer into the water in the box (the quantity of which fluid amounted to 18.77 pounds avoirdupois, or 2¼ wine gallons) that its temperature had been raised no less than 47 degrees; being now 107° of Fahrenheit's scale.

When thirty minutes more had elapsed, or one hour and thirty minutes after the machinery had been put in motion, the heat of the water in the box was 142°.

At the end of two hours, reckoning from the beginning of the experiment, the temperature of the water was found to be raised to 178°.

At two hours twenty minutes it was 200°; and at two hours thirty minutes it *actually boiled!*

It would be difficult to describe the surprise and astonishment expressed in the countenances of the bystanders, on seeing so large a quantity of cold water heated and actually made to boil without any fire.

Though there was, in fact, nothing that could justly be considered as surprising in this event, yet I acknowledge fairly that it afforded me a degree of childish pleasure, which, were I ambitious of the reputation of a grave philosopher, I ought most certainly rather to hide than to discover.

The quantity of heat excited and accumulated in this experiment was very considerable; for not only the water in the box, but also the box itself (which weighed 15¼ pounds) and the hollow metallic cylinder, and that part of the iron bar which, being situated within the cavity of the box, was immersed in the water, were heated 150 degrees of Fahrenheit's scale; viz., from 60° (which was the temperature of the water, and of the machinery, at the beginning of the experiment) to 210°, the heat of boiling water at Munich.

The total quantity of heat generated may be estimated with some considerable degree of precision. . . .

From the result of these computations it appears that the quantity of heat produced equably, or in a continual stream (if I may use that expression), by the friction of the blunt steel borer against the bottom of the hollow metallic cylinder, in the experiment under consideration, was greater than that produced equably in the combustion of nine wax candles, each three quarters of an inch in diameter, all burning together, or at the same time, with clear bright flames.

As the machinery used in this experiment could easily be carried round by the force of one horse (though, to render the work lighter, two horses were actually employed in doing it), these computations show further how large a quantity of heat might be produced by proper mechanical contrivance, merely by the strength of a horse, without either fire, light, combustion, or chemical decomposition; and, in a case of necessity, the heat thus produced might be used in cooking victuals.

But no circumstances can be imagined in which this method of procuring heat would not be disadvantageous; for more heat might be obtained by using the fodder necessary for the support of a horse, as fuel.

By meditating on the results of all these experiments we are naturally brought to that great question which has so often been the subject of speculation among philosophers; namely:

What is heat? Is there any such thing as an *igneous fluid*? Is there anything that can with propriety be called *caloric*?

We have seen that a very considerable quantity of heat may be excited in the friction of two metallic surfaces and given off in a constant stream or flux, *in all directions*, without interruption or intermission, and without any signs of diminution or exhaustion.

From whence came the heat which was continually given off in this manner, in the foregoing experiments? Was it furnished by the small particles of metal, detached from the larger solid masses, on their being rubbed together? This, as we have already seen, could not possibly have been the case.

Was it furnished by the air? This could not have been the case; for, in three of the experiments, the machinery being kept immersed in water, the access of the air of the atmosphere was completely prevented.

Was it furnished by the water which surrounded the machinery? That this could not have been the case is evident: first, because this water was continually *receiving heat* from the machinery and could not, at the same time, be *giving to*, and *receiving heat from*, the same body; and secondly, because there was no chemical decomposition of any part of this water. Had any such decomposition taken place (which indeed could not reasonably have been expected), one of its component elastic fluids (most probably inflammable air) must, at the same time, have been set at liberty, and in making its escape into the atmosphere would have been detected; but though I frequently examined the water to see if any air bubbles rose up through it, and had even made preparations for catching them, in order to examine them, if any should appear, I could perceive none; nor was there any sign of decomposition of any kind whatever, or other chemical process, going on in the water.

Is it possible that the heat could have been supplied by means of the iron bar to the end of which the blunt steel borer was fixed? Or by the small neck of gun metal by which the hollow cylinder was united to the cannon? These suppositions appear more improbable even than either of those before mentioned; for heat was continually going off, or *out of the machinery*, by both these passages, during the whole time the experiment lasted.

And, in reasoning on this subject, we must not forget to consider that most remarkable circumstance, that the source of the heat generated by friction, in these experiments, appeared evidently to be *inexhaustible*.

It is hardly necessary to add that anything which any *insulated* body, or system of bodies, can continue to furnish *without limitation* cannot possibly be *a material substance*: and it appears to me to be extremely difficult, if not quite impossible, to form any distinct idea of anything, capable of being excited and communicated, in the manner the heat was excited and communicated in these experiments, except it be MOTION.

WILLIAM HERSCHEL[1]

1 7 3 8 · 1 8 2 2

WHEN HERSCHEL turned his telescope to the sun, his eyes were troubled by the heat, and he noticed that the colored glasses which were best in cutting down the amount of light that came through them were not necessarily the best in limiting the heat. He therefore started a long series of experiments, reported in two lengthy essays in the Philosophical Transactions of the Royal Society of London for 1800, to find if light of different colors really had a different heating quality.

Herschel set a prism in the sun and measured the difference between the room temperature and the thermometer readings in the light of various colors. He first found the red light far warmer than the blue. He then put the thermometer in the dark just beyond the red band and found an even higher heat; farther out yet, the heat diminished again to room temperature.

Soon afterwards, J. W. Ritter found rays above the visible violet which would blacken nitrate of silver. (Scheele had discovered this photographic action in 1777.) This gave support to what Herschel had already suggested, that the visible rays of light are but a part of the rays sent by the sun to earth, and that the rays that carry most heat are invisible.

[1] For material on Herschel as astronomer, see above, p. 112.

INFRA-RED AND THE CONTINUITY OF
LIGHT AND HEAT

Investigation of the Powers of the prismatic Colours to
heat and illuminate Objects; with Remarks, that prove
the different Refrangibility of Radiant Heat.

Read March 27, 1800.

It is sometimes great use in natural philosophy, to doubt of things
that are commonly taken for granted; especially as the means of
resolving any doubt, when once it is entertained, are often within
our reach. We may therefore say that any experiment which leads
us to investigate the truth of what was before admitted upon trust
may become of great utility to natural knowledge. Thus, for instance, when we see the effect of the condensation of the sun's rays
in the focus of a burning lens, it seems to be natural to suppose that
every one of the united rays contributes its proportional share to the
intensity of the heat which is produced; and we should probably
think it highly absurd if it were asserted that many of them had but
little concern in the combustion, or vitrification, which follows,
when an object is put into that focus. It will therefore not be amiss
to mention what gave rise to a surmise that the power of heating
and illuminating objects might not be equally distributed among
the variously coloured rays.

In a variety of experiments I have occasionally made, relating to
the method of viewing the sun with large telescopes to the best
advantage, I used various combinations of differently-coloured darkening glasses. What appeared remarkable was, that when I used
some of them, I felt a sensation of heat, though I had but little light;

while others gave me much light, with scarce any sensation of heat. Now, as in these different combinations the sun's image was also differently coloured, it occurred to me, that the prismatic rays might have the power of heating bodies very unequally distributed among them; and, as I judged it right in this respect to entertain a doubt, it appeared equally proper to admit the same with regard to light.

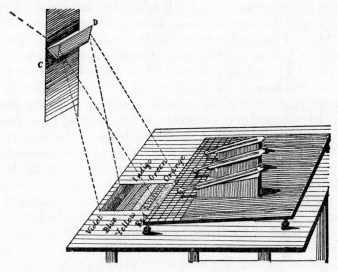

Diagram illustrating Herschel's experiment with prismatic colors.

[In a series of experiments, Herschel placed the ball of a thermometer in the spectral band of one color after another, while two control thermometers remained apart in the darkened room. He noted the increase in the number of degrees registered by the thermometer in the spectrum, and found that in the red light the thermometer rose over twice as far as when in the green, and over three times as far as when in the violet light.

In another series, he found that the thermometer was most heated when placed in the dark just beyond the red band, while the place of greatest light intensity was in the yellow and light green in the middle of the visible spectrum.]

Radiant Heat is of different Refrangibility

I must now remark that my foregoing experiments ascertain beyond a doubt that radiant heat, as well as light, whether they be the same or different agents, is not only refrangible, but is also subject to the laws of the dispersion arising from its different refrangibility. . . . May not this lead us to surmise that radiant heat consists of particles of light of a certain range of momenta, and which range may extend a little farther, on each side of refrangibility, than that of light? We have shewn, that in a gradual exposure of the thermometer to the rays of the prismatic spectrum, beginning from the violet, we come to the maximum of light long before we come to that of heat, which lies at the other extreme. By several experiments, which time will not allow me now to report, it appears that the maximum of illumination has little more than half the heat of the full red rays; and, from other experiments, I likewise conclude that the full red falls still short of the maximum of heat; which perhaps lies even a little beyond visible refraction. In this case, radiant heat will at least partly, if not chiefly, consist, if I may be permitted the expression, of invisible light; that is to say, of rays coming from the sun, that have such a momentum as to be unfit for vision. And, admitting, as is highly probable, that the organs of sight are only adapted to receive impressions from particles of a certain momentum, it explains why the maximum of illumination should be in the middle of the refrangible rays; as those which have greater or less momenta are likely to become equally unfit for impressions of sight. Whereas, in radiant heat, there may be no such limitation to the momentum of its particles. From the powerful effects of a burning lens, however, we gather the information, that the momentum of terrestrial radiant heat is not likely to exceed that of the sun; and that, consequently, the refrangibility of *calorific* rays cannot extend much beyond that of *colourific* light.

Hence we may also infer, that the invisible heat of red-hot iron, gradually cooled till it ceases to shine, has the momentum of the invisible rays which, in the solar spectrum viewed by daylight, go to the confines of red; and this will afford an easy solution of the reflection of invisible heat by concave mirrors. . . .

Experiments on the Refrangibility of the Invisible Rays of the Sun

Read April 24, 1800.

In that section of my former paper which treats of radiant heat it was hinted, though from imperfect experiments, that the range of its refrangibility is probably more extensive than that of the prismatic colours; but, having lately had some favourable sunshine, and obtained a sufficient confirmation of the same, it will be proper to add the following experiments to those which have been given.

[The following paragraphs are greatly condensed from Herschel's report.]

I provided a small stand, covered with white paper. On this I drew five lines, parallel to one end of the stand, at half an inch distance from each other, but so that the first of the lines might only be ¼ of an inch from the edge.

The same thermometers were then placed to have the centres of the shadow of their balls thrown on these lines. Now I caused the prismatic spectrum to fall with its extreme colour [red] upon the edge of the paper, so that none might advance beyond the first line. In this arrangement, all the [visible] spectrum, except the vanishing last quarter of an inch, passed down by the edge of the stand, and could not interfere with the experiments.

During the experiment, I kept the last termination of visible red carefully to the first line, as a limit assigned to it, by gently moving the stand when required; and I found that thermometer No. 1 rose 6½ degrees, in ten minutes, when its centre was placed ½ inch beyond visible light.

It being now evident that there was a refraction of rays coming from the sun, which, though not fit for vision, were yet highly invested with a power of occasioning heat, I proceeded to examine its extent as follows.

The thermometers were arranged on the third line, instead of the second; here the thermometer No. 1 rose 5¼ degrees, in 13 minutes, at 1 inch behind the visible light of the red rays. On the 4th line. thermometer No. 1 rose 3⅛ degree, in 10 minutes, at 1½ inch beyond the visible light of the red rays.

I might now have gone on to the 5th line; but, so fine a day, with regard to clearness of sky and perfect calmness, was not to be expected often, at this time of the year; I therefore hastened to make a trial of the other extreme of the prismatic spectrum. I placed the thermometers one inch beyond the reach of the violet rays, and found the several indications afford no ground for ascribing any of their small changes to other causes than the accidental disturbance which will arise from the motion of the air, in a room where some employment is carried on.

It will now be easy to draw the result of these observations into a very narrow compass.

The first four experiments prove that there are rays coming from the sun which are less refrangible than any of those that affect the sight. They are invested with a high power of heating bodies, but with none of illuminating objects; and this explains the reason why they have hitherto escaped unnoticed.

My present intention is not to assign the angle of the least refrangibility belonging to these rays, for which purpose more accurate, repeated, and extended experiments are required. But, at the distance of 52 inches from the prism, there was still a considerable heating power exerted by our invisible rays, one inch and a half beyond the red ones, measured upon their projection on a horizontal plane. I have no doubt but that their efficacy may be traced still somewhat farther.

The 5th and 6th experiments shew that the power of heating is extended to the utmost limits of the visible violet rays, but not beyond them; and that it is gradually impaired, as the rays grow more refrangible.

The four last experiments prove that the maximum of the heating power is vested among the invisible rays; and is probably not less than half an inch beyond the last visible ones, when projected in the manner before mentioned. The same experiments also shew, that the sun's invisible rays, in their less refrangible state, and considerably beyond the maximum, still exert a heating power fully equal to that of red-coloured light; and that, consequently, if we may infer the quantity of the efficient [cause] from the effect produced, the invisible rays of the sun probably far exceed the visible ones in number.

To conclude, if we call *light* those rays which illuminate objects, and *radiant heat* those which heat bodies, it may be inquired, whether light be essentially different from radiant heat? In answer to which I would suggest that we are not allowed, by the rules of philosophizing, to admit two different causes to explain certain effects, if they may be accounted for by one. A beam of radiant heat, emanating from the sun, consists of rays that are differently refrangible. The range of their extent, when dispersed by a prism, begins at violet-coloured light, where they are most refracted, and have the least efficacy. We have traced these calorific rays throughout the whole extent of the prismatic spectrum; and found their power increasing, while their refrangibility was lessened, as far as to the confines of red-coloured light. But their diminishing refrangibility, and increasing power, did not stop here; for we have pursued them a considerable way beyond the *prismatic spectrum*, into an invisible state, still exerting their increasing energy, with a decrease of refrangibility up to the maximum of their power; and have also traced them to that state where, though still less refracted, their energy, on account, we may suppose, of their now failing density, decreased pretty fast; after which, the invisible *thermometrical spectrum*, if I may so call it, soon vanished.

If this be a true account of solar heat, for the support of which I appeal to my experiments, it remains only for us to admit that such of the rays of the sun as have the refrangibility of those which are contained in the prismatic spectrum, by the construction of the organs of sight are admitted, under the appearance of light and colours; and that the rest, being stopped in the coats and humours of the eye, act upon them, as they are known to do upon all the other parts of our body, by occasioning a sensation of heat.

III

The Study of Air and of Chemistry

EARLY CHEMISTRY followed three somewhat independent but overlapping lines of investigation. First there was the search of the alchemists for a method of transmuting base metals into gold—taking weight from one, color from another, and so on. Secondly, following Paracelsus, there was medicinal chemistry, directed not only to healing specific ills, but also to the search for a universal cure and the elixir of life. Thirdly, there was the practical chemistry of the miner and metalworker.

Clarification of thought and development of experimental techniques usually go together where there is progress in science. Chemistry developed more slowly than astronomy and mechanics, largely because of the difficulty of finding a starting place for a basic theory. It has often been said that a wrong theory is far better than no theory as a starting point for experiment, and the fruitfulness to physics of the false "heat-fluid" theory proves this. But apparently it is much harder to think about the commonplace materials we meet every day than it is to measure the speed of light, or the orbits of stellar bodies.

Newton himself spent far more time on chemical and alchemistic research than he did on the work which brought him his fame. His notebooks show that he was a careful observer of chemical processes, and some of his ideas were well ahead of his time. But, in spite of his genius for organization, he was unable to bring order into the thinking about chemistry, as he had done in the fields of celestial mechanics and light. Consequently, he did not publish many of his results.

The four primitive elements—earth, air, fire, water—were said by the "Aristotelian" or "peripatetic" or "Hermetic" philosophers to be the basis of all matter. There has been much debate as to the meaning of these "elements" to the philosophers of one generation or another, but it is certain that they are frequently considered as the pure, intangible essences of things. Paracelsus, however, and his followers, the "Spagyrists" of the sixteenth and seventeenth centuries, contended that the first principles of things were three in number—salt, sulphur, and mercury. Van Helmont (1577-1644) demonstrated the material character of "airs" or gases, but held the view that "all salt, clay, and indeed all tangible bodies are really and materially the product of water only, and may be reduced to water again by nature or art." The famous German medical chemist, Johann Rudolf Glauber (1604-1668), maker of "Glauber's salts," compromised between Paracelsus and Van Helmont by substituting water for mercury in Paracelsus' list of elements. "The principles of vegetables," he said, "are water, salt, and sulphur, from which the metals are also derived."

In the course of an argument against such lists, Robert Boyle made one of the first modern definitions of an element. "I now mean by elements," he wrote, "certain primitive and simple or perfectly unmingled bodies, which, not being made of any other bodies, or of one another, are the ingredients of which all those called perfectly mixed bodies are immediately compounded, and into which they are ultimately resolved." It was on this broad definition that Lavoisier was to base his list of elements a century later.

The physical and chemical study of gases is the theme of many of the selections in the following section. After the three paragraphs from Paracelsus, the discussion of the nature of a vacuum by Descartes and Galileo provides a background for the seventeenth century barometric experiments on air pressure by Torricelli, Pascal, and Boyle. Meanwhile Jean Rey's essay on the increase of weight in metals during calcination or burning argues that the increase is caused by something taken from the air. This is a purely chemical discussion, and leads up to the work of Priestley, Cavendish, Lavoisier, and Nicholson in which, a century later, they isolate gases, synthesize water from oxygen and hydrogen, and disintegrate water into oxygen and hydrogen.

In addition to their experimental work, Boyle and Lavoisier are represented here by selections from two dynamically important books on theory: Boyle's *Sceptical Chymist* destroyed mediaeval chemistry; Lavoisier's *Elements of Chemistry* created modern chemical language.

PARACELSUS

1493 · 1541

AT A TIME when chemistry was alchemy, mixed with notions from astrology, Paracelsus broke violently with the old ideas. The noise of the argument was so violent that Paracelsus' middle name (he was christened Theophrastus Bombastus von Hohenheim) is still used to denote pompous ranting.

Though his writing sounds to us hopelessly vague and mystical, there is much sound chemistry and clear observation hidden in the language. He was an early advocate of chemical drugs in medicine; he prescribed remedies containing mercury, antimony, copper, iron, lead, and milk of sulphur.

The passage below, from his Heaven of Philosophy, translated from the Latin by Arthur Edward Waite for the Hermetic and Alchemical Writings of Paracelsus, London, 1894, is typical of his satirical vein and his ridicule of current alchemical jargon.

THE RECEIPTS OF ALCHEMY

THE PREFACE

You who are skilled in alchemy, and as many others as promise yourselves great riches or chiefly desire to make gold and silver, which alchemy in different ways promises and teaches; equally, too, you who willingly undergo toil and vexations, and wish not to be freed from them until you have attained your rewards and the fulfillment of the promises made to you: experience teaches this every day, that out of thousands of you not even one accomplishes his desire. Is this a failure of nature or of art? I say no; but it is rather the fault of fate, or of the unskillfulness of the operator. . . .

How to Make Gold and Silver (Sol and Luna)[1]

What, then, shall we say about the receipts of alchemy, and about the diversity of its vessels and instruments? These are furnaces, glasses, jars, waters, oils, limes, sulphurs, salts, saltpeters, alums, vitriols, chrysocollae, copper greens, atraments, auripigments, fel vitri, ceruse, red earth, thucia, wax, lutum sapientiae, pounded glass, verdigris, soot, crocus of Mars, soap, crystal, arsenic, antimony, minium, elixir, lazarium, gold leaf, salt niter, sal ammoniac, calamine stone, magnesia, bolus armenus, and many other things. Moreover, [what shall we say] concerning preparations, putrefactions, digestions, probations, solutions, cementings, filtrations, reverberations, calcinations, graduations, rectifications, amalgamations, purgations, et cetera; with these alchemical books are crammed.

[1] Sol and Luna, Latin names for Sun and Moon, were used very commonly by the alchemists to mean gold and silver. According to ancient theory, each of the seven planets was in some way associated with one of the so-called seven metals. To this day the planet Mercury and its metal keep the same name.

Then, again, concerning herbs, roots, seeds, woods, stones, animals, worms, bone dust, snail shells, other shells, and pitch. These and the like, whereof there are some very farfetched in alchemy, are mere incumbrances of work; since even if Sol and Luna could be made by them they rather hinder and delay than further one's purpose. But it is not from these—to say the truth—that the art of making Sol and Luna is to be learned. So, then, all these things should be passed by, because they have no effect with the five metals, so far as Sol and Luna are concerned. Someone may ask, "What, then, is this short and easy way, which involves no difficulty, and yet whereby Sol and Luna can be made?" Our answer is: this has been fully and openly explained in the Seven Canons. It would be lost labor should one seek further to instruct one who does not understand these. It would be impossible to convince such a person that these matters could be so easily understood, but in an occult rather than in an open sense.

The art is this: after you have made heaven, or the sphere of Saturn, with its life to run over the earth, place it on all the planets, or such, one or more, as you wish, so that the portion of Luna may be the smallest. Let all run, until heaven, or Saturn, has entirely disappeared. Then all those planets will remain dead with their old corruptible bodies, having meanwhile obtained another new, perfect, and incorruptible body.

That body is the spirit of heaven. From it these planets again receive a body and life, and live as before. Take this body from the life and the earth. Keep it. It is Sol and Luna. Here you have the art altogether, clear and entire. If you do not yet understand it, or are not practiced therein, it is well. It is better that it should be kept concealed, and not made public.

RENÉ DESCARTES[1]

1 5 9 6 · 1 6 5 0

THE FOLLOWING observations of Descartes on the impossibility of obtaining a vacuum and on the non-existence of atoms, are included here to show the great difficulties encountered by even so astute a genius in thinking about these important matters, and to give a basis of comparison for the later points of view of Galileo, Torricelli, and Pascal, who were more experimentally minded. Men became less and less interested in this sort of metaphysical speculation as they became more absorbed in experiment.

The selection is from Part II of The Principles of Philosophy, 1644, translated by John Veitch, 1853 (Everyman's Edition, E. P. Dutton, New York).

[1] For Descartes' opposition to old methods of thinking, see below, p. 595.

OF THE PRINCIPLES OF

MATERIAL THINGS

XVI. THAT A VACUUM or space in which there is absolutely no body is repugnant to reason.

With regard to a vacuum, in the philosophical sense of the term, that is, a space in which there is no substance, it is evident that such does not exist, seeing the extension of space or internal place is not different from that of body. For since from this alone, that a body has extension in length, breadth, and depth, we have reason to conclude that it is a substance, it being absolutely contradictory that nothing should possess extension, we ought to form a similar inference regarding the space which is supposed void, viz., that since there is extension in it there is necessarily also substance.

XVII. That a vacuum in the ordinary use of the term does not exclude all body.

And, in truth, by the term vacuum in its common use, we do not mean a place or space in which there is absolutely nothing, but only a place in which there is none of those things we presume ought to be there. Thus, because a pitcher is made to hold water, it is said to be empty when it is merely filled with air; or if there are no fish in a fish-pond, we say there is nothing in it, although it be full of water; thus a vessel is said to be empty, when, in place of the merchandise which it was designed to carry, it is loaded with sand only, to enable it to resist the violence of the wind; and, finally, it is in the same sense that we say space is void when it contains nothing sensible, although it contain created and self-subsisting matter; for we are not in the habit of considering the bodies near us, unless in so far as they cause in our organs of sense impressions strong enough to enable us to perceive them. And if, in place of keeping in mind what ought to be understood by these terms a vacuum and nothing, we afterwards suppose that in the space we called a vacuum, there is not only no sensible object, but no object at all, we will fall into the same error as if, because a pitcher in which there is nothing but air, is, in common speech, said to be empty, we were therefore to judge that the air contained in it is not a substance.

XVIII. How the prejudice of an absolute vacuum is to be corrected.

We have almost all fallen into this error from the earliest age, for, observing that there is no necessary connection between a vessel and the body it contains, we thought that God at least could take from a vessel the body which occupied it, without it being necessary that any other should be put in the place of the one removed. But that we may be able now to correct this false opinion, it is necessary to remark, that there is in truth no connection between the vessel and the particular body which it contains, but that there is an absolutely necessary connection between the concave figure of the vessel and the extension considered generally which must be comprised in this cavity; so that it is not more contradictory to conceive a mountain without a valley than such a cavity without the extension it contains, or this extension apart from an extended substance, for, as we have often said, of nothing there can be no extension. And accordingly, if it be asked what would happen were God to remove from a vessel all the body contained in it, without permitting another body to occupy its place, the answer must be that the sides of the vessel would thus come into proximity with each other. For two bodies must touch each other when there is nothing between them, and it is manifestly contradictory for two bodies to be apart, in other words, that there should be a distance between them, and this distance yet be nothing; for all distance is a mode of extension, and cannot therefore exist without an extended substance.

XIX. That this confirm what was said of rarefaction.

After we have thus remarked that the nature of corporeal substance consists only in its being an extended thing, and that its extension is not different from that which we attribute to space, however empty, it is easy to discover the impossibility of any one of its parts in any way whatsoever occupying more space at one time than at another, and thus of being otherwise rarefied than in the way explained above; and it is easy to perceive also that there cannot be more matter or body in a vessel when it is filled with lead or gold, or any other body however heavy and hard, than when it but contains air and is supposed to be empty: for the quantity of the parts of which a body is composed does not depend on their weight or hardness, but only on the extension, which is always equal in the same vase.

XX. That from this the non-existence of atoms may likewise be demonstrated.

We likewise discover that there cannot exist any atoms or parts of matter that are of their own nature indivisible.[1] For however small we suppose these parts to be, yet because they are necessarily extended, we are always able in thought to divide any one of them into two or more smaller parts, and may accordingly admit their divisibility. For there is nothing we can divide in thought which we do not thereby recognize to be divisible; and, therefore, were we to judge it indivisible our judgment would not be in harmony with the knowledge we have of the thing; and although we should even suppose that God had reduced any particle of matter to a smallness so extreme that it did not admit of being further divided, it would nevertheless be improperly styled indivisible, for though God had rendered the particle so small that it was not in the power of any

1 Descartes is here wrongly arguing that a bit of gold, or any other metal, is infinitely divisible without changing its essential character. Today we "split atoms," but protons and electrons are parts of atoms somewhat in the way that lamb chops are parts of sheep, or nails are parts of a house, rather than in the way that a small bit of gold is part of a large piece of gold.

creature to divide it, he could not however deprive himself of the ability to do so, since it is absolutely impossible for him to lessen his own omnipotence, as was before observed. Wherefore, absolutely speaking, the smallest extended particle is always divisible, since it is such of its very nature.

GALILEO GALILEI

1 5 6 4 · 1 6 4 2

THIS BRIEF SELECTION from Galileo's Dialogues Concerning Two New Sciences,[1] translated by H. Crew and A. de Salvio (Macmillan, 1914; Northwestern University, 1939), clearly explains the principle of the common lift pump. The statement that "on weighing the water contained in a tube eighteen cubits long . . . we shall obtain the value of the resistance of a vacuum," may have stimulated his assistant and disciple, Torricelli, to formulate his famous principle, and to construct a barometer, as described in a later selection.

The characters who take part in the following dialogue, Sagredo and Salviati, were actual friends and followers of Galileo, and speak of his views.

[1] For another selection from this dialogue, see above, p. 44.

HOW A PUMP LIFTS WATER

SAGREDO. Thanks to this discussion, I have learned the cause of a certain effect which I have long wondered at and despaired of understanding. I once saw a cistern which had been provided with a pump, under the mistaken impression that the water might thus be drawn with less effort or in greater quantity than by means of the ordinary bucket. The stock of the pump carried its sucker and valve in the upper part so that the water was lifted by attraction and not by a push as is the case with pumps in which the sucker is placed lower down. This pump worked perfectly so long as the water in the cistern stood above a certain level; but below this level the pump failed to work. When I first noticed this phenomenon I thought the machine was out of order; but the workman whom I called in to repair it told me the defect was not in the pump but in the water which had fallen too low to be raised through such a height; and he added that it was not possible, either by a pump or by any other machine working on the principle of attraction, to lift water a hair's breadth above eighteen cubits;[1] whether the pump be large or small this is the extreme limit of the lift. Up to this time I had been so thoughtless that, although I knew a rope, or rod of wood, or of iron, if sufficiently long, would break by its own weight when held by the upper end, it never occurred to me that the same thing would happen, only much more easily, to a column of water. And really is not that thing which is attracted in the pump a column of water attached at the upper end and stretched more and more until finally a point is reached where it breaks, like a rope, on account of its excessive weight?

SALVIATI. That is precisely the way it works; this fixed elevation of

[1] That is, nearly 34 feet.

219

eighteen cubits is true for any quantity of water whatever, be the pump large or small or even as fine as a straw. We may therefore say that, on weighing the water contained in a tube eighteen cubits long, no matter what the diameter, we shall obtain the value of the resistance of the vacuum in a cylinder of any solid material having a bore of this same diameter. . . .

JEAN REY

1 5 7 5 (?) - 1 6 4 5

OCCASIONAL ACHIEVEMENTS in the history of science appear so far ahead of their time that they actually fail to affect the course of thought until much later. The work of Jean Rey, a medical doctor of Bergerac, France, is an example. We know very little about Rey except what is printed in a single brief pamphlet: Essays of Jean Rey, doctor of medicine, on his search for the reason why tin and lead gain in weight when they are calcined. This pamphlet passed unnoticed until it was brought forward, a century and a half later, to prove that one of Lavoisier's experiments had been already anticipated.

Rey said that the Sieur Brun, Master Apothecary in Bergerac, had asked him why lead and tin gain weight when they are calcined or roasted in great heat, and that he had written this essay to give the answer. First he had to demonstrate that air has weight, contrary to the prevailing ideas of the day. "The error I have combatted [that air is without weight]," he said, "rests on an argument which may dazzle feeble eyes, though not clearseeing ones. For, balancing air in air itself, and finding no weight in it, they believed that it had none. But let them balance water (which they believe to be heavy) in water itself, and they will find no weight in it either; the fact being that no element shows weight when weighed in itself." The main part of his argument follows. The translation is from the Alembic Club Reprint No. 11, and was taken from John F. Fulton's Readings in the History of Physiology (Charles C. Thomas, Springfield, Ill., 1930).

WHY TIN AND LEAD INCREASE
IN WEIGHT WHEN CALCINED

Now I HAVE made the preparations, nay, laid the foundations for
my answer to the question of the sieur Brun, which is, that having
placed two pounds six ounces of fine English tin in an iron vessel
and heated it strongly on an open furnace for the space of six hours
with continual agitation and without adding anything to it, he
recovered two pounds thirteen ounces of a white calx; which filled
him at first with amazement, and with a desire to know whence the
seven ounces of surplus had come. And to increase the difficulty,
I say that it is necessary to enquire not only whence these seven
ounces have come, but besides them what has replaced the loss of
weight which occurred necessarily from the increase of volume of the
tin on its conversion into calx, and from the loss of the vapours and
exhalations which were given off. To this question, then, I respond
and sustain proudly, resting on the foundations already laid, "That
this increase in weight comes from the air, which in the vessel has
been rendered denser, heavier, and in some measure adhesive, by
the vehement and long-continued heat of the furnace: which air
mixes with the calx (frequent agitation aiding) and becomes attached to its most minute particles: not otherwise than water makes
heavier sand which you throw into it and agitate, by moistening it
and adhering to the smallest of its grains." I fancy there are many
who would have been alarmed by the sole mention of this response
if I had given it at the beginning, who will now willingly receive it,
being as it were tamed and rendered tractable by the evident truth
of the preceding Essays. For those without doubt whose minds were
preoccupied with the opinion that air was light, would have rushed

to oppose it. Why (they would have said) does not one extract cold from heat, white from black, light from darkness, since so much heaviness is extracted from air, a thing inherently light? And those who chanced to have bestowed their credence on the heaviness of air, would not have been able to persuade themselves that it can ever increase weight, being balanced in itself. On this account I was constrained to show that air had weight; which was recognisable by other means than the balance: and that even with the latter, a portion previously changed and made denser could manifest its weight. All this I have done as briefly as I found possible, and without advancing anything not strictly germane to this matter: to elucidate which at all points it only remains for me to state and refute succinctly some opinions which others have held or might hold; and to resolve the objections which might be made to my answer.

[The author then considers possible objections under the following headings]

Essay XVII. That it is not the disappearance of the celestial heat giving life to the lead, or the death of the latter, which augments its weight on calcination.

Essay XVIII. That it is not the consumption of the aërated particles which augments the weight of the lead.

Essay XIX. That it is not soot which augments the weight of the calx.

Essay XX. That the augmentation of the calx of tin and lead does not come from the vessel.

Essay XXI. That it is not the vapours from the charcoal that augment the weight.

Essay XXII. That it is not the volatile salt of the charcoal which augments the weight.

Essay XXIII. That the mercurial volatile salt is not the cause of this augmentation.

Essay XXIV. That it is not humidity attracted by the calx which augments its weight.

Essay XXV. By a single experiment all opinions contrary to mine are entirely destroyed.

Essay XXVI. Why the calx does not increase in weight infinitely.

Essay XXVII. Why all other calces and ashes do not increase in weight.

Essay XXVIII. Whether lead increases in weight as well as tin.

CONCLUSION

Behold now this truth, whose brilliance strikes the eye, which I have drawn from the deepest dungeons of obscurity. This it is to which the path has been hitherto inaccessible. This it is which has distressed with toil so many learned men, who, wishing to know it, have striven to clear the difficulties which held it encircled. Cardan, Scaliger, Fachsius, Cæsalpinus, Libavius, have curiously sought it, but never perceived it. Others may be on its quest, but vainly if they fail to follow the road which I first of all have made clear and royal: all others being but thorny footpaths and inextricable byways which lead never to the goal. The labour has been mine; may the profit be to the reader, and to God alone the glory.

EVANGELISTA TORRICELLI

1 6 0 8 · 1 6 4 7

TORRICELLI SET OUT deliberately to measure the pressure of air and constructed the first mercury barometer, though he did not at first know how to make the necessary temperature corrections. Written two years after the death of his master and patron, Galileo, the following brilliant letter to Michelangelo Ricci summarized existing thought about the vacuum, described his own experiment, and theorized about it in a way which showed him to be well ahead of the English scientists of his day.

Torricelli was a student at Padua while William Harvey, the physician, was there, and succeeded Galileo as professor of mathematics at Florence. He was a moving spirit in the group which later founded the Accademia del Cimento (Academy of Experiment) at Florence in 1757. The present translation of his letter is taken from The Physical Treatises of Pascal, by I. H. B. and A. G. H. Spiers (Columbia University Press, New York, 1937).

ON THE PRESSURE OF THE
ATMOSPHERE

Letter from Torricelli to Michelangelo Ricci

Florence, June 11, 1644.

MY MOST ILLUSTRIOUS Sir and most cherished Master:

Several weeks ago I sent some demonstrations of mine on the area of the cycloid to Signor Antonio Nardi, entreating him to send them directly to you or to Signor Magiotti after he had seen them. I have already intimated to you that a certain physical experiment was being performed on the vacuum; not simply to produce a vacuum, but to make an instrument which would show the changes in the air, which is at times heavier and thicker and at times lighter and more rarefied. Many have said that a vacuum cannot be produced, others that it can be produced, but with repugnance on the part of Nature and with difficulty; so far, I know of no one who has said that it can be produced without effort and without resistance on the part of Nature. I reasoned in this way: if I were to find a plainly apparent cause for the resistance which is felt when one needs to produce a vacuum, it seems to me that it would be vain to try to attribute that action, which patently derives from some other cause, to the vacuum; indeed, I find that by making certain very easy calculations, the cause I have proposed (which is the weight of air) should in itself have a greater effect than it does in the attempt to produce a vacuum. I say this because some Philosopher, seeing that he could not avoid the admission that the weight of the air causes the resistance which is felt in producing a vacuum, did not say that he admitted the effect of the weight of the air, but persisted in asserting that Nature also contributes at least to the abhorrence of a vacuum.

We live submerged at the bottom of an ocean of the element of air, which by unquestioned experiments is known to have weight, and so much, indeed, that near the surface of the earth where it is most dense, it weighs [volume for volume] about the four-hundredth part of the weight of water.[1] Those who have written about twilight, moreover, have observed that the vaporous and visible air rises above us about fifty or fifty-four miles; I do not, however, believe its height is as great as this, since if it were, I could show that the vacuum would have to offer much greater resistance than it does—even though there is in their favor the argument that the weight referred to by Galileo applies to the air in very low places where men and animals live, whereas that on the tops of high mountains begins to be distinctly rare and of much less weight than the four-hundredth part of the weight of water.

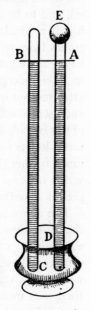

We have made glass vessels like the following marked A and B with necks two cubits.[2] We filled these with quicksilver, and then, the mouths being stopped with a finger and being inverted in a basin where there was quicksilver C, they seemed to become empty and nothing happened in the vessel that was emptied; the neck AD, therefore, remained always filled to the height of a cubit and a quarter and an inch besides [29¾ inches]. To show that the vessel was perfectly empty, the underlying basin was filled with water up to D, and as the vessel was slowly raised, when its mouth reached the water, one could see the quicksilver fall from the neck, whereupon with a violent impetus the vessel was filled with water

[1] Modern computations show that the density of water is 775 times that of air, at sea level.
[2] About 46 inches.

completely to the top. This experiment was performed when the vessel was empty and the quicksilver, although very heavy, was held up in the neck AD.

The force which holds up that quicksilver, against its nature to fall down again, has been believed hitherto to be inside of the vessel, and to be due either to vacuum or to that material [mercury] highly rarefied; but I maintain that it is external and that the force comes from without. On the surface of the liquid which is in the basin, there gravitates a mass of air fifty miles high; is it therefore to be wondered at if in the glass CE, where the mercury is not attracted nor indeed repelled, since there is nothing there, it enters and rises to such an extent as to come to equilibrium with the weight of this outside air which presses upon it? Water also, in a similar but much longer vessel, will rise up to almost eighteen cubits, that is, as much further than the quicksilver rises as quicksilver is heavier than water, in order to come to equilibrium with the same force, which presses alike the one and the other.

The above conclusion was confirmed by an experiment made at the same time with a vessel A and a tube B, in which the quicksilver always came to rest at the same level, AB. This is an almost certain indication that the force was not within; because if that were so, the vessel AE would have had greater force, since within it there was more rarefied material to attract the quicksilver, and a material much more powerful than that in the very small space B, on account of its greater rarefaction.

I have since tried to consider from this point of view all the kinds of repulsions which are felt in the various effects attributed to vacuum, and thus far I have not encountered anything which does not go [to confirm my opinion]. I know that you will think up many objections, but I also hope that, as you think about them, you will overcome them. I must add that my principal intention—which was to determine with the instrument EC when the air was thicker and heavier and when it was more rarefied and light—has not been fulfilled; for the level AB changes from another cause (which I never would have believed), namely, on account of heat and cold; and changes very appreciably, exactly as if the vase AE were full of air.

BLAISE PASCAL

1 6 2 3 · 1 6 6 2

THREE YEARS after the invention of the barometer, the brilliant
French philosopher and mathematician, Pascal, verified Torricelli's
guess that the pressure of air was less on high mountains than in low
places. Thus he demonstrated beyond question the fact that as Torricelli had said, "we live at the bottom of a great, deep sea of air,"
which presses down with what was later calculated to be a force of
fifteen pounds for every square inch, or a ton for every square foot.
It also put an end to the myth that "nature abhors a vacuum."

In his childhood Pascal was so quick in his studies that his father,
a cultured government official, tried to keep mathematics from him
in fear that he might overtax himself. But at the age of eleven, he
taught geometry to himself, and at sixteen proved one of the important theorems in projective geometry, a newly developed branch of
geometry in which magnitudes, including the lengths of lines, are
not considered. Later he constructed the first calculating machine,
and, with Fermat, developed the basis for the theory of probability,[1]
which is now of tremendous importance to insurance companies
and to every worker in statistical analysis.

The actual experiment on the weight of the air was performed at
Pascal's request by his brother-in-law, Périer. Pascal immediately
published their correspondence, together with his own conclusions.
The quotation below is from The Physical Treatises of Blaise Pascal,
translated by I. H. B. and A. H. G. Spiers (Columbia University
Press, New York, 1937).

[1] On this theory, see below, p. 622.

THE GREAT EXPERIMENT
ON THE WEIGHT OF
THE MASS OF THE AIR

The Mass of the Air Has Weight and with This Weight Presses
upon All the Bodies It Surrounds

It is no longer open to discussion that the air has weight. It is common knowledge that a balloon is heavier when inflated than when empty, which is proof enough. For if the air were light, the more the balloon was inflated the lighter the whole would be, since there would be more air in it. But since, on the contrary, when more air is put in, the whole becomes heavier, it follows that each part has a weight of its own, and consequently that the air has weight.

Whoever wishes for more elaborate proofs can find them in the writings of those who have devoted special treatises to the subject.

If it be objected that air is light when pure, but that the air that surrounds us is not pure, being mixed with vapor and impurities which alone give it weight, my answer is brief: I am not acquainted with "pure" air, and believe that it might be very difficult to find it. But throughout this treatise I am referring solely to the air such as we breathe, regardless of its component elements. Whether it be compound or simple, that is the body which I call the air, and which I declare to have weight. This cannot be denied, and I require nothing more for my further proof. . . .

If there were collected a great bulk of wool, say twenty or thirty fathoms high, this mass would be compressed by its own weight; the bottom layers would be far more compressed than the middle or top layers, because they are pressed by a greater quantity of wool. Similarly the mass of the air, which is a compressible and heavy body like wool, is compressed by its own weight, and the air at the bottom, in the lowlands, is far more compressed than the higher layers on the mountain tops, because it bears a greater load of air.

In the case of that bulk of wool, if a handful of it were taken from the bottom layer, compressed as it is, and lifted, in the same state of compression, to the middle of the mass, it would expand of its own accord; for it would then be nearer the top and subjected there to the pressure of a smaller quantity of wool. Similarly if a body of air, as found here below in its natural state of compression, were by some device transferred to a mountaintop, it would necessarily expand and come to the condition of the air around it on the mountain; for then it would bear a lesser weight of air than it did below. Hence if a balloon, only half inflated—not fully so, as they generally are—were carried up a mountain, it would necessarily be more inflated at the mountaintop, and would expand in the degree to which it was less burdened. The difference will be visible, provided the quantity of air along the mountain slope, from the pressure of which it is now relieved, has a weight great enough to cause a sensible effect.

The Great Experiment on the Equilibrium of Fluids

At the time when I published my pamphlet entitled *New Experiments touching the Vacuum*, etc., I used the phrase "Abhorrence of the Vacuum" because it was universally accepted and because I had not then any convincing evidences against it; but nevertheless sensed certain difficulties which made me doubt the truth of the conception. To clarify these doubts, I conceived at that very time the experiment here described, which I hoped would yield definite knowledge as a ground for my opinion, I have called it the Great Experiment on the Equilibrium of Fluids, because it is the most conclusive of all that can be made on this subject, inasmuch as it shows the equilibrium of air and quicksilver, which are, respectively, the lightest and the heaviest of all the fluids known in nature.

But since it was impossible to carry out this experiment here, in the City of Paris, and because there are very few places in France that are suitable for this purpose and the town of Clermont in Auvergne is one of the most convenient of these, I requested my brother-in-law, M. Périer, counsellor in the Court of Aids in Auvergne, to be so kind as to conduct it there. What my difficulties were and what the experiment is will be made clear by the accompanying letter concerning it, which I wrote him at the time.

Copy of the letter of Monsieur Pascal the Younger to Monsieur Périer, November 15, 1647.

Monsieur:

I should not break in upon the constant calls made on you by your official duties to submit to you considerations of Physical Science, were I not fully aware that they will be a refreshment to you in your hours of relaxation, and will be as entertaining to you as they would be burdensome to others. I hesitate the less to do this, also, because I know full well the delight you take in these pursuits.

You will find here but a continuation of our former discussions concerning the vacuum. You know the views of the Philosophers on this subject. They have all endorsed the principle that nature abhors a vacuum, and most of them have gone further and maintained that nature cannot admit of it, and would perish sooner than suffer it. Thus opinions have been divided: some have been content to say that nature abhors a vacuum, others have maintained that she could not tolerate it. I have tried in my pamphlet on the vacuum to refute the latter opinion, and I believe that the experiments recorded there suffice to show undubitably that nature can, and does, tolerate any amount of space empty of any of the substances that we are acquainted with, and that are perceptible to our senses.

I am now engaged in testing the truth of the former statement, namely, that nature abhors a vacuum, and am trying to find experimental ways to show whether the effects ascribed to the abhorrence of a vacuum are really attributable to that abhorrence, or to the weight and pressure of the air. For, to reveal to you frankly my whole thought on the matter,

I can hardly admit that nature, which is not at all animated nor sensible, can be capable of abhorrence, since the passions presuppose a soul capable of experiencing them. I feel much more inclined to attribute all these effects to the weight and pressure of the air, because I consider them only as particular cases of a universal principle concerning the Equilibrium of Fluids, which is to be the greater part of the Treatise I have promised.

Not but that I had the same thoughts when I brought out my abridgment; but for lack of convincing experiments, I dared not then (and I dare not yet) give up the idea of the abhorrence of a vacuum. I even used it as a premise in my abridgment, not having then any other design than to controvert the opinion of those who hold that the void is absolutely impossible, and that nature would rather suffer her destruction than the least empty space. Indeed I do not consider that it is permissible for us lightly to discard the maxims handed down to us by the ancients unless we are compelled to do so by indubitable and unanswerable proofs. But in that case I maintain that it would be the extremity of weakness to have the least scruple in the matter. We must have more respect for evident truths than obstinacy in clinging to accepted opinions.

I cannot better illustrate the circumspection which I exercise before rejecting ancient maxims than to recall to you the experiment I made lately in your presence with the two tubes, one inside the other, which exhibit a vacuum within a vacuum.[1] You saw that the quicksilver of the inner tube hung suspended at the usual height when it was counterpoised and pressed by the weight of the whole mass of the air, but that it dropped altogether, so that it was no longer suspended at all, when by removing all the surrounding air we made a complete vacuum about it so that it was no longer pressed by it and counterbalanced. Afterward, you saw that the height or suspension of the quicksilver increased or decreased as the pressure of the air increased or decreased, and finally that all these various heights or suspensions of the quicksilver were always proportional to the pressure of the air.

After that experiment we certainly had reason to believe, as we do believe, that it is not the abhorrence of the vacuum that causes the quicksilver to stand suspended in the usual experiment, but really the weight and pressure of the air, which balances the weight of the quick-

[1] Essentially a barometer inside a tube from which the air was pumped.

silver. But seeing that all the effects of this last experiment with the two tubes, which is so naturally explained by the mere pressure and weight of the air, can also be explained, probably enough, by the abhorrence of a vacuum, I still hold to that ancient principle, although I am determined to seek a thorough elucidation of this difficulty by means of a decisive experiment.

To this end I have devised one that is in itself sufficient to give us the light we seek if it can be carried out with accuracy. This is to perform the usual experiment with a vacuum several times over in one day, with the same tube and with the same quicksilver, sometimes at the base and sometimes at the summit of a mountain at least five or six hundred fathoms [2] high, in order to ascertain whether the height of the quicksilver suspended in the tube will be the same or different in the two situations. You see at once, doubtless, that such an experiment is decisive. If it happens that the height of the quicksilver is less at the top than at the base of the mountain (as I have many reasons to believe it is, although all who have studied the matter are of the opposition opinion), it follows of necessity that the weight and pressure of the air is the sole cause of this suspension of the quicksilver, and not the abhorrence of a vacuum: for it is quite certain that there is much more air that presses on the foot of the mountain than there is on its summit, and one cannot well say that nature abhors a vacuum more at the foot of the mountain than at its summit.

But since difficulty, as a rule, attends great achievement, I foresee much trouble in carrying out this plan, because for the purpose a very high mountain must be selected, in the vicinity of a town where a person may be found who is competent to bring to bear upon the task all the precision of measurement that it demands. If the mountain were very distant it would be difficult to carry to it the vessels, the quicksilver, the tubes, and many other necessary accessories, and to undertake the many laborious journeys that would be necessary in order to find upon these heights the suitably calm weather which is seldom to be met with there. And since it is as uncommon to find outside of Paris persons who have these qualifications as it is to find places that meet the conditions, I have been highly gratified by my good fortune in having on this occasion

[2] The French *toise*, translated as *fathom*, is about six feet long.

found both; for our town of Clermont is at the foot of the lofty Puy de Dôme,[3] and I hope that you will be good enough to grant me the favor of conducting the experiment yourself. Being assured of this, I have encouraged all our interested Parisians to expect it, among others the Rev. Father Mersenne,[4] who has already pledged himself by letters to Italy, Poland, Sweden, Holland, and elsewhere, to convey the result to the friends his great merit has won him in those countries. I say nothing about the means of performing the experiment, because I well know that you will omit none of the precautions necessary to carry it out with precision.

I would only beg of you to choose the earliest date you can, and to excuse the liberty I am taking, to which I am driven by my impatience to hear of the success of the experiment.

Monsieur,

Your very humble and very obedient servant,

PASCAL

M. Périer received this letter at Moulins, where he was discharging duties which forbade him full freedom of action. Anxious though he was to carry out the experiment at once, he was not at liberty to do so before the month of September last.

The reasons for this delay, the story of the experiment, and the precision with which he conducted it are made plain by the following letter with which he honored me.

Copy of the letter sent by Monsieur Périer to Monsieur Pascal the Younger, September 22, 1648.

Monsieur,

At last I have carried out the experiment you have so long wished for. I would have given you this satisfaction before now, but have been prevented both by the duties I have had to perform in Bourbonnais, and by

---

[3] The Puy de Dôme is 4817 feet high; about 3000 feet above the town of Clermont.

[4] Father Mersenne was an enthusiastic French scientist who had published a popular book on *Theological, Physical, Moral, and Mathematical Questions.*

the fact that ever since my return the Puy de Dôme, where the experiment is to be made, has been so wrapped in snow and fog that even in this season, which here is the finest of the year, there was hardly a day when one could see its summit, which is usually in the clouds and sometimes above them even while the weather is clear in the plains. I was unable to adjust my own convenience to a favorable state of the weather before the nineteenth of this month. But my good fortune in performing the experiment on that day has amply repaid me for the slight vexation caused by so many unavoidable delays.

I send you herewith a complete and faithful account of it, in which you will find evidence of the painstaking care I bestowed upon the undertaking, which I thought it proper to carry out in the presence of a few men who are as learned as they are irreproachably honest, so that the sincerity of their testimony should leave no doubt as to the certainty of the experiment.

Copy of the account of the experiment submitted by Monsieur Périer.

The weather on Saturday last, the nineteenth of this month, was very unsettled. At about five o'clock in the morning, however, it seemed sufficiently clear; and since the summit of the Puy de Dôme was then visible, I decided to go there to make the attempt. To that end I notified several people of standing in this town of Clermont, who had asked me to let them know when I would make the ascent. Of this company some were clerics, others laymen. Among the clerics was the Very Rev. Father Bannier, one of the Minim Fathers [5] of this city, who has on several occasions been "corrector" (that is, father superior), and Monsieur Mosnier, canon of the Cathedral Church of this city; among the laymen were Messieurs la Ville and Begon, councilors to the Court of Aids, and Monsieur la Porte, a doctor of medicine, practicing here. All these men are very able, not only in the practice of their professions, but also in every field of intellectual interest. It was a delight to have them with me in this fine work.

[5] Members of a strict order of monks, called the Minimi Eremitae, Least Hermits, shortened here to "the Minims."

On that day, therefore, at eight o'clock in the morning, we started off all together for the garden of the Minim Fathers, which is almost the lowest spot in the town, and there began the experiment in this manner.

First, I poured into a vessel six pounds of quicksilver which I had rectified during the three days preceding; and having taken glass tubes of the same size, each four feet long and hermetically sealed at one end but open at the other, I placed them in the same vessel and carried out with each of them the usual vacuum experiment. Then, having set them up side by side without lifting them out of the vessel, I found that the quicksilver left in each of them stood at the same level, which was twenty-six inches and three and a half lines [6] above the surface of the quicksilver in the vessel. I repeated this experiment twice at this same spot, in the same tubes, with the same quicksilver, and in the same vessel; and found in each case that the quicksilver in the two tubes stood at the same horizontal level, and at the same height as in the first trial.

That done, I fixed one of the tubes permanently in its vessel for continuous experiment. I marked on the glass the height of the quicksilver, and leaving that tube where it stood, I requested the Rev. Father Chastin, one of the brothers of the house, a man as pious as he is capable, and one who reasons very well upon these matters, to be so good as to observe from time to time all day any changes that might occur. With the other tube and a portion of the same quicksilver, I then proceeded with all these gentlemen to the top of the Puy de Dôme, some five hundred fathoms above the convent. There, after I had made the same experiments in the same way that I had made them at the Minims, we found that there remained in the tube a height of only twenty-three inches and two lines of quicksilver; whereas in the same tube, at the Minims, we had found a height of twenty-six inches and three and a half lines. Thus between the heights of the quicksilver in the two experiments there proved to be a difference of three inches, one line and a half.

We were so carried away with wonder and delight, and our surprise was so great, that we wished, for our own satisfaction, to repeat the experiment. So I carried it out with the greatest care five times more at different points on the summit of the mountain, once in the shelter of

[6] A line is one-twelfth of an inch.

the little chapel that stands there, once in the open, once shielded from the wind, once in the wind, once in fine weather, once in the rain and fog which visited us occasionally. Each time I most carefully rid the tube of air; and in all these experiments we invariably found the same height of quicksilver. This was twenty-three inches, and two lines, which yields the same discrepancy of three inches, one line and a half in comparison with the twenty-six inches, three lines and a half which had been found at the Minims. This satisfied us fully.

Later, on the way down at a spot called Lafon de l'Arbre, far above the Minims but much farther below the top of the mountain, I repeated the same experiment, still with the same tube, the same quicksilver, and the same vessel, and there found that the height of the quicksilver left in the tube was twenty-five inches. I repeated it a second time at the same spot; and Monsieur Mosnier, one of those previously mentioned, having the curiosity to perform it himself, then did so again, at the same spot. All these experiments yielded the same height of twenty-five inches, which is one inch, three lines and a half less than that which we had found at the Minims, and one inch and ten lines more than we had just found at the top of the Puy de Dôme. It increased our satisfaction not a little to observe in this way that the height of the quicksilver diminished with the altitude of the site.

On my return to the Minims I found that the [quicksilver] in the vessel I had left there in continuous operation was at the same height at which I had left it, that is, at twenty-six inches, three lines and a half; and the Rev. Father Chastin, who had remained there as observer, reported to us that no change had occurred during the whole day, although the weather had been very unsettled, now clear and still, now rainy, now very foggy, and now windy.

Here I repeated the experiment with the tube I had carried to the Puy de Dôme, but in the vessel in which the tube used for the continuous experiment was standing. I found that the quicksilver was at the same level in both tubes and exactly at the height of twenty-six inches, three lines and a half, at which it had stood that morning in this same tube, and as it had stood all day in the tube used for the continuous experiment.

I repeated it again a last time, not only in the same tube I had used on the Puy de Dôme, but also with the same quicksilver and in the same vessel that I had carried up the mountain; and again I found the quicksilver at the same height of twenty-six inches, three lines and a half which I had observed in the morning, and thus finally verified the certainty of our results.

The next day, the Very Revd. Father De la Mare, priest of the Oratory and Lecturer in Divinity of the Cathedral Church, who had witnessed all that had taken place on the morning before in the garden of the Minims, and to whom I had reported all that had occurred on the Puy de Dôme, proposed to me that I carry out the same experiment at the base and on the top of the highest tower of Notre Dame de Clermont, to see whether there would be any difference [between pres- sures at these heights]. To gratify the curiosity of a man of such great distinction who has given all France many proofs of his ability, I car- ried out that very day the ordinary experiment of the vacuum in a private residence which stands on the highest ground in the city, some six or seven fathoms above the garden of the Minims, and on a level with the base of the tower. There we found the quicksilver at the height of about twenty-six inches and three lines, which is less than that which was found at the Minims by about half a line. I next made the experiment on the top of the tower, which was twenty fathoms higher than its base and about twenty-six or twenty-seven fathoms above the garden of the Minims. There I found the quicksilver at the height of about twenty-six inches and one line, that is, about two lines less than its height at the base of the tower, and about two and a half lines lower than it stood in the garden of the Minims.

Thus, collecting results and comparing the various elevations of the places where the experiments were made with the corresponding heights of quicksilver which were left in the tubes . . . it is found that about seven fathoms of altitude give a difference in the height of the quick- silver of half a line; about twenty-seven fathoms give a difference of two lines and a half; about one hundred and fifty fathoms, fifteen lines and a half, which makes one inch, three lines and a half; and about five hundred fathoms, thirty-seven lines and a half, or three inches, one line and a half. . . .

If you find any obscurities in this recital I shall be able in a few days to

clear them up in conversation with you, since I am about to take a little trip to Paris, when I shall assure you that I am,
Monsieur,
Your very humble and very affectionate servant,

PÉRIER

This narrative cleared up all my difficulties and, I am free to say, afforded me great satisfaction. Seeing that a difference of twenty fathoms of altitude made a difference of two lines in the height of the quicksilver, and six or seven fathoms one of about half a line, facts which it was easy for me to verify in this city, I made the usual vacuum experiment on the top and at the base of the tower of St. Jacques de la Boucherie, which is some twenty-four or twenty-five fathoms high, and found a difference of more than two lines in the height of the quicksilver. I then repeated it in a private house ninety steps high, and found a clearly perceptible difference of half a line. These results are in perfect agreement with those given in M. Périer's narrative.

Any who care to do so, may, for themselves, confirm them at their pleasure.

ROBERT BOYLE

1 · 6 2 7 · 1 6 9 1

THE HONORABLE Robert Boyle, seventh son of the Earl of Cork, was "the father of modern chemistry." He was born in Ireland, studied at Eton and on the Continent; and was in Italy in 1642, the year Galileo died and Newton was born. In 1644 he returned to England, where in time he became a leading member of the brilliant group of scientists who in 1662 founded the Royal Society of London. He was an ardent disciple of the mechanical philosophy of Galileo, Bacon, and Descartes. Few men have made more important original contributions to science than Robert Boyle.

We present here two of these contributions. A Defense of the Doctrine Touching the Spring and Weight of the Air describes the experiment proving what is now commonly known as Boyle's Law; namely, that at a constant temperature, if the pressure on a quantity of gas be doubled (twice atmospheric pressure, for instance), the volume will be halved; if tripled, the volume will be decreased to one third, and so on. Boyle stated this law first in 1660, in a tract on the elasticity of the air. The next year an objector published a pamphlet in refutation, and in 1662 Boyle published A Defense as an appendix to the second edition of his earlier tract. We quote below from this work.

Our second selection is from Boyle's Sceptical Chymist, published in 1661, which marked the beginning of modern chemistry. It was composed as a diologue on elements in nature, between three scholars, Themistius, a believer in Aristotle, Carneades, who speaks for Boyle himself, and Philoponus, an exponent of the theories of Paracelsus,[1] each one laboring to convince Eleutherius, a common friend, of the truth of his opinion. The plan of the discussion, as agreed on in advance, is that Themistius is to argue for the four traditional "elements," Philoponus for Paracelsus' three, while Carneades, speaking for Boyle, has to prove, if he can, that both these numbers are artificial and absurd; that there must surely be either more elements, or less. In the course of the discussion, Carneades makes the first modern statement of the nature of a chemical element.

[1] For the theories of Paracelsus, see pp. 208 and 211.

A DEFENSE OF THE DOCTRINE
TOUCHING THE SPRING AND
WEIGHT OF THE AIR

℈

THE OTHER THING that I would have considered touching our Adversaries Hypothesis is, That it is needless. For whereas he denies not that the Air has some Weight and Spring, but affirms that it is very insufficient to perform such great matters as the counterpoising of a Mercurial Cylinder of 29. Inches, as we teach that it may: We shall now endeavour to manifest by Experiments purposely made, that the Spring of the Air is capable of doing far more than 'tis necessary for us to ascribe to it, to salve the Phænomena of the Torricellian Experiment.[1]

We took then a long Glass-Tube, which by a dexterous hand and the help of Lamp was in such a manner crooked at the bottom, that the part turned up was almost parallel to the rest of the Tube, and the Orifice of this shorter leg of the Siphon (if I may so call the whole Instrument) being Hermetically seal'd, the length of it was divided into Inches, (each of which was subdivided into eight parts) by a straight list of paper, which containing those Divisions was carefully pasted all along it: then putting in as much Quicksilver as served to fill the Arch or bended part of the Siphon, that the Mercury standing in a level might reach in the one leg to the bottom of the divided paper, and just to the same height or horizontal line in the other; we took care, by frequently inclining the Tube, so that the Air might freely pass from one leg into the other by the sides of the Mercury, (We took (I say) care) that the Air at last included

[1] For this experiment, see above, p. 226.

244

in the shorter Cylinder should be of the same laxity with the rest of the Air about it. This done, we began to pour Quicksilver into the longer leg of the Siphon, which by its weight pressing up that in the shorter leg, did by degrees streighten the included Air: and continuing this pouring in of Quicksilver till the Air in the shorter leg was by condensation reduced to take up but half the space it possess'd (I say, possess'd, not fill'd) before; we cast our eyes upon the longer leg of the Glass, on which was likewise pasted a list of Paper carefully divided into Inches and parts, and we observed, not without delight and satisfaction, that the Quicksilver in that longer part of the Tube was 29. Inches higher then the other. Now that this Observation does both very well agree with and confirm our Hypothesis, will be easily discerned by him that takes notice that we teach, and Monsieur Paschall and our English friends Experiments prove, that the greater the weight is that leans upon the Air, the more forcible is its endeavour of Dilatation, and consequently its power of resistance (as other Springs are stronger when bent by greater weights). For this being considered it will appear to agree rarely-well with the Hypothesis, that as according to it the Air in that degree

Boyle's first air-pump.

of density and correspondent measure of resistance to which the weight of the incumbent Atmosphere had brought it, was able to counter-balance and resist the pressure of a Mercurial Cylinder of about 29. Inches, as we are taught by the Torricellian Experiment; so here the same Air being brought to a degree of density about twice as great as that it had before, obtains a Spring

twice as strong as formerly. As may appear by its being able to sus
tain or resist a Cylinder of 29. Inches in the longer Tube, together
with the weight of the Atmospherical Cylinder, that lean'd upon

A Table of the Condensation of the Air.

A	A	B	C	D	E
48	12	00		$29\frac{2}{16}$	$29\frac{2}{16}$
46	$11\frac{1}{2}$	$01\frac{7}{16}$		$30\frac{9}{16}$	$30\frac{6}{16}$
44	11	$02\frac{11}{16}$		$31\frac{11}{16}$	$31\frac{12}{16}$
42	$10\frac{1}{2}$	$04\frac{6}{16}$		$33\frac{8}{16}$	$33\frac{7}{3}$
40	10	$06\frac{3}{16}$		$35\frac{5}{16}$	$35.--$
38	$9\frac{1}{2}$	$07\frac{14}{16}$		$37.--$	$36\frac{11}{19}$
36	9	$10\frac{7}{16}$		$39\frac{5}{16}$	$38\frac{8}{7}$
34	$8\frac{1}{2}$	$12\frac{8}{16}$		$41\frac{10}{16}$	$41\frac{17}{7}$
32	8	$15\frac{1}{16}$		$44\frac{3}{16}$	$43\frac{11}{16}$
30	$7\frac{1}{2}$	$17\frac{12}{16}$		$47\frac{1}{16}$	$46\frac{5}{7}$
28	7	$21\frac{11}{16}$		$50\frac{5}{16}$	$50.--$
26	$6\frac{1}{2}$	$25\frac{1}{16}$		$54\frac{5}{16}$	$53\frac{12}{13}$
24	6	$29\frac{11}{16}$		$58\frac{11}{16}$	$58\frac{8}{7}$
23	$5\frac{3}{4}$	$32\frac{1}{16}$		$61\frac{5}{16}$	$60\frac{11}{18}$
22	$5\frac{1}{2}$	$34\frac{7}{16}$		$64\frac{1}{16}$	$63\frac{6}{11}$
21	$5\frac{1}{4}$	$37\frac{1}{16}$		$67\frac{1}{16}$	$66\frac{4}{7}$
20	5	$41\frac{1}{16}$		$70\frac{11}{16}$	$70.--$
19	$4\frac{3}{4}$	$45.--$		$74\frac{4}{7}$	$73\frac{19}{7}$
18	$4\frac{1}{2}$	$48\frac{12}{16}$		$77\frac{1}{16}$	$77\frac{3}{7}$
17	$4\frac{1}{4}$	$53\frac{1}{16}$		$82\frac{12}{16}$	$82\frac{2}{7}$
16	4	$58\frac{2}{16}$		$87\frac{1}{16}$	$87\frac{8}{7}$
15	$3\frac{3}{4}$	$63\frac{1}{16}$		$93\frac{1}{16}$	$93\frac{3}{7}$
14	$3\frac{1}{2}$	$71\frac{1}{16}$		$100\frac{7}{16}$	$99\frac{7}{7}$
13	$3\frac{1}{4}$	$78\frac{11}{16}$		$107\frac{11}{16}$	$107\frac{1}{13}$
12	3	$88\frac{7}{16}$		$117\frac{2}{16}$	$116\frac{8}{1}$

(Column C: Added to $29\frac{1}{2}$ makes)

AA. The number of equal spaces in the
 shorter leg, that contained the same
 parcel of Air diversly extended.

B. The height of the Mercurial Cylinder in the longer leg, that compress'd
 the Air into those dimensions.

C. The height of a Mercurial Cylinder
 that counterbalanc'd the pressure of
 the Atmosphere.

D. The Aggregate of the two last Columns B and C, exhibiting the pressure
 sustained by the included Air.

E. What that pressure should be according to the *Hypothesis*, that supposes
 the pressures and expansions to be in
 reciprocal proportion.

Boyle's table showing the figures which proved that the volume of a gas
decreases as the pressure increases.

those 29. Inches of Mercury; and, as we just now inferr'd from the
Torricellian Experiment, was equivalent to them.

We were hindered from prosecuting the tryal at that time by the
casual breaking of the Tube. But because an accurate Experiment

of this nature would be of great importance to the Doctrine of the Spring of the Air, and has not yet been made (that I know) by any man; and because also it is more uneasie to be made than one would think, in regard of the difficulty as well of procuring crooked Tubes fit for the purpose, as of making a just estimate of the true place of the Protuberant Mercury's surface; I suppose it will not be unwelcome to the Reader, to be informed that after some other tryals, one of which we made in a Tube whose longer leg was perpendicular, and the other, that contained the Air, parallel to the Horizon, we at last procured a Tube of the Figure exprest in the Scheme; which Tube, though of a pretty bigness, was so long, that the Cylinder whereof the shorter leg of it consisted admitted a list of Paper, which had before been divided into 12. Inches and their quarters, and the longer leg admitted another list of Paper of divers foot in length, and divided after the same manner: then Quicksilver being poured in to fill up the bended part of the Glass, that the surface of it in either leg might rest in the same Horizontal line, as we lately taught, there was more and more Quicksilver poured into the longer Tube; and notice being watchfully taken how far the Mercury was risen in that longer Tube, when it appeared to have ascended to any of the divisions in the shorter Tube, the several Observations that were thus successively made, and as they were made set down, afforded us the ensuing Table.

WHAT IS AN ELEMENT?

♪

*Touching the experiments wont to be employed to evince
either the four peripatetick [Aristotelian] Elements, or the
three [Paracelsian] chymical principles of mixt bodies.*

Part of the first Dialogue.

. . . (THEMISTIUS SPEAKS) . . . "If I were allowed the freedom,
in pleading for the four elements, to employ the arguments suggested
to me by reason to demonstrate them, I should almost as little doubt
of making you a proselyte to those unsevered teachers, Truth and
Aristotle, as I do of your candour and your judgement. And I hope
you will, however, consider that that great favourite and interpreter
of nature, Aristotle, who was (as his *Organum* witnesses) the greatest master of logic that ever lived, disclaimed the course taken by
other petty philosophers (antient and modern), who not attending
the coherence and consequences of their opinions, are more solicitous to make each particular opinion plausible independently upon
the rest, than to frame them all so, as not only to be consistent
together, but to support each other.

"For that great man in his vast and comprehensive intellect, so
framed each of his notions, that being curiously adapted into one
systeme, they need not each of them any other defence than that
which their mutual coherence gives them: as 'tis in an arch, where
each single stone, which if severed from the rest would be perhaps
defenceless, is sufficiently secured by the solidity and entireness of
the whole fabric of which it is a part. How justly this may be applied
to the present case, I could easily shew you, if I were permitted to
declare to you, how harmonious Aristotle's doctrine of the elements

is with his other principles of philosophy; and how rationally he has deduced their number from that of the combinations of the four first qualities, from the kinds of simple motion belonging to simple bodies, and from I know not how many other principles and phae-nomena of nature, which so conspire with his doctrine of the ele-ments, that they mutually strengthen and support each other.

"But since 'tis forbidden me to insist on reflections of this kind, I must proceed to tell you that though the assertors of the four ele-ments value reason so highly, and are furnished with arguments enough drawn from thence to be satisfied that there must be four elements, though no man had ever yet made any sensible trial to discover their number, yet they are not destitute of experience to satisfie others that are wont to be more swayed by their senses than their reason. And I shall proceed to consider the testimony of experience, when I shall have first advertised you, that if men were as perfectly rational as 'tis to be wished they were, this sensible way of probation would be as needless as 'tis wont to be imperfect.

"For it is much more high and philosophical to discover things *a priore* than *a posteriore*. And therefore the peripatetics have not been very solicitous to gather experiments to prove their doctrines, contenting themselves with a few only, to satisfy those that are not capable of a nobler conviction. And indeed they employ experiments rather to illustrate than to demonstrate their doctrines, as astrono-mers use sphaeres of pasteboard, to descend to the capacities of such as must be taught by their senses, for want of being arrived to a clear apprehension of purely mathematical notions and truths.

"I speak thus, Eleutherius (adds Themistius), only to do right to reason, and not out of diffidence of the experimental proof I am to alledge. For though I shall name but one, yet it is such a one as will make all others appear as needless as itself will be found satis-factory. For if you but consider a piece of green wood burning in a chimney, you will readily discern in the disbanded parts of it the four elements, of which we teach it and other mixt bodies to be composed. The fire discovers itself in the flame by its own light;

the smoake by ascending to the top of the chimney, and there read-ily vanishing into air, like a river losing itself in the sea, sufficiently manifests to what element it belongs and gladly returnes. The water in its own form boiling and hissing at the ends of the burning wood betrays itself to more than one of our senses; and the ashes by their weight, their firiness, and their dryness, put it past doubt that they belong to the element of earth.[1]

"If I spoke (continues Themistius) to less knowing persons, I would perhaps make some excuse for building upon such an obvious and easie analysis, but 'twould be, I fear, injurious, not to think such an apology needless to you, who are too judicious either to think it necessary that experiments to prove obvious truths should be far-fetched, or to wonder that among so many mixt bodies that are compounded of the four elements, some of them should upon a slight analysis manifestly exhibit the ingredients they consist of. Especially since it is very agreeable to the goodness of nature to disclose, even in some of the most obvious experiments that men make, a truth so important and so requisite to be taken notice of by them. Besides that our analysis by how much the more obvious we make it, by so much the more suitable it will be to the nature of that doctrine which 'tis alledged to prove, which being as clear and intelligible to the understanding as obvious to the sense, 'tis no marvel the learned part of mankind should so long and so generally imbrace it.

"For this doctrine is very different from the whimseys of chymists and other modern innovators, of whose hypotheses we may observe, as naturalists do of less perfect animals, that as they are hastily formed, so they are commonly short-lived. For so these, as they are often framed in one week, are perhaps thought fit to be laughed at the next; and being built perchance but upon two or three experi-ments are destroyed by a third or fourth; whereas the doctrine of the four elements was framed by Aristotle after he had leasurely consid-

[1] The elements, according to Aristotle and most of the later Greek and medieval philosophers, were, it will be remembered, fire, air, water, and earth.

ered those theories of former philosophers which are now with great applause revived as discovered by these latter ages; and had so judiciously detected and supplied the errors and defects of former hypotheses concerning the elements, that his doctrine of them has been ever since deservedly embraced by the lettered part of mankind: all the philosophers that preceded him having in their several ages contributed to the compleatness of this doctrine, as those of succeeding times have acquiesced in it.

"Nor has an hypothesis, so deliberately and maturely established, been called in question till in the last century Paracelsus and some few other sooty empirics, rather than (as they are fain to call themselves) philosophers, having their eyes darkened, and their braines troubled with the smoak of their own furnaces, began to rail at the peripatetic doctrine, which they were too illiterate to understand, and to tell the credulous world, that they could see but three ingredients in mixt bodies; which, to gain themselves the repute of inventors, they endeavoured to disguise by calling them (instead of earth, and fire, and vapour) salt, sulphur, and mercury; to which they gave the canting title of hypostatical principles.

"But when they came to describe them, they shewed how little they understood what they meant by them, by disagreeing as much from one another, as from the truth they agreed in opposing: for they deliver their hypotheses as darkly as their processes; and 'tis almost as impossible for any sober man to find their meaning, as 'tis for them to find their elixir. And indeed nothing has spread their philosophy, but their great brags and undertakings; notwithstanding all which (says Themistius smiling), I scarce know anything they have performed worth wondering at, save that they have been able to draw Philoponus to their party, and to engage him to the defence of an unintelligible hypothesis, who knowes so well as he does, that principles ought to be like diamonds, as well very clear as perfectly solid."

Themistius having after these last words declared by his silence that he had finished his discourse, Carneades addressing himself, as his adversary had done, to Eleutherius, returned this answer to it. "I hoped for a demonstration, but I perceive Themistius hopes to put me off with an harangue, wherein he cannot have given me a greater opinion of his parts, than he has given me distrust for his hypothesis, since for it even a man of such learning can bring no better arguments. The rhetorical part of his discourse, though it make not the least part of it, I shall say nothing to, designing to examine only the argumentative part, and leaving it to Philoponus to answer those passages wherein either Paracelsus or chymists are concerned.

"I shall observe to you, that in what he has said besides, he makes it his business to do these two things. The one to propose and make out an experiment to demonstrate the common opinion about the four elements; and the other, to insinuate divers things which he thinks may repair the weakness of his argument from experience, and upon other accounts bring some credit to the otherwise defenceless doctrine he maintains.

"To begin then with his experiment of the burning wood, it seems to me to be obnoxious to not a few considerable exceptions.

"And first, if I would now deal rigidly with my adversary, I might here make a great question of the very way of probation which he and others employ, without the least scruple, to evince that the bodies commonly called mixt are made up of earth, air, water, and fire, which they are pleased also to call elements; namely that upon the supposed analysis made by the fire, of the former sort of concretes, there are wont to emerge bodies resembling those which they take for the elements.

"For not to anticipate here what I foresee I shall have occasion to insist on, when I come to discourse with Philoponus concerning the right that fire has to pass for the proper and universal instrument of analysing mixt bodies, not to anticipate that, I say, if I were disposed to wrangle, I might alledge, that by Themistius his experiment it would appear rather that those he calls elements are made of those he calls mixt bodies, than mixt bodies of the elements. For in Themistius's analysed wood, and in other bodies dissipated and altered by the fire, it appears, and he confesses, that which he takes for elementary fire and water are made out of the concrete; but it appears not that the concrete was made up of fire and water. Nor has either he, or any man, for ought I know, of his persuasion, yet proved that nothing can be obtained from a body by the fire that was not pre-existent in it. . . .

"I consider then (says Carneades), in the next place, that there are divers bodies out of which Themistius will not prove in haste that there can be so many elements as four extracted by the fire. And I should perchance trouble him if I should ask him what peripatetic can shew us (I say not all the four elements, for that would be too rigid a question, but) any one of them extracted out of gold by any degree of fire whatsoever. Nor is gold the only bodie in nature that would puzzle an Aristotelian, (that is no more) to analyse by the fire into elementary bodies, since, for ought I have yet observed, both silver and calcined Venetian talc, and some other concretes, not necessary here to be named, are so fixed, that to reduce any of them into four heterogeneous substances has hitherto proved a task much too hard, not only for the disciples of Aristotle, but those of Vulcan,[2] at least whilst the latter have employed only fire to make the analysis.

"The next argument (continues Carneades) that I shall urge against Themistius's opinion shall be this, That as there are divers bodies whose analysis by fire cannot reduce them into so many heterogeneous substances or ingredients as four, so there are others which may be reduced into more, as the blood (and divers other parts) of men and other animals, which yield when analysed five distinct substances, phlegme, spirit, oile, salt, and earth, as experience has shewn us in distilling man's blood, harts-horns, and divers other bodies that belonging to the animal-kingdom abound with not uneasily sequestrable salt. . . ."

[2] That is, the practical workers in metal. Vulcan was the god of the forge.

A *Paradoxical Appendix to the Foregoing Treatise*

(Carneades speaks) . . . "And, to prevent mistakes, I must advertize you, that I now mean by elements, as those chymists that speak plainest do by their principles, certain primitive and simple, or perfectly unmingled bodies; which not being made of any other bodies, or of one another, are the ingredients of which all those called perfectly mixt bodies are immediately compounded, and into which they are ultimately resolved: now whether there be any one such body to be constantly met with in all and each of those that are said to be elemented bodies, is the thing I now question.

"By this state of the controversie you will, I suppose, guess, that I need not be so absurd, as to deny that there are such bodies as earth and water, and quicksilver, and sulphur: but I look upon earth and water, as component parts of the universe, or rather of the terrestrial globe, not of all mixt bodies. And though I will not peremptorily deny that there may sometimes either a running mercury or a combustible substance be obtained from a mineral, or even a metal; yet I need not concede either of them to be an element in the sence above declared; as I shall have occasion to shew you by and by.

"To give you then a brief account of the ground I intend to proceed upon, I must tell you that in matters of philosophy, this seems to me a sufficient reason to doubt of a known and important proposition, that the truth of it is not yet by any competent proof made to appear. And congruously hereunto, if I shew that the grounds, upon which men are perswaded that there are elements, are unable to satisfie a considering man, I suppose my doubts will appear rational.

"Now the considerations that induce men to think that there are elements, may be conveniently enough referred to two heads. Namely, the one, that it is necessary that nature make use of elements to constitute the bodies that are reputed mixt. And the other, that the resolution of such bodies manifests that nature had compounded them of elementary ones.

"In reference to the former of these considerations, there are two or three things that I have to represent.

"And I will begin with reminding you of the experiments I not long since related to you concerning the growth of pompions, mint, and other vegetables out of fair water. For by those experiments it seems evident that water may be transmuted into all the other elements; from whence it may be inferred, both, that 'tis not everything chymists will call salt, sulphur, or spirit, that needs alwaies be a primordiate and ingenerable body. And, that nature may contex [compound] a plant (though that be a perfectly mixt concrete) without having all the elements previously presented to her to compound it of. And, if you will allow the relation I mentioned . . . to be true; then may not only plants, but animals and minerals too, be produced out of water. And however there is little doubt to be made, but that the plants my tryals afforded me, as they were like in so many other respects to the rest of the plants of the same denomination; so they would, in case I had reduced them to putrefaction, have likewise produced wormes or other insects, as well as the resembling vegetables are wont to do; so that water may, by various seminal principles, be successively transmuted into both plants and animals. And if we consider that not only men, but even sucking children are, but too often, tormented with solid stones; and that divers sorts of beasts themselves (whatever Helmont against experience thinks to the contrary) may be troubled with great and heavy stones in their kidneys and bladders, though they feed but upon grass and other vegetables that are perhaps but disguised water, it will not seem improbable that even some concretes of a mineral nature, may likewise be formed of water.

"We may further take notice, that as a plant may be nourisht, and consequently may consist of common water; so may both plants and animals (perhaps even from their seminal rudiments) consist of compound bodies, without having anything merely elementary brought them by nature to be compounded by them: this is evident in divers men, who whilst they were infants were fed only with milk, afterwards live altogether upon flesh, fish, wine, and other perfectly mixt bodies. It may be seen also in sheep, who on some of our English downs or plains, grow very fat by feeding upon the grass, without scarce drinking at all. And yet more manifestly in the magots that breed and grow up to their full bignesse within the pulps of apples, pears, or the like fruit. We see also, that dungs that abound with a mixt salt give a much more speedy increment to corn and other vegetables, than water alone would do. . . .

"And thus (continues Carneades) having given you some reasons why I refuse to admit elementary water for a constant ingredient of mixt bodies, it will be easie for me to give you an account why I also reject earth.

"For first, it may well be suspected that many substances pass among chymists under the name of earth, because, like it, they are dry, and heavy, and fixt, which yet are very farr from an elementary nature. . . .

"To be short, as the difference of bodies may depend merely upon that of the schemes whereinto their common matter is put; so the seeds of things, the fire and the other agents are able to alter the minute parts of a body (either by breaking them into smaller ones of differing shapes, or by uniting together these fragments with the unbroken corpuscles, or such corpuscles among themselves) and the same agents partly by altering the shape or bigness of the constituent corpuscles of a body, partly by driving away some of them, partly by blending others with them, and partly by some new manner of connecting them, may give the whole portion of matter a new texture of its minute parts, and thereby make it deserve a new and distinct name. So that according as the small parts of matter recede from each other, or work upon each other, or are connected together after this or that determinate manner, a body of this or that denomination is produced, as some other body happens thereby to be altered or destroyed

"Since then those things which chymists produce by the help of the fire are but inanimate bodies; since such fruits of the chymists' skill differ from one another but in so few qualities that . . . we can easily enough work as great alterations upon matter, as those that are requisite to change one of these chymical productions into another; since, I say, these things are so, I see not why we must needs believe that there are any primogeneal and simple bodies, of which, as of pre-existent elements, nature is obliged to compound all others. Nor do I see why we may not conceive that she may produce the bodies accounted mixt out of one another by variously altering and contriving their minute parts, without resolving the matter into any such simple or homogeneous substances as are pretended. Neither, to dispatch, do I see why it should be counted absurd to think, that when a body is resolved by the fire into its supposed simple ingredients, those substances are not true and proper elements, but rather were, as it were, accidentally produced by the fire, which by dissipating a body into minute parts does, if those parts be shut up in close vessels, for the most part necessarily bring them to associate themselves after another manner than before, . . ."

HENRY CAVENDISH[1]

1 7 3 1 · 1 8 1 0

BRITISH CHEMISTS made great strides in their study of gases in spite of the difficulty they found in explaining their experiments by means of the faulty phlogiston theory. Before reading Cavendish's account of his synthesis of water by burning pure hydrogen in "common air," it may be interesting to read Lavoisier's attack on the theory a few years later, after he himself had abandoned it: "Chemists have made of phlogiston a vague principle which is not rigorously defined, and which consequently adapts itself to all explanations into which it may be introduced. Sometimes this principle is heavy, sometimes it is not; sometimes it is free fire, sometimes it is fire combined with the earthy elements. . . . It is a veritable Proteus which changes form at every instant."

Cavendish's account is continued in a report of "Experiments on Air," which he read before the Royal Society of London in January, 1784. If we translate the word "phlogisticate," as Cavendish used it, to mean "burn" or "combine with," it will be possible to understand the report.

Following these experiments, Cavendish found that "when five parts of pure, dephlogisticated air [oxygen] were mixed with three parts of common air," almost the whole of the air was made to disappear, "when the mixture was sparked in the presence of soapsuds." About one one hundred and twentieth (1/120) part of the air remained, with what we now know was nitric acid. The remaining gas was found, in 1894, to be argon.

[1] For one of Cavendish's physical experiments, see above, p. 105.

THE SYNTHESIS OF WATER

In Dr. Priestley's last volume of experiments [1] is related an experiment of Mr. Warltire's, in which it is said that, on firing a mixture of common and inflammable air (hydrogen) by electricity . . . in glass vessels, the inside of the glass, though clean and dry before, immediately became dewy; which confirmed an opinion he had long entertained that common air deposits its moisture by phlogistication. As the experiment seemed likely to throw great light on the subject I had in view, I thought it well worth examining more closely. . . .

In all the experiments, the inside of the glass globe became dewy, as observed by Mr. Warltire; but not the least sooty matter could be perceived. Care was taken in all of them to find how much the air was diminished by the explosion, and to observe its test. . . .

In these experiments the inflammable air was procured from zinc [and acid], as it was in all my experiments, except where otherwise expressed; but I made two more experiments, to try whether there was any difference between the air from zinc and that from iron, the quantity of inflammable air being the same in both, namely, 0,331 of the common; but I could not find any difference to be depended on between the two kinds of air, either in the diminution which they suffered by the explosion, or the test of the burnt air.

From the fourth experiment it appears that 423 measures of inflammable air [that is, 423 measures of hydrogen] are all that can be burned in 1000 measures of air; and that the bulk of the air remaining after the explosion is then very little more than four-fifths of the common air employed; so that as common air cannot be reduced to a much less bulk than that by any method of phlogistication, we

[1] For an example of Priestley's experiments with air, see below, p. 443.

may safely conclude that when they are mixed in this proportion, and exploded, almost all the inflammable air, and about one-fifth part of the common air, lose their elasticity, and are condensed into the dew which lines the glass.

The better to examine the nature of this dew, 500,000 grain measures of inflammable air were burnt with about 2½ times that quantity of common air, and the burnt air made to pass through a glass cylinder eight feet long and three-quarters of an inch in diameter, in order to deposit the dew. The two airs were conveyed slowly into this cylinder by separate copper pipes, passing through a brass plate which stopped up the end of the cylinder; and as neither inflammable nor common air can burn by themselves, there was no danger of the flame spreading into the magazines from which they were conveyed. Each of these magazines consisted of a large tin vessel, inverted into another vessel just big enough to receive it. The inner vessel communicated with the copper pipe, and the air was forced out of it by pouring water into the outer vessel; and in order that the quantity of common air expelled should be 2½ times that of the inflammable, the water was let into the outer vessels by two holes in the bottom of the same tin pan, the hole which conveyed the water into that vessel in which the common air was confined being 2½ times as big as the other.

In trying the experiment, the magazines being first filled with their respective airs, the glass cylinder was taken off, and water let, by the two holes, into the outer vessels, till the airs began to issue from the ends of the copper pipes; they were then set on fire by a candle, and the cylinder put on again in its place. By this means upwards of 135 grains of water were condensed in the cylinder, which had no taste nor smell, and which left no sensible sediment when evaporated to dryness; neither did it yield any pungent smell during the evaporation; in short, it seemed pure water.

In my first experiment, the cylinder near that part where the air was fired was a little tinged with sooty matter, but very slightly so; and that little seemed to proceed from the putty with which the apparatus was luted, and which was heated by the flame; for in another experiment, in which it was contrived so that the luting should not be much heated, scarce any sooty tinge could be perceived.

By the experiments with the globe it appeared that when inflammable and common air are exploded in a proper proportion, almost all the inflammable air, and near one-fifth of the common air, lose their elasticity, and are condensed into dew. And by this experiment it appears that this dew is plain water, and consequently that almost all the inflammable air, and about one-fifth of the common air, are turned into pure water. . . .

ANTOINE LAVOISIER[1]

1 7 4 3 · 1 7 9 4

LAVOISIER'S INTRODUCTION of exact measurement into chemistry led to his remarkable contributions to that science. He proved, for example, that water is not reducible to earth, as one old theory had it, by demonstrating that distilled water loses nothing in weight and does not change in any way when it is repeatedly re-distilled. He showed that burning and respiration were the same; that both were oxidation, one fast and the other slow, and both resulted in an increase of weight equal to the weight of the oxygen taken into combination. Perhaps most important of all was his demonstration that matter persists through all chemical changes; that throughout the most involved reactions, the total mass, as measured by its weight, does not vary. Other results of Lavoisier's emphasis on precision were his recognition that the phlogiston theory was wrong and unnecessary, and his establishment of a sound method of chemical terminology.

Lavoisier brought together the great body of chemical research from the time of Jean Rey to the era in which he worked. He borrowed freely from everywhere, sometimes without crediting others with their help, but he usually had something valuable to add to previous efforts.

The following selections are from Lavoisier's Elements of Chemistry, translated in 1799 by Robert Kerr. The first is an account of an experiment performed in 1775, in which he calcined mercury—that is, combined it with the oxygen in the air by heat. He reduced the

[1] For other work of Lavoisier, see below, p. 610.

262

mercury, obtaining the exact amount of gas that had been with-drawn from the air, and found that it answered the tests for oxygen. In passages from the introduction to the same work he gave oxy-gen, hydrogen, and many other substances the names which have been used ever since, though it will be noted that azot, his name for nitrogen, has not survived.

ANALYSIS OF ATMOSPHERIC AIR

From what has been premised, it appears that our atmosphere is composed of a mixture of every substance capable of retaining the gaseous or aëriform state in the common temperatures, and under the usual degrees of pressure which it experiences. These fluids constitute a mass, in some measure homogeneous, extending from the surface of the earth to the greatest height hitherto attained, of which the density continually decreases in the inverse ratio of the superincumbent weight. But, as I have before observed, it is possible that this first stratum may be surmounted by several others consisting of different fluids.

Our business, in this place, is to endeavour to determine, by experiments, the nature of the elastic fluids which compose the inferior stratum of air which we inhabit. Modern chemistry has made great advances in this research; and it will appear, by the following details, that the analysis of atmospherical air has been more rigorously determined than that of any other substance of the class.

Chemistry affords two general methods of determining the constituent principles of bodies, the method of analysis, and that of synthesis. When, for instance, by combining water with alcohol, we form the species of liquor called, in commercial language, brandy, or spirit of wine, we certainly have a right to conclude that brandy, or spirit of wine, is composed of alcohol combined with water. We can procure the same result by the analytical method; and in general it ought to be considered as a principle in chemical science, never to rest satisfied without both these species of proofs. We have this advantage in the analysis of atmospherical air; being able both to decompound it, and to form it anew in the most satisfactory manner. I shall, however, at present confine myself to recount such

experiments as are most conclusive upon this head; and I may consider most of these as my own, having either first invented them, or
having repeated those of others, intended for analysing atmospherical air, in perfectly new points of view.

I took a flask of about 36 cubical inches capacity, having a long
neck of six or seven lines [half an inch] internal diameter, and having bent the neck, as in Plate IV. Fig. 2. C D, to allow of its being
placed in the furnace in such a manner that the extremity of its neck
might be inserted under a bell-glass F G, placed in a trough of

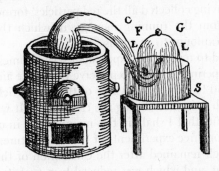

quicksilver S S; I introduced four ounces of pure mercury into the
flask, and, by means of a syphon, exhausted the air in the bell-glass,
so as to raise the quicksilver to L L, and I carefully marked the
height at which it stood, by pasting on a slip of paper. Having accurately noted the height of the thermometer and barometer, I lighted
a fire in the furnace, which I kept up almost continually during
twelve days, so as to keep the quicksilver always very near its boiling
point. Nothing remarkable took place during the first day. The mercury, though not boiling, was continually evaporating, and covered
the interior surface of the vessel with small drops, which gradually
augmenting to a sufficient size, fell back into the mass at the bottom
of the vessel. On the second day, small red particles began to appear
on the surface of the mercury, these, during the four or five following days, gradually increased in size and number, after which they

ceased to increase in either respect. At the end of twelve days, seeing that the calcination of the mercury did not at all increase, I extinguished the fire, and allowed the vessels to cool. The bulk of air in the body and neck of the flask, and in the bell-glass, reduced to a medium of 28 inches of the barometer and 54.5° of the thermometer, at the commencement of the experiment was about 50 cubical inches. At the end of the experiment the remaining air, reduced to the same medium pressure and temperature, was only between 42 and 43 cubical inches; consequently it had lost about 1/6 of its bulk. Afterwards, having collected all the red particles, formed during the experiment, from the running mercury in which they floated, I found these to amount to 45 grains.

I was obliged to repeat this experiment several times, as it is difficult, in one experiment, both to preserve the whole air upon which we operate, and to collect the whole of the red particles, or calx of mercury, which is formed during the calcination. It will often happen in the sequel that I shall, in this manner, give in one detail the results of two or three experiments of the same nature.

The air which remained after the calcination of the mercury in this experiment, and which was reduced to 5/6 of its former bulk, was no longer fit either for respiration or for combustion; animals being introduced into it were suffocated in a few seconds, and when a taper was plunged into it, it was extinguished, as if it had been immersed in water.

In the next place, I took the 45 grains of red matter formed during this experiment, which I put into a small glass retort, having a proper apparatus for receiving such liquid, or gaseous product, as might be extracted. Having applied a fire to the retort in the furnace, I observed that, in proportion as the red matter became heated, the intensity of its colour augmented. When the retort was almost red hot, the red matter began gradually to decrease in bulk, and in a few minutes after it disappeared altogether; at the same time 41½ grains of running mercury were collected in the recipient, and 7 or 8 cubical inches of elastic fluid, greatly more capable of supporting both respiration and combustion than atmospherical air, were collected in the bell-glass.

A part of this air being put into a glass tube of about an inch diameter, shewed the following properties: A taper burned in it with a dazzling splendour, and charcoal, instead of consuming quietly, as it does in common air, burnt with a flame, attended with a decrepitating noise, like phosphorus, and threw out such a brilliant light that the eyes could hardly endure it. This species of air was discovered almost at the same time by Dr. Priestley, Mr. Scheele, and myself. Dr. Priestley gave it the name of *dephlogisticated air*;[1] Mr. Scheele called it *empyreal air*; at first I named it *highly respirable air*, to which has since been substituted the term of *vital air*. We shall presently see what we ought to think of these denominations.

In reflecting upon the circumstances of this experiment, we readily perceive that the mercury, during its calcination, absorbs the salubrious and respirable part of the air, or, to speak more strictly, the base of this respirable part; that the remaining air is . . . incapable of supporting combustion or respiration; and, consequently, that atmospheric air is composed of two elastic fluids of different and opposite qualities. As a proof of this important truth, if we recombine these two elastic fluids, which we have separately obtained in the above experiment, viz., the 42 cubical inches of mephitis [noxious air], with the 8 cubical inches of highly respirable air, we reproduce an air precisely similar to that of the atmosphere, and possessing nearly the same power of supporting combustion and respiration, and of contributing to the calcination of metals. . . .

Nomenclature of the several Constituent Parts of Atmospheric Air

Hitherto I have been obliged to make use of circumlocution, to express the nature of the several substances which constitute our

[1] Now called oxygen. See below, pp. 270 and 451 ff. For Priestley on oxygen and phlogiston, see p. 443; for Scheele on phlogiston, see p. 169.

atmosphere, having provisionally used the terms of *respirable*, and *noxious* or *non-respirable*, *parts of the air*. But the investigations I mean to undertake, require a more direct mode of expression; and, having now endeavoured to give simple and distinct ideas of the different substances which enter into the composition of the atmosphere, I shall henceforth express these ideas by words equally simple.

The temperature of our earth being very near to that at which water becomes solid, and at which reciprocally it changes from solid to fluid; and as this phenomenon takes place frequently under our observation, it has very naturally followed that, in the languages of at least every climate subject to any degree of winter, a term has been used for signifying water in the state of solidity, or when deprived of its caloric [heat]. The same precision has not been found necessary with respect to water reduced to the state of vapour by an additional quantity of caloric. Those persons who do not make a particular study of objects of this kind, are still ignorant that water, when in a temperature only a little above the boiling heat, is changed into an elastic aëriform fluid, susceptible, like all other gases, of being received and contained in vessels, and of preserving its gaseous form so long as it remains at the temperature of 212°, and under a pressure not exceeding 28 inches of the mercurial barometer. As this phenomenon has not been very generally observed, no language has used a particular term for expressing water in this state; and the same thing occurs with all fluids, and all substances, which do not evaporate in the common temperature, and under the usual pressure of our atmosphere.

For similar reasons, names have not been given to the liquid or concrete states of most of the aëriform fluids. These were not known to arise from the combination of caloric with certain bases; and, as they had not been seen either in the liquid or solid states, their existence, under these forms, was even unknown to natural philosophers.

We have not pretended to make any alteration upon such terms as are sanctified by ancient custom; and, therefore, continue to use tne words *water* and *ice* in their common acceptation. We likewise retain the word *air*, to express that collection of elastic fluids which composes our atmosphere. But we have not thought it necessary to preserve the same respect for modern terms, adopted by the later philosophers, having considered ourselves as at liberty to reject such as appeared liable to give erroneous ideas of the substances they are meant to express, and either to substitute new terms, or to employ the old ones, after having modified them in such a manner as to convey more determinate ideas. New words, when necessary, have been borrowed chiefly from the Greek language, in such a manner as to make their etymology convey some idea of what was meant to be represented by them; and we have always endeavoured to make these short, and of such a form as to admit of being changed into adjectives and verbs.

Following these principles, we have, after the example of Mr. Macquer, retained the term *gas*, employed by van Helmont;[2] having arranged the numerous class of elastic aëriform fluids under the name, excepting only atmospheric air. *Gas*, therefore, in our nomenclature, becomes a generic term, expressing the fullest degree of saturation in any body with caloric; being, in fact, a term expressive of a mode of existence. To distinguish the species of gas, we employ a second term derived from the name of the base, which, saturated with caloric, forms each particular gas. Thus, we name water combined to saturation with caloric, so as to form an elastic fluid, *aqueous gas*; ether combined in the same manner, *ethereal gas*; the combination of alkohol with caloric, becomes *alkoholic gas*; and, following the same principles, we have *muriatic acid gas, ammoniacal gas*, and so on of every substance susceptible of being combined with caloric, in such a manner as to assume the gaseous or elastic aëriform state.

We have already seen that the atmospheric fluid, or common air, is composed of two gases, or aëriform fluids; one of which is capable,

[2] On van Helmont, see below, p. 393.

by respiration, of contributing to support animal life; and in it metals are calcinable, and combustible bodies may burn. The other, on the contrary, is endowed with directly opposite qualities; it cannot be breathed by animals, neither will it admit of the combustion of inflammable bodies, nor of the calcination of metals. We have given to the base of the former, which is the respirable portion of atmospheric air, the name of *oxygen*, from ὀξύς, acidum, and γείνομχι, gignor, because one of the most general properties of this base is to form acids, by combining with many different substances. The union of this base with caloric, which is the same with what was formerly named *pure*, or *vital*, or *highly respirable air*, we now call *oxygen gas*. The weight of this gas, at the temperature of 54.50°, and under a pressure equal to 28 inches of the barometer, is half a grain for each cubical inch nearly, or one ounce and a half to each cubical foot.

The chemical properties of the noxious portion of atmospheric air being hitherto but little known, we have been satisfied to derive the name of its base from its known quality of killing such animals as are forced to breathe it, giving it the name of *azot*, from the Greek privative particle *a*, and ςωή, vita; hence the name of the noxious part of atmospheric air is *azotic gas*. The weight of this, in the same temperature, and under the same pressure, is 1 *oz.* 2 *drams* and 48 *grs.* to the cubical foot, or 0.4444 of a grain to the cubical inch. We cannot deny that this name appears somewhat extraordinary; but this must be the case with all new terms, which cannot be expected to become familiar until they have been some time in use. We long endeavoured to find a more proper designation without success. It was at first proposed to call it *alkaligen gas*, as, from the experiments of Mr. Berthollet, it appears to enter into the composition of ammoniac, or volatile alkali; but then, we have as yet no proof of its making one of the constituent elements of the other alkalies; besides, it is proved to form a part of the nitric acid, which gives a good reason to have it called *nitrigen*. For these reasons, finding it necessary to reject any name upon systematic principles, we have considered that we run no risk of mistake, in adopting the terms of *azot*, and *azotic gas*, which only express a matter of fact, or that property which it possesses, of depriving such animals as breathe it of their lives.

I should anticipate subjects more properly reserved for the subsequent chapters, were I in this place to enter upon the nomenclature of the several species of gases. It is sufficient, in this part of the work, to establish the principles upon which their denominations are founded. The principal merit of the nomenclature we have adopted is, that, when once the simple elementary substance is distinguished by an appropriate term, the names of all its compounds derive readily, and necessarily, from this first denomination. . . .

WILLIAM NICHOLSON

1 7 5 3 · 1 8 1 5

ANTHONY CARLISLE

1 7 6 8 · 1 8 4 0

A MONTH AFTER VOLTA had written his famous letter describing his new electric battery to Sir Joseph Banks, president of the Royal Society,[1] Carlisle, a London surgeon and professor of anatomy, read the letter and constructed a similar instrument. During his first experiments with it, in the company of William Nicholson, they observed the decomposition of water.

Nicholson, a civil engineer as well as publisher of Nicholson's Journal of Natural Philosophy, Chemistry and the Arts, carried the experiments to a successful conclusion, and published the results in his Journal for July, 1800.

Lavoisier had previously remarked that it ought to be considered a principle in chemical science not to be satisfied with a proof of the chemical constituents of a body until the body had been analyzed by breaking it down into its parts, and also synthesized by building it up from its parts. In the preceding essay, Cavendish described the creation of water by burning hydrogen in air. Here Nicholson describes the dissolution of water by electrical current into hydrogen and oxygen.

[1] See below, p. 331.

THE DECOMPOSITION OF WATER

IN ALL THESE experiments it was observed that the action of the instrument [Voltaic pile][2] was freely transmitted through the usual conductors of electricity, but stopped by glass and other non-conductors. Very early in this course, the contacts being made sure by placing a drop of water upon the upper plate, Mr. Carlisle observed a disengagement of gas round the touching wire. This gas, though very minute in quantity, evidently seemed to me to have the smell afforded by hydrogen when the wire of communication was steel. This, with some other facts, led me to propose to break the circuit by the substitution of a tube of water between two wires. On the 2nd of May we, therefore, inserted a brass wire through each of two corks inserted in a glass tube of half an inch internal diameter. The tube was filled with New River water, and the distance between the points of the wires in the water was one inch and three quarters. This compound discharger was applied so that the external ends of its wire were in contact with the two extreme plates of a [Voltaic] pile of 36 half crowns with the correspondent pieces of zinc and pasteboard. A fine stream of minute bubbles immediately began to flow from the point of the lower wire in the tube, which communicated with the silver, and the opposite point of the upper wire became tarnished, first deep orange and then black. On reversing the tube, the gas came from the other point, which was now lowest, while the upper in its turn became tarnished and black. Reversing the tube again, the phenomena again changed their order. . . .

The product of gas, during the whole two hours and a half, was two-thirtieths of a cubic inch. It was then mixed with an equal quan-

[2] Concerning the Voltaic pile, a form of electric battery, see p. 334.

tity of common air, and exploded by the application of a lighted waxed thread.

It might seem almost unnecessary to have reversed the order of the pile in building up, as reversing the tube must have answered exactly the same purpose. We chose, however, to do this, and found that when the zinc was at the bottom, its effects were reversed, that is to say, the gas still came from the wire communicating with the silver, etc.

We had been led by our reasoning on the first appearance of hydrogen to expect a decomposition of the water; but it was with no little surprise that we found the hydrogen extricated at the contact with one wire, while the oxygen fixed itself in combination with the other wire at the distance of almost two inches. This new fact still remains to be explained, and seems to point at some general law of the agency of electricity in chemical operations. As the distance between the wires formed a striking feature in this result, it became desirable to ascertain whether it would take place to greater distances. When a tube three-quarters of an inch in diameter, and thirty-six inches long, was made use of, the effect failed, though the very same wires, inserted into a shorter tube, operated very briskly. The solicitation of other objects of enquiry prevented trial being made of all the various intermediate distances; but from the general tenor of experiments, it appears to be established that this decomposition is more effectual the less the distance between the wires, but that it ceases altogether when the wires come into contact.

The decomposition of water, and oxidation of metallic wire, gave birth to a variety of speculations and projects of experiments. Among others it became a question what would be the habitude of metals of different oxidation. Two wires of platina, one of which was round, and one fortieth of an inch in diameter, and the other nearly of the same mass, but flatted to the breadth of one twenty-fifth of an inch, were inserted into a short tube of one fourth of an inch inside diameter. When placed in the circuit, the silver side gave a plentiful stream of fine bubbles, and the zinc side also a stream less plentiful. . . .

The simple decomposition of water by platina wires without oxidation offered a means of obtaining the gases separate from each other. With this intention, Mr. Carlisle's [Voltaic] pile of thirty-six was combined with my two sets of sixteen repetitions. His pile was built with zinc uppermost, and mine in the reverse order; so that by connecting the upper plates the whole constituted one range, and the communications could be made from the bottom of the one to the bottom of the other. The two platina wires were made to protrude out of two separate tubes, each containing a little water, and through the opposite corks of each were passed copper wires of communication. These tubes were slightly greased on the outside to prevent their becoming damp; and in this state the extremities, armed with the platina, were plunged in a shallow glass vessel of water, in which two small inverted vessels, quite full of water, were so disposed, that the platina of one tube was beneath one vessel, and the platina of the other tube was beneath the other, the distance between their extremities being about two inches. The copper wires of these tubes respectively were made to communicate with the extremities of the entire pile of sixty-eight sets. A cloud of gas arose from each wire, but most from the silver, or minus, side. Bubbles were extricated from all parts of the water, and adhered to the whole internal surface of the vessels. The process was continued for thirteen hours, after which the wires were disengaged, and the gases decanted into separate bottles. On measuring the quantities, which was done by weighing the bottles, it was found that the quantities of water displaced by the gases were, respectively, 72 grains by the gas from the zinc side, and 142 grains by the gas from the silver side; so that the whole volume of gas was 1.17 cubic inches, or near an inch and a quarter. These are nearly the proportions in bulk of what are stated to be the component parts of water.

JOHN DALTON

1 7 6 6 · 1 8 4 4

FROM THE FOURTH century before Christ until the end of the eighteenth century the argument had persisted as to whether or not matter is made up of atoms. Since Dalton's time, the atomic point of view has been taken for granted, for he showed that when elements combine to form compounds, they combine in simple proportions, as if one, two, three, or even more, distinct atoms of one were to combine with a small and definite number of atoms of another. It is this principle we use when we say water may be symbolized by H_2O, (two atoms of hydrogen to one of oxygen); or CO for carbon monoxide, or CO_2 for carbon dioxide.

John Dalton, a school teacher, son of a Westmoreland handloom weaver, first applied his atomic theory to gases, and later extended it to all chemical substances. He made some errors in his original essay, a part of which is quoted here, but they do not detract from the importance of his discovery that elements combine exactly as if they were made up of small, indivisible particles. This theory, one of the greatest forward steps in the history of science, opened the way for the amazing progress of the great chemists of the nineteenth century. The essay from which we quote is from Papers and Extracts by John Dalton.

THE FOUNDATIONS OF ATOMIC THEORY

THERE ARE THREE distinctions in the kinds of bodies, or three states, which have more especially claimed the attention of philosophical chemists; namely, those which are marked by the terms *elastic fluids, liquids,* and *solids.* A very familiar instance is exhibited to us in water, of a body which in certain circumstances is capable of assuming all the three states. In steam we recognize a perfectly elastic fluid, in water a perfect liquid, and in ice a complete solid. These observations have tacitly led to the conclusion, which seems universally adopted, that all bodies of sensible magnitude, whether liquid or solid, are constituted of a vast number of extremely small particles, or atoms, of matter bound together by a force of attraction, which is more or less powerful according to circumstances, and which as it endeavors to prevent their separation, is very properly called in that view, *attraction of cohesion;* but as it collects them from a dispersed state (as from steam into water) it is called, *attraction of aggregation,* or more simply, *affinity.* Whatever names it may go by, they still signify one and the same power. It is not my design to call in question this conclusion, which appears completely satisfactory; but to show that we have hitherto made no use of it, and that the consequence of this neglect has been a very obscure view of chemical agency, which is daily growing more so in proportion to the new lights attempted to be thrown upon it.

The opinions I more particularly allude to are those of Berthollet on the Laws of chemical affinity; such as that chemical agency is proportional to the mass, and that in all chemical unions, there exist insensible gradations in the proportions of the constituent principles. The inconsistence of these opinions, both with reason and observation, cannot, I think, fail to strike everyone who takes a proper view of the phenomena.

Whether the ultimate particles of a body, such as water, are all alike, that is, of the same figure, weight, etc., is a question of some importance. From what is known, we have no reason to apprehend a diversity in these particulars; if it does exist in water, it must equally exist in the elements constituting water, namely, hydrogen and oxygen. Now it is scarcely possible to conceive how the aggregates of dissimilar particles should be so uniformly the same. If some of the particles of water were heavier than others, if a parcel of the liquid on any occasion were constituted principally of these heavier particles, it must be supposed to affect the specific gravity of the mass, a circumstance not known. Similar observations may be made on other substances. Therefore we may conclude that *the ultimate particles of all homogeneous bodies are perfectly alike in weight, figure, etc.* In other words, every particle of water is like every other particle of water; every particle of hydrogen is like every other particle of hydrogen, etc.

On Chemical Synthesis

When any body exists in the elastic state, its ultimate particles are separated from each other to a much greater distance than in any other state; each particle occupies the center of a comparatively large sphere, and supports its dignity by keeping all the rest, which by their gravity, or otherwise, are disposed to encroach upon it, at a respectful distance. When we attempt to conceive the *number* of particles in an atmosphere, it is somewhat like attempting to conceive the number of stars in the universe; we are confounded with the thought. But if we limit the subject, by taking a given volume of any gas, we seem persuaded that, let the divisions be ever so minute, the number of particles must be finite; just as in a given space of the universe, the number of stars and planets cannot be infinite.

Chemical analysis and synthesis go no farther than to the separation of particles one from another, and to their reunion. No new creation or destruction of matter is within the reach of chemical agency. We might as well attempt to introduce a new planet into the solar system, or to annihilate one already in existence, as to create or destroy a particle of hydrogen. All the changes we can produce consist in separating particles that are in a state of cohesion or combination, and joining those that were previously at a distance.

In all chemical investigations, it has justly been considered an important object to ascertain the relative *weights* of the simples which constitute a compound. But unfortunately the enquiry has terminated here; whereas from the relative weights in the mass, the relative weights of the ultimate particles or atoms of the bodies might have been inferred, from which their number and weight in various other compounds would appear, in order to assist and to guide future investigations, and to correct their results. Now it is one great object of this work, to show the importance and advantage of ascertaining *the relative weights of the ultimate particles, both of simple and compound bodies, the number of simple elementary particles which constitute one compound particle, and the number of less compound particles which enter into the formation of one more compound particle.*

If there are two bodies, A and B, which are disposed to combine, the following is the order in which the combinations may take place, beginning with the most simple, namely:

1 atom of A + 1 atom of B = 1 atom of C, binary.
1 atom of A + 2 atoms of B = 1 atom of D, ternary.
2 atoms of A + 1 atom of B = 1 atom of E, ternary.
1 atom of A + 3 atoms of B = 1 atom of F, quaternary.
3 atoms of A + 1 atom of B = 1 atom of G, quaternary.

etc., etc.

IV

Electricity

IT IS A GREAT *recommendation of the study of electricity, that it now appears to be by no means a small object. The electric fluid is no local or occasional agent in the theatre of the world. Late discoveries show that its presence and effects are everywhere, and that it acts a principal part in the grandest and most interesting scenes of nature. It is not, like magnetism, confined to one kind of bodies, but everything we know is a conductor or non-conductor of electricity. These are properties as essential and important as any they are possessed of, and can hardly fail to show themselves wherever the bodies are concerned.*

Hitherto philosophy has been chiefly conversant about the more sensible properties of bodies; electricity, together with chymistry, and the doctrine of light and colours, seems to be giving us an inlet into their internal structure, on which all their sensible properties depend. By pursuing this new light, therefore, the bounds of natural science may possibly be extended beyond what we can now form an idea of. New worlds may open to our view, and the glory of the great Sir Isaac Newton himself and all his contemporaries be eclipsed by a new set of philosophers, in quite a new field of speculation.

This prophetic statement was contained in Priestley's *History of Electricity*, published in 1767. When it was written, electricity was still only a laboratory curiosity and a source of parlor tricks. Thirty-three years later Volta invented the first electric battery and produced the first sustained electric current.

From early antiquity four different electric phenomena had been familiar to everyone: the lightning flash, the sting of the electric eel or torpedo, the attraction that amber and other materials, when rubbed, have for bits of paper (which phenomenon gave us the name "electricity," from the Greek ελεκτϱoy or amber), and the glow called St. Elmo's fire, which sometimes appears at the metal ends of ship spars and masts. "In one sense, perhaps," says Lloyd W. Taylor,[1] "these illustrations are trivial. They have no inescapable connection with the action of familiar electrical accessories. Yet in another sense, they constitute a complete index to the history of electricity up to the eighteenth century. . . . Until the eighteenth century they were four separate and unconnected effects, only one of which, the attraction exhibited by rubbed bodies for light particles, was termed electric."

In the late sixteenth century the Englishman William Gilbert made the first serious study of static electricity, and included accounts of many experiments in his great work on magnetism, *De magnete*. He constructed the first electroscope, out "of any sort of metal, three or four fingers long, pretty light, and poised on a sharp point after the manner of magnetic pointers." Either end of this device was attracted, he found, by rubbed amber and other stones. Other of his experiments are described in the quotation reprinted below. Gilbert's theories were not always right, and he failed to notice magnetic and electrostatic repulsion; but he was a tireless experimenter. His work meant a definite break with tradition; a fact as important as any of his actual discoveries.

Experimenters after Gilbert grew tired of rubbing objects to produce electricity, and developed a number of machines to reduce the labor. Otto von Guericke (1602-1686), mayor of Magdeburg and experimenter with vacuums and electricity, made great globes of solid sulphur, which could be rapidly twirled without much effort, while the experimenter touched the surfaces. He noticed that a "sulphur globe, having been previously excited by rubbing, can exercise its virtue through a linen thread an ell or more long." This sensational discovery, however, was not followed up. It remained to be re-discovered a half century later by Stephen Gray, who transmitted static electricity as far as 765 feet.

[1] *Physics, the Pioneer Science*, Lloyd William Taylor, Houghton Mifflin Co., 1941. p. 601.

Charles Du Fay repeated Gray's experiments, finding that wet strings conducted electricity very well, and that the metals which Gilbert had called non-electrics were actually good conductors. Du Fay noticed, too, that there appeared to be two sorts of electricity, *vitreous* (produced from glass) and resinous (from amber). But Benjamin Franklin soon afterward called these two aspects *positive* and *negative* respectively, asserting that one indicated the presence and the other the absence of electricity. Du Fay was mistaken in his idea that both forms of electricity moved with equal facility; we know now that both kinds exist, but that only the negative or resinous kind is able to move.

Franklin went on to prove the identity of lightning with frictional electricity by conducting a charge from the clouds to a Leyden jar, where it behaved in the same way as the electricity produced by a friction machine.

Galvani started investigation into electricity in living bodies, when he found that the discharge of an electric spark would cause the leg of a frog to twitch, as would also the touching of the frog with a pair of electric conductors in a special way. He believed, however, that the cause of the electricity was in the frog, rather than that the junction of the two metals created the electric current.

The year 1800 marks the beginning of the modern phase of electrical study. In 1801 the heating effect of an electric current was noticed; in 1802 light was produced in the form of a carbon arc; in the same year the art of electroplating was discovered and experiments begun for an electric telegraph; in 1808 electricity was first used to ignite blasting powder. By 1818 John Bostock, in his history of "galvanism," thought it safe to declare that just about everything possible had been done with electricity. But in the very next year Oersted found a connection between electricity and magnetism; a flowing electric current, he observed, would deflect a magnet. With this discovery, which underlies the theory of the generator and the motor, the modern study of electricity got under way.

WILLIAM GILBERT

1 5 4 0 · 1 6 0 3

THE COMPASS HAD been in common use for four or five hundred years before William Gilbert, about 1600, wrote his great book on magnetism and electricity. As early as the year 1269 Peter Peregrine, a friend of Roger Bacon, wrote a remarkable Letter on Magnets, which contained a clear statement of magnetic polarity, and described how to trace out lines of force. For some unknown reason the author failed to notice the repulsion of like poles, but he presented the first known picture of the mariners' needle compass, pivoted in the middle.

At the end of the fifteenth century Christopher Columbus remarked the fact that the compass did not always point to the geographic north, but deviated from it in varying amounts. Others of that time noticed that the compass needle tended to dip towards the earth, and that the intensity of the earth's magnetic field seemed to vary.

A hundred years later, England was beginning to take Spain's place as the leading maritime power. It was not then strange that William Gilbert, physician to Queen Elizabeth, should interest himself in a science of so much interest to Her Majesty's captains. His book On Magnets is an encyclopedia of the existing knowledge of the subject, tried and tested by careful experiment. This work of a generation before Galileo contains the first serious discussion of electrostatics; it also presents Gilbert's great conception that the earth is nothing but a large magnet. This treatise, written in the spirit of modern science, laid a firm foundation for later scientists to build upon.

284

The translation here used of the De magnete magneticisque cor-
poribus et de magno magnete tellure physiologia nova *(The Magnet,
and Magnetic Bodies, and the Great Magnet, the Earth, a new
Physiology) was made by E. Fleury Mottelay in 1893.*

MAGNETISM AND ELECTRICITY

The Loadstone Possesses Parts Differing In Their Natural Powers, And Has Poles Conspicuous For Their Properties

THE MANY QUALITIES exhibited by the loadstone itself, qualities hitherto recognized yet not well investigated, are to be pointed out in the first place, to the end the student may understand the powers of the loadstone and of iron, and not be confused through want of knowledge at the threshold of the arguments and demonstrations. In the heavens, astronomers give to each moving sphere two poles; thus do we find two natural poles of excelling importance

This bar of iron is being magnetized by pounding it while it is cooling. Note that it is being held in a north-south direction. (From Gilbert's *De magnete*.)

even in our terrestrial globe, constant points related to the movement of its daily revolution, to wit, one pole pointing to Arctos (Ursa) and the north; the other looking toward the opposite part of the heavens. In like manner the loadstone has from nature its two poles, a northern and a southern; fixed, definite points in the stone, which are the primary termini of the movements and effects, and the limits and regulators of the several actions and properties. It is to be understood, however, that not from a mathematical point does the force of the stone emanate, but from the parts themselves; and all these parts in the whole—while they belong to the whole— the nearer they are to the poles of the stone, the stronger virtues do they acquire and pour out on other bodies. These poles look toward the poles of the earth, and move toward them, and are subject to them. The magnetic poles may be found in every loadstone, whether strong and powerful (male, as the term was in antiquity) or faint, weak, and female; whether its shape is due to design or to chance, and whether it be long, or flat, or four-square, or three-cornered, or polished; whether it be rough, broken-off, or unpolished: the loadstone ever has and ever shows its pole. . . .

One Loadstone Appears To Attract Another In The Natural Position; But In The Opposite Position Repels It And Brings It To Rights

First we have to describe in popular language the potent and familiar properties of the stone; afterward, very many subtle properties, as yet recondite and unknown, being involved in obscurities, are to be unfolded; and the causes of all these (nature's secrets being unlocked) are in their place to be demonstrated in fitting words and with the aid of apparatus. The fact is trite and familiar, that the loadstone attracts iron; in the same way, too, one loadstone attracts another. Take the stone on which you have designated the poles, N. and S., and put it in its vessel so that it may float; let the poles lie just in the plane of the horizon, or at least in a plane not very oblique to it; take in your hand another stone the poles of which are also known, and hold it so that its south pole shall lie toward the north pole of the floating stone, and near it alongside; the floating loadstone will straightway follow the other (provided it be within the range and dominion of its powers), nor does it cease to move nor does it quit the other till it clings to it, unless by moving your hand away, you manage skilfully to prevent the conjunction.

In like manner, if you oppose the north pole of the stone in your hand to the south pole of the floating one, they come together and follow each other. For opposite poles attract opposite poles. But, now, if in the same way you present N. to N. or S. to S., one stone repels the other; and as though a helmsman were bearing on the rudder it is off like a vessel making all sail, nor stands nor stays as long as the other stone pursues. One stone also will range the other, turn the other around, bring it to right about and make it come to agreement with itself. But when the two come together and are conjoined in nature's order, they cohere firmly. For example, if you present the north pole of the stone in your hand to . . . any point between the equator and the south pole: immediately the floating stone turns round and so places itself that its south pole touches the north pole of the other and is most closely joined to it.

In the same way you will get like effect at the other side of the equator by presenting pole to pole; and thus by art and contrivance we exhibit attraction and repulsion, and motion in a circle toward the concordant position, and the same movements to avoid hostile meetings. Furthermore, in one same stone we are thus able to demonstrate all this: but also we are able to show how the self-same part of one stone may by division become either north or south. Take the oblong stone *ad* (Fig. 19) in which *a* is the north pole and *d* the south. Cut the stone in two equal parts, and put part *a* in a vessel and let it float in water.

You will find that *a*, the north point, will turn to the south [1] as

---

[1] Today we name the poles the other way. The "north pole" of a magnet is the "north-seeking" pole.

before; and in like manner the point *d* will move to the north, in
the divided stone, as before division. But *b* and *c*, before connected,
now separated from each other, are not what they were before. *b* is
now south while *c* is north. *b* attracts *c*, longing for union and for
restoration of the original continuity. They are two stones made out
of one, and on that account the *c* of one turning toward the *b* of
the other, they are mutually attracted, and being freed from all
impediments and from their own weight, borne as they are on the

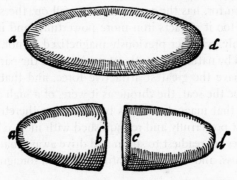

Gilbert's original illustration to demonstrate
that a magnet, when broken, forms two magnets.

surface of the water, they come together and into conjunction. But
if you bring the part or point *a* up to *c* of the other, they repel one
another and turn away; for by such a position of the parts nature is
crossed and the form of the stone is perverted: but nature observes
strictly the laws it has imposed upon bodies: hence the flight of one
part from the undue position of the other, and hence the discord
unless everything is arranged exactly according to nature. And nature will not suffer an unjust and inequitable peace, or agreement,
but makes war and employs force to make bodies acquiesce fairly
and justly. Hence, when rightly arranged the parts attract each other,

i.e., both stones, the weaker and the stronger, come together and with all their might tend to union: a fact manifest in all loadstones, and not, as Pliny supposed, only in those from Ethiopia.

The Ethiopic stones if strong, and those brought from China, which are all powerful stones, show the effect most quickly and most plainly, attract with most force in the parts nighest the pole, and keep turning till pole looks straight on pole. The pole of a stone has strongest attraction for that part of another stone which answers to it (the *adverse* as it is called); e.g., the north pole of one has strongest attraction for, has the most vigorous pull on, the south part of another; so too it attracts iron more powerfully, and iron clings to it more firmly, whether previously magnetized or not. Thus it has been settled by nature, not without reason, that the parts nigher the pole shall have the greatest attractive force; and that in the pole itself shall be the seat, the throne as it were, of a high and splendid power; and that magnetic bodies brought near thereto shall be attracted most powerfully and relinquished with most reluctance. So, too, the poles are readiest to spurn and drive away what is presented to them amiss, and what is inconformable and foreign. . . .

Of Magnetic Coition; And, First, Of The Attraction Exerted By Amber, or More Properly The Attachment of Bodies to Amber

Great has ever been the fame of the loadstone and of amber in the writings of the learned: many philosophers cite the loadstone and also amber whenever, in explaining mysteries, their minds become obfuscated and reason can no farther go. Over-inquisitive theologians, too, seek to light up God's mysteries and things beyond man's understanding by means of the loadstone as a sort of Delphic sword and as an illustration of all sorts of things. Medical men also (at the bidding of Galen), in proving that purgative medicines exercise attraction through likeness of substance and kinships of juices (a silly error and gratuitous!), bring in as a witness the loadstone, a substance of great authority and of noteworthy efficiency, and a body of no common order.

Thus in very many affairs persons who plead for a cause the merits of which they cannot set forth, bring in as masked advocates the loadstone and amber. But all these, besides sharing the general misapprehension, are ignorant that the causes of the loadstone's movements are very different from those which give to amber its properties; hence they easily fall into errors, and by their own imaginings are led farther and farther astray. For in other bodies is seen a considerable power of attraction, differing from that of the loadstone,—in amber, for example. Of this substance a few words must be said, to show the nature of the attachment of bodies to it, and to point out the vast difference between this and the magnetic actions; for men still continue in ignorance, and deem that inclination of bodies to amber to be an attraction, and comparable to the magnetic coition. . . .

The ancients as well as moderns tell (and their report is confirmed by experience) that amber attracts straws and chaff. The same is done by jet, a stone taken out of the earth in Britain, Germany, and many other regions: it is a hard concretion of black bitumen—a sort of transformation of bitumen to stone. Many modern authors have written about amber and jet as attracting chaff and about other facts unknown to the generality, or have copied from other writers: with the results of their labors booksellers' shops are crammed full. Our generation has produced many volumes about recondite, abstruse, and occult causes and wonders, and in all of them amber and jet are represented as attracting chaff; but never a proof from experiments, never a demonstration do you find in them. The writers deal only in words that involve in thicker darkness subject-matter; they treat the subject esoterically, miracle-mongeringly, abstrusely, reconda, recondently, mystically.

Hence such philosophy bears no fruit; for it rests simply on a few Greek or unusual terms—just as our barbers toss off a few Latin words in the hearing of the ignorant rabble in token of their learning, and thus win reputation—bears no fruit, because few of the philosophers themselves are investigators, or have any first-hand acquaintance with things; most of them are indolent and untrained, add nothing to knowledge by their writings, and are blind to the things that might throw a light upon their reasonings. For not only do amber and jet, as they suppose attract light substances: the same is done by diamond, sapphire, carbuncle, iris stone, opal, amethyst, vincentina, Bristol stone, beryl, rock crystal. Like powers of attracting are possessed by glass, especially clear, brilliant glass; by artificial gems made of (paste) glass or rock crystal, antimony glass, many fluor-spars, and belemnites. Sulphur also attracts, and likewise mastich, and sealing-wax (of lac), hard resin, orpiment (weakly). Feeble power of attraction is also possessed in favoring dry atmosphere by sal gemma [native chloride of sodium], mica, rock alum. This we may observe when in mid-winter the atmosphere is very cold, clear, and thin; when the electrical effluvia of the earth offers less impediment, and electric bodies are harder: of all this later. These several bodies (electric) not only draw to themselves straws and chaff, but all metals, wood, leaves, stones, earths, even water and oil; in short, whatever things appeal to our senses or are solid: yet we are told that it attracts nothing but chaff and twigs. Hence Alexander Aphrodiseus incorrectly declares the question of amber to be unsolvable, because that amber does attract chaff, yet not the leaves of basil; but such stories are false, disgracefully inaccurate.

Now in order clearly to understand by experience how such attraction takes place, and what those substances may be that so attract other bodies (and in the case of many of these electrical substances, though the bodies influenced by them lean toward them, yet because of the feebleness of the attraction they are not drawn clean up to them, but are easily made to rise), make yourself a rotating-needle (electroscope—*versorium*) (See fig.), of any sort of metal, three or four fingers long, pretty light, and poised on a sharp point after the manner of a magnetic pointer. Bring near to one end of it a piece of amber or a gem, lightly rubbed, polished and shining: at once the instrument revolves. Several objects are seen to attract not only natural objects, but things artificially prepared, or manufactured, or formed by mixture. Nor is this a rare property possessed by one object or two (as is commonly supposed), but evidently belongs to a multitude of objects, both simple and compound, e.g., sealingwax and other unctuous mixtures. But why this inclination and what these forces,—on which points a few writers have given a very small amount of information, while the common run of philosophers give us nothing—these questions must be considered fully. . . .

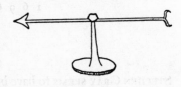

STEPHEN GRAY

1 6 9 6 · 1 7 3 6

STEPHEN GRAY SEEMS to have been a pensioner at the Charterhouse, an anciently endowed home for decayed gentlemen and a school for boys, in London. To him belongs the credit for discovering the conduction of electricity. Otto von Guericke [1] (1602-1686), famous scientist and mayor of Magdeburg, had earlier noted that a "sulphur globe, that had been previously excited by rubbing, could exercise its virtue through a linen thread an ell or more long," but had failed to recognize the significance of this great discovery. If Gray had known of von Guericke's electrical machine and his experiment, his own results might have been even more sensational.

The passage below, from the Philosophical Transactions for 1731, abridged, vol. VI. part II, shows the development of an idea as worked out by a tenacious experimenter. For a conductor Gray used linen thread, damp from the atmosphere. When the linen thread was suspended by short lengths of the same material hanging from nails, the "electric virtue" was dissipated; so he used silk thread, thinking that the virtue would escape less easily through slender supports. Later he found that the finest wire insulated as poorly as the damp linen, and correctly concluded that the failure was due to the material he was using rather than to its thickness. In the course of his experiments, he identified silk, horsehair and glass as insulators; and succeeded in electrifying metals, which Gilbert had erroneously classed as non-electrics.

[1] See above, p. 282.

EXPERIMENTS WITH
CONDUCTORS AND NON-CONDUCTORS

❧

HAVING OFTEN OBSERVED in the electrical experiments made with a glass tube and a down feather tied to the end of a small stick that after its fibers had been drawn towards the tube, when that had been withdrawn, most of them would be drawn to the stick, as if it had been an electric body, or as if there had been some electricity communicated to the stick or feather; this put me upon thinking, whether if a feather were drawn through my fingers, it might not produce the same effect, by acquiring some degree of electricity. This succeeded accordingly upon my first trial, the small downy fibers next the quill being drawn by my finger when held near it; and sometimes the upper part of the feather, with its stem, would be attracted also; but not always with the same success. I then proceeded to try whether hair might not have the same property, by taking one from my wig, and drawing it three or four times through my fingers, or rather between my thumb and forefinger, and soon found it would come to my finger at the distance of half an inch; and soon after I found that the fine hair of a dog's ear was strongly electrical; for upon taking the ear and drawing it through my fingers, great numbers of them would be attracted to my fingers at once. The next thing which I thought of was threads of silk of several colors, and of several finenesses, which I found to be all electrical, but sometimes I could not succeed, the reason of which I afterward found, as will appear in the sequel to this discourse.

Having succeeded so well in these, I proceeded to larger quantities of the same materials, as pieces of ribband both of coarse and fine silk of several colors, and found that by taking a piece of either of these of about half a yard long, and by holding the end in one hand, and drawing it through my other hand between my thumb and fingers, it would acquire an electricity, so that if the hand were held near the lower end of it, it would be attracted by it at the distance of five or six inches; but at some times the electricity would be much weaker than at others, the reason of which I conjectured to be that the ribband might have imbibed some aqueous particles from the moist air, which I found to be upon trial the occasion of it; for when I had well warmed the ribband by the fire, it never failed to be strongly electrical.

After this I made trial of several other bodies, as linen of several sorts, viz, Holland, muslin, etc. And woolen, as of several sorts of cloth and other stuffs of the same materials. From these I proceeded to paper, both white and brown, finding them, after they had been well heated before rubbing, to emit copiously their electric effluvia. The next body in which I found the same property, was thin shavings of wood; I have only as yet tried the fir shavings, which are strongly electrical. The three last substances which I found to have the same property are leather, parchment, and those thin guts wherein leaf-gold is beaten.

All these bodies will not only by their electricity be drawn to the hand, or any other solid body that is near them; but they will, as other electric bodies do, draw all small bodies to them, and that to the distance of sometimes eight or ten inches. Heating them by the fire before rubbing very much increases their force. There is another property in some of these bodies which is common to glass, that when they are rubbed in the dark there is a light follows the fingers through which they are drawn; this holds both in silk and linen, but is strongest in pieces of white pressing papers, which are much the same with card-paper; this not only yields a light as above, but when the fingers are held near it, there proceeds a light from them with a crackling noise, like that produced by a glass tube, though not at so great a distance from the fingers; to perform this, the paper before rubbing must be heated as hot as the fingers can well bear.

A down feather being tied to the end of a fine thread of raw silk and the other end to a small stick, which was fixed to a foot, that it might stand upright on the table; there was taken a piece of brown paper, which by the above-mentioned method was made to be strongly electrical, which being held near the feather, it came to the paper, and I carried it with the same till it came near the perpendicular of the stick; then lifting up my hand till the paper was got beyond the feather, the thread was extended and stood upright in the air, as if it had been a piece of wire, though the feather was distant from the paper near an inch. If the finger were held near the feather in this position, the greatest part of the fibers next the paper would be repelled, when at the same time if a finger were held to the fibers that were more remote from the paper, they would be drawn by it.

I then repeated this experiment without the feather, viz, by a single thread of silk only, of about five or six inches long, which was made to stand upright, as above-mentioned, without touching the paper; then placing my finger near the end, it would avoid or was repelled by it, but when I had placed my finger at about the same distance from a part of the thread that was about two inches from the end, it was then attracted by it.

An enumeration of the several bodies mentioned herein that are found to be electrical: 1. Feathers. 2. Hair. 3. Silk. 4. Linen. 5. Woolen. 6. Paper. 7. Leather. 8. Wood. 9. Parchment. 10. Ox-guts, wherein leaf-gold is beaten.

More Experiments Concerning Electricity, by Mr. Gray

In February, 1728-9, I repeated some of the experiments I had formerly made, in the first discovery of an electrical attraction in many bodies not before known to have that property. I made several attempts on the metals, to see whether they might not be made attractive by the same method as other bodies were, viz, by heating, rubbing, and hammering, but without any success. I then resolved to procure me a large flint-glass tube, to see if I could make any farther discovery with it, having called to mind a suspicion which some years ago I had, that as the tube communicated a light to bodies when it was rubbed in the dark, whether it might not at the same time communicate an electricity to them, though I never till now tried the experiment, not imagining the tube could have so great and wonderful an influence, as to cause them to attract with so much force, or that the attraction would be carried to such prodigious distances, as will be found in the sequel of this discourse.

Before I proceed to the experiments, it may be necessary to give a description of the tube. Its length is three feet five inches, and near one inch two tenths in diameter: I give the mean dimensions, the tube being larger at each end than in the middle, the bore about one inch. To each end I fitted a cork, to keep the dust out when the tube was not in use.

The first experiment I made was to see if I could find any difference in its attraction when the tube was stopped at both ends by the corks, or when left open, but could perceive no sensible difference; but upon holding a down feather over against the upper end of the tube, I found that it would go to the cork, being attracted and repelled by it, as by the tube when it had been excited by rubbing. I then held the feather over against the flat end of the cork, which attracted and repelled many times together; at which I was much surprised, and concluded that there was certainly an attractive virtue communicated to the cork by the excited tube.

I fixed an ivory ball of about one inch three tenths diameter, with a hole through it, upon a fir stick about four inches long, thrusting the other end into the cork, and upon rubbing the tube found that the ball attracted and repelled the feather with more vigor than the cork had done, repeating its attractions and repulsions for many times together. I then fixed the ball on longer sticks, first upon one of eight inches, and afterwards upon one of twenty-four inches long, and found the effect the same. Then I made use first of iron, and then of brass wire, to fix the ball on, inserting the other end of the wire in the cork as before, and found that the attraction was the same as when the fir sticks were made use of, and that when the feather was held over against any part of the wire, it was attracted by it; but though it was then nearer the tube, yet its attraction was not so strong as that of the ball. When the wire of two or three feet long was used, its vibrations caused by rubbing the tube, made it somewhat troublesome to be managed. This put me upon thinking whether if the ball was hung by a pack-thread and suspended by a loop on the tube, the electricity would not be carried down the line to the ball. I found it to succeed accordingly, for upon suspending the ball on the tube by a pack-thread about three feet long, when the tube had been excited by rubbing, the ivory ball attracted and repelled the leaf-brass, over which it was held, as freely as it had done when it was suspended on sticks or wire; as did also a ball of cork, and another of lead that weighed one pound and a quarter.

After I had found that the several bodies above-mentioned had an electricity communicated to them, I then went on to see upon what other bodies the tube would have the same effect, beginning with the metals, suspending them on the tube by the method above-mentioned, first in small pieces, as with a guinea, a shilling, a half-penny, a piece of block tin, a piece of lead; then with larger quantities of metal, suspending them on the tube by pack-thread. Here I made use of a fire-shovel, tongs, and iron poker, a copper teakettle, which succeeded the same, whether empty, or full of either cold or hot water, a silver pint pot; all of which were strongly electrical, attracting the leaf-brass to the height of several inches. After I had found that the metals were thus electrical, I went on to make trials on other bodies, as flintstone, sandstone, loadstone, bricks, tiles, chalk; and then on several vegetable substances, as well green as dry, and found that they had all of them an electric virtue communicated to them, either by being suspended on the tube by a line, or fixed on the end of it by the method above-mentioned.

I next proceeded to try at what greater distances the electric virtue might be carried, and having by me part of a hollow walking cane, which I suppose was part of a fishing rod, two feet seven inches long, I cut the great end of it, to fit it into the bore of the tube, into which it went about five inches; then when the cane was put into the end of the tube, and this excited, the cane drew the leaf-brass to the height of more than two inches, as did also the ivory ball, when by a cork and stick it had been fixed to the end of the cane. A solid cane had the same effect, when inserted in the tube after the same manner as the hollow one had been. I then took the two upper joints of a large fishing-rod, the one of Spanish cane, the other partly wood and the upper end whale-bone, which, together with the tube, made a length of more than fourteen feet. Upon the lesser end of the whale-bone was fixed a ball of cork of about an inch and a quarter diameter; then the great end of the rod being inserted in the tube, the leaf-brass laid on the table, and the tube excited, the ball attracted the leaf-brass to the height of about three inches by estimation. With several pieces of Spanish cane and fir-sticks I afterwards made a rod, which together with the tube, was somewhat more than eighteen feet long, which was the greatest length I could conveniently use in my chamber, and found the attraction very nearly, if not altogether, as strong, as when the ball was placed on shorter rods.

May 14, 1729, between six and seven o'clock in the evening. Having provided a rod of about twenty-four feet, that consisted of a fir pole, of cane, and the top of reed, upon the end of which the ball of cork was placed, and the great end of the rod put into the tube about seven or eight inches; then the leaf-brass being laid down, and the tube rubbed, the ball attracted and repelled the leaf-brass with vigor; so that it was not at all to be doubted but with a longer pole the electricity would have been carried much farther.

May the 16th, I made a rod thirty-two feet long, including the tube; the bigger part of it was a fir-staff about six feet and a half long, the rest was of cane, and reed for the top part of it. All things being prepared, as before, the effect was the same as in the last experiment, only the pole bending so much, and vibrating by rubbing the tube, made it more troublesome to manage the experiment. This put me upon making the following experiments.

May the 19th, about six in the morning, the ivory ball being suspended on the tube by a line of pack-thread twenty-six feet long, which was the height I stood at in the balcony from the court where he stood that held the board with the leaf-brass on it; then the tube being rubbed, attracted the leaf-brass to the height of near two inches, as he that assisted informed me. This was repeated with the cork ball with the same success.

May the 31st, in the morning, to a pole of eighteen feet there was tied a line of thirty-four feet in length; so that the pole and line together were fifty-two feet. With the pole and tube I stood in the balcony, the assistant below in the court, where he held the board with the leaf-brass on it; then the tube being excited as usual, the electric virtue passed from the tube up the pole, and down the line to the ivory ball, which attracted the leaf-brass, and as the ball passed over it in its vibrations, the leaf-brass would follow it, till it was carried off the board: but these experiments are difficult to make in the open air, the least wind that is stirring carrying away the leaf-brass.

Some time after I made several attempts to carry the electric virtue in a line horizontally, since I had not the opportunity here of carrying it from greater heights perpendicularly, but without success, for want of then making use of proper materials, as will appear from what follows. The first method I made trial of was by making a loop at each end of a line, and hanging it on a nail driven into a beam, the other end hanging downwards; through the loop at this end the line with the ivory ball was put; the other end of the line was by a loop hung on the tube, so that that part of the line next the ball hung perpendicular, the rest of the line horizontal; then the leaf-brass being laid under the ball, and the tube rubbed, not the least sign of attraction was perceived. Upon this I concluded that when the electric virtue came to the loop that was suspended on the beam, it went up the same to the beam; so that none, or very little of it at least, came down to the ball, which was afterward verified, as will appear by the experiments that will be mentioned hereafter.

June 30th, 1729, I went to Otterden Place to wait on Mr. Wheler, carrying with me a small solid glass cane of about eleven inches long and seven-eighths of an inch in diameter, designing only to give him a specimen of my experiments. The first was from the window in the long gallery that opened into the hall, the height about sixteen feet; the next from the battlements of the house down into the fore court, twenty-nine feet; then from the clock turret to the ground, which was thirty-four feet, this being the greatest height we could come at; and notwithstanding the smallness of the cane, the leaf-brass was attracted and repelled beyond what I expected. As we had no greater heights here, Mr. Wheler was desirous to try whether we could not carry the electric virtue horizontally. I then told him of the attempt I had made with that design, but without success, tell-ing him the method and materials made use of, as mentioned above. He then proposed a silk line to support the line, by which the electric virtue was to pass. I told him it might do better upon the account of its smallness; so that there would be less virtue carried from the line of communication, with which, together with the apt method Mr. Wheler contrived, and with the great pains he took himself, and the assistance of his servants, we succeeded far beyond our expecta-tion.

The first experiment was made in the matted gallery July 2, 1729, about ten in the morning. About four feet from the end of the gal-lery there was a cross line that was fixed by its ends to each side of the gallery by two nails; the middle part of the line was silk, the rest at each end was pack-thread; then the line to which the ivory ball was hung, and by which the electric virtue was to be conveyed to it from the tube, being eighty feet and a half in length, was laid on the cross silk line, so as the ball hung about nine feet below it. Then the other end of the line was by a loop suspended on the glass cane, and the leaf-brass held under the ball on a piece of white paper; when the tube being rubbed, the ball attracted the leaf-brass, and kept it suspended on it for some time.

This experiment succeeded so well, and the gallery not permitting us to go any farther in one length, Mr. Wheler thought of another expedient, by which we might increase the length of our line, which was by putting up another cross line near the other end of the gallery; and over the silk part of both the lines there was laid a line that was long enough to be returned to the other end, where the ball hung; and though now both ends of the line were at the same end of the gallery, yet care was taken that the tube was far enough off from having any influence upon the leaf-brass, except what passed by the line of communication; then the cane being rubbed and the leaf-brass held under the ivory ball, the electric virtue passed by the line of communication to the other end of the gallery, and returned back again to the ivory ball, which attracted the leaf-brass, and suspended it as before. The whole length of the line was 147 feet.

We then thought of trying whether the attraction would not be stronger without doubling or returning the line, which we found means of doing in the barn, where we had a line of 124 feet long, fourteen feet of which hung perpendicular from the silk line; and now the attraction was, as we then concluded, stronger than when the line was returned, as in the matted gallery.

July 3, between ten and eleven in the morning we went again into the barn, and repeated the last experiment with both the tube and the cane; but the attraction was not so strong as in the preceding evening, nor was there so great a difference in the attraction communicated by the solid cane and glass tube, as one would have expected, considering the difference of their lengths and diameters.

We then proceeded farther by adding so much more line as would make a return to the other end of the barn, the whole length of the line being now 293 feet; and though the line was so much lengthened, we found no perceivable difference in the attraction, the ball attracting as strongly as before. This encouraged us to add another return; but upon beginning to rub the tube, our silk lines broke, being not strong enough to bear the weight of the line, when shaken by the motion given it by rubbing the tube. Upon this, having brought with me both brass and iron wire, instead of the silk we put up small iron wire; but this was too weak to bear the weight of the line. We then took brass wire of a somewhat larger size than that of iron. This supported our line of communication; but though the tube was well rubbed, yet there was not the least motion or attraction given by the ball, neither with the great tube, which we made use of when we found the small solid cane to be ineffectual; by which we were now convinced that the success we had before depended upon the lines that supported the line of communication being silk, and not upon their being small, as before trial I imagined it might be; the same effect happening here as it did when the line that is to convey the electric virtue is supported by pack-thread; viz, that when the effluvia comes to the wire or pack-thread that supports the line, it passes by them to the timber, to which each end of them is fixed, and so goes no farther forward in the line that is to carry it to the ivory ball. . . .

CHARLES FRANCIS
DE CISTERNAY DU FAY

1 6 9 8 · 1 7 3 9

RUBBING GLASS tubes was a tiresome business; many types of friction machines were accordingly devised by lazy experimenters to simplify the work of producing electricity. The first of these utilized a globe of sulphur, constructed by pouring melted sulphur into a glass globe and then breaking the glass. Otto von Guericke, who made this device, did not know that the empty glass globe would have done just as well.

While experimenting with the sulphur globe, Du Fay, Director of the Dyeing Industry of France, not only verified Gray's findings, but noticed that there were two sorts of electrical charges. He correctly said: "Electricity is a quality universally expanded in all the matter we know, and which influences the mechanism of the universe more than we think," but his "two-fluid" theory dropped from favor when Franklin, in 1747, observed that electrical phenomena could be explained in terms of a single fluid, the absence of which would leave a body negatively charged.[1] The extract below is taken from the Philosophical Transactions of 1734.

[1] See below, p. 314.

THE TWO-FLUID THEORY

OF ELECTRICITY

ON MAKING THE experiment related by Otho de Guerik, in his Collection of experiments *de Spatio Vacuo*, which consists in making a ball of sulphur render'd electrical, to repel a down-feather, I perceived that the same effects were produced not only by the tube, but by all electrick bodies whatsoever; and I discovered a very simple principle, which accounts for a great part of the irregularities, and if I may use the term, of the caprices that seem to accompany most of the experiments on electricity. This principle is, that electrick bodies attract all those that are not so, and repel them as soon as they are become electrick, by the vicinity or contact of the electrick body. Thus leaf-gold is first attracted by the tube; and acquires an electricity by approaching it; and of consequence is immediately repell'd by it. Nor is it re-attracted, while it retains its electrick quality. But if, while it is thus sustain'd in the air, it chance to light on some other body, it straightways loses its electricity; and consequently is re-attracted by the tube, which, after having given it a new electricity, repels it a second time; which continues as long as the tube keeps its electricity.

Upon applying this principle to the various experiments of electricity, one will be surprised at the number of obscure and puzzling facts it clears up. For Mr. Hauksbee's famous experiments of the glass globe, in which silk threads are put, is a necessary consequence of it. When these threads are ranged in form of rays by the electricity of the sides of the globe, if the finger be put near the outside of the globe, the threads within fly from it, as is well known; which happens only because the finger, or any cther body applied near the glass globe, is thereby rendered electrical, and consequently repels the silk threads, which are endowed with the like quality. With a little reflection one may in the same manner account for most of the other phenomena, and which seem inexplicable, without attending to this principle.

Chance has thrown in my way another principle, more universal and remarkable than the preceding one, and which casts a new light on the subject of electricity. This principle is, that there are two distinct electricities, very different from one another; one of which I call *vitreous electricity*, and the other *resinous electricity*. The first is that of glass, rock-crystal, precious stones, hair of animals, wool, and many other bodies; the second is that of amber, copal, gum-lack, silk, thread, paper, and a vast number of other substances. The characteristick of these two electricities is, that a body of the *vitreous electricity*, for example, repels all such as are of the same electricity; and on the contrary, attracts all those of the *resinous electricity*; so that the tube, made electrical, will repel glass, crystal, hair of animals, etc., when render'd electrick and will attract silk, thread, paper, etc., though render'd electrical likewise. Amber on the contrary will attract electrick glass, and other substances of the same class, and will repel gum-lac, copal, silk, thread, etc. Two silk ribbons rendered electrical, will repel each other; two woolen threads will do the like; but a woolen thread and a silk thread will mutually attract one another. This principle very naturally explains why the ends of threads, of silk, or wool, recede from one another in form of a pencil or broom, when they have acquired an electrick quality. From this principle one may with the same ease deduce the explanation of a great number of other phenomena. And it is probable, that this truth will lead us to the further discovery of many other things.

In order to know immediately, to which of the two classes of electricity belongs any body whatsoever, one need only render electrical a silk thread, which is known to be of the *resinous electricity*, and see whether that body, rendered electrical, attracts or repels it. If it attracts, it is certainly of that kind of electricity which I call *vitreous;* if on the contrary it repels, it is of the same kind of electricity with the silk, that is, of the *resinous.* I have likewise observed that communicated electricity retains the same properties: for if a ball of ivory, or wood, be set on a glass stand, and this ball be rendered electrick by the tube, it will repel all such substances as the tube repels; but if it be rendered electrick by applying a cylinder of gum-lac near it, it will produce quite contrary effects, viz., precisely the same as gum-lac would produce. In order to succeed in these experiments, it is requisite that the two bodies, which are put near one another, to find out the nature of their electricity, be rendered as electrical as possible; for if one of them was not at all, or but weakly electrical, it would be attracted by the other, though it be of that sort, that should naturally be repelled by it. But the experiment will always succeed perfectly well, if both the bodies are sufficiently electrical.

ABBÉ JEAN ANTOINE NOLLET

1 7 0 0 · 1 7 7 0

TAKING ELECTRICAL shocks from friction machines became a pastime, as did charging with electricity almost anything movable. But with the invention, in 1745, of the Leyden jar, a form of electrical condenser, the sport became a bit rough. With the idea perhaps of storing electricity in a jar, Ewald von Kleist, dean of the cathedral of Kammin, Pomerania, had driven a nail through a cork in a jar, and then held the nail to an electrical machine. When he touched the nail, he received a stunning shock. The shock occurred however only when he held the jar in one hand, while touching the nail with the other. A little later, Pieter van Musschenbroek (1692-1761), professor of mathematics at the University of Leyden, made a similar instrument out of a very thin glass bowl, which "condensed" so much electricity that he was two days getting over the effects of the shock and the fright.

It was soon recognized that the essential characteristics of a condenser were two conductors, separated by a narrow space. In the early forms, the nail or water inside the jar and the hand outside, formed the conductors, while the jar was a method of keeping them apart. Benjamin Franklin later used a pane of glass coated on both sides with tinfoil.

The reporter of van Musschenbroek's experiments to the French Academy of Sciences was the Abbé Nollet, professor of physics first at the University of Turin and later at Paris. He also attempted in several essays to defend Du Fay's theory of two electric fluids against Franklin. The following extract from the Memoires de l'Académie Royale des Sciences, Paris, 1746, is taken from A Source Book in Physics, by William Francis Magie (McGraw-Hill Book Co., New York, 1935).

INVENTION OF THE CONDENSER

IN THE MONTH of January of the present year M. de Réaumur showed me a letter from M. Musschenbroek, Professor of Philosophy and Mathematics in the University of Leyden: among several matters which this letter contained there was one which particularly attracted the attention of the Academy. I give here its content translated from the Latin. "I am going to tell you about a new but terrible experiment which I advise you not to try yourself. . . . I was making some investigations on the force of electricity (this is the account of M. Musschenbroek); for this purpose I had suspended by two threads of blue silk a gun-barrel AB (Fig. 80) which received by communication the electricity of a glass globe which was turned rapidly on its axis while it was rubbed by the hands placed against it; at the other end B there hung freely a brass wire, the end of which passed into a round glass flask D, partly filled with water, which I held in my right hand F, and with the other hand E, I tried to draw sparks from the electrified gun-barrel: all at once my right hand F was struck so violently that all my body was affected as if it had been struck by lightning; the flask, although made of thin glass, ordinarily does not break, and the hand is not displaced by this disturbance; but the arm and all the body are affected in a terrible way that I cannot describe: in a word I thought that it was all up with me. But it is very remarkable (adds the author of the letter) that when the experiment is tried with an English glass there is no effect or almost none; the glass must be German, it does not even do to have it from Holland; it is all the same whether it is rounded in the form of a sphere or of any other figure: we may use an ordinary goblet, large or small, thick or thin, deep or not; but what is absolutely necessary is that it be made of

German or Bohemian glass; the one which I thought had killed me was made of a white thin glass and five inches in diameter. The person who tries the experiment may simply stand on the floor, but it is important that the same man holds the flask D in one hand and tries to draw the spark with the other; the effect is very slight

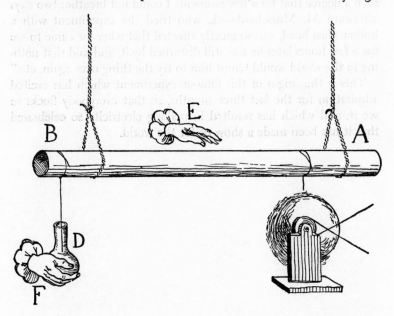

if these actions are performed by two different persons: if the flask D is placed on a metal support standing on a wooden table, then the one who touches this metal even with the end of his finger and draws the spark with his other hand receives a great shock, etc."

Some days after I had read this letter, a letter reached me from M. Allaman, who also lives in Leyden, and who has devoted himself for a long time to experimental physics; he reports the following on the subject of electricity.

"You have learned by a letter from M. Musschenbroek to M. de

Réaumur of a new experiment which we have made here which is very remarkable. It is as follows." (He then describes the procedure as it has been reported, and adds) "You will receive a prodigious shock which will affect all your arm and even all your body; it is a stroke of lightning; the first time that I received it I was affected to such a degree that for a few moments I could not breathe: two days afterward M. Musschenbroek, who tried the experiment with a hollow glass bowl, was so greatly affected that when he came to see me a few hours later he was still disturbed by it, and said that nothing in the world would tempt him to try the thing over again, etc."

This is the origin of this famous experiment which has excited admiration for the last three months, so that everybody flocks to see it, and which has resulted in making electricity so celebrated that it has been made a show of for the world.

BENJAMIN FRANKLIN[1]

1 7 0 6 · 1 7 9 0

FRANKLIN'S INTEREST in electricity dated from 1746, when in Boston he saw a certain Dr. Spence, from Scotland, perform several electrical experiments. The next year, as he relates in the letter quoted below, he formulated a "one-fluid" theory of electricity, describing its aspects as "positive" and "negative." In 1748, at the age of forty-two, he sold his Almanack, his newspaper, and his printing house, and retired from business, planning to devote all his time to electrical experimentation, with the idea particularly of discovering how to prevent damage from lightning.

One of Franklin's notebooks contains the following entry: "November 7, 1749. Electrical fluid agrees with lightning in these particulars. 1. Giving light. 2. Colour of the light. 3. Crooked direction. 4. Swift motion. 5. Being conducted by metals. 6. Crack or noise in exploding. 7. Subsisting in water or ice. 8. Rending bodies it passes through. 9. Destroying animals. 10. Melting metals. 11. Firing inflammable substances. 12. Sulphureous smell. The electric fluid is attracted by points. We do not know whether this property is in lightning. But since they agree in all particulars wherein we can already compare them, is it not probable they agree likewise in this? Let the experiment be made!"

The famous kite experiment, described in the second letter below, was devised as the final test to prove that lightning was the same as man-made electricity. He brought it down from the clouds, charged a Leyden jar with it, tested it in every known way and found it was the same. The letters are quoted from Franklin's Experiments and Observations on Electricity.

[1] For other work of Franklin, see above, p. 162 and below, p. 360.

THE ONE-FLUID THEORY

OF ELECTRICITY

❦

PETER COLLINSON, ESQ.; F. R. S. LONDON

July 11, 1747.

SIR,

In my last I informed you that, in pursuing our electrical en-quiries, we had observed some particular phenomena, which we looked upon to be new, and of which I promised to give you some account, though I apprehended they might not possibly be new to you, as so many hands are daily employed in electrical experiments on your side the water, some or other of which would probably hit on the same observations.

The first is the wonderful effect of pointed bodies, both in *draw-ing off* and *throwing off* the electrical fire. For example,

Place an iron shot of three or four inches diameter on the mouth of a clean dry glass bottle. By a fine silken thread from the ceiling, right over the mouth of the bottle, suspend a small cork-ball, about the bigness of a marble; the thread of such a length as that the cork-ball may rest against the side of the shot. Electrify the shot, and the ball will be repelled to the distance of four or five inches, more or less, according to the quantity of Electricity.—When in this state, if you present to the shot the point of a long, slender, sharp bodkin, at six or eight inches distance, the repellency is instantly destroyed, and the cork flies to the shot. A blunt body must be brought within an inch, and draw a spark to produce the same effect. To prove that the electrical fire is *drawn off* by the point, if you take the blade of the bodkin out of the wooden handle, and fix it in a stick of sealing-

314

wax, and then present it at the distance aforesaid, or if you bring it very near, no such effect follows; but sliding one finger along the wax till you touch the blade, and the ball flies to the shot immediately.—If you present the point in the dark, you will see, sometimes at a foot distance and more, a light gather upon it, like that of a fire-fly, or glow-worm; the less sharp the point, the nearer you must bring it to observe the light; and at whatever distance you see the light, you may draw off the electrical fire, and destroy the repellency. —If a cork-ball so suspended be repelled by the tube, and a point be presented quick to it, though at a considerable distance, 'tis surprising to see how suddenly it flies back to the tube. Points of wood will do near as well as those of iron, provided the wood is not dry; for perfectly dry wood will no more conduct electricity than sealing-wax.

To shew that points will *throw off* as well as *draw off* the electrical fire; lay a long sharp needle upon the shot, and you cannot electrise the shot so as to make it repel the cork-ball.—Or fix a needle to the end of a suspended gun-barrel, or iron-rod, so as to point beyond it like a little bayonet; and while it remains there, the gun-barrel, or rod, cannot by applying the tube to the other end be electrised so as to give a spark, the fire continually running out silently at the point. In the dark you may see it make the same appearance as it does in the case before-mentioned.

The repellency between the cork-ball and the shot is likewise destroyed. 1. By sifting fine sand on it; this does it gradually. 2. By breathing on it. 3. By making a smoke about it from burning wood.[1] 4. By candle-light, even though the candle is at a foot distance; these do it suddenly.—The light of a bright coal from a wood fire; and the light of a red-hot iron do it likewise; but not at so great a distance.

[1] We suppose every particle of sand, or smoke, being first attracted and then repelled, carries off with it a portion of the electrical fire; but that the same subsists in those particles till they communicate it to something else; and that it is never really destroyed . . . so when water is thrown on a common fire, we do not imagine the element is thereby destroyed or annihilated, but only dispersed, each particle of water carrying off in vapor its portion of the fire, which it had attracted and attached to itself. [Franklin's note to the first edition.]

Smoke from dry rosin dropt on hot iron, does not destroy the repellency; but is attracted by both shot and cork-ball, forming proportionable atmospheres round them, making them look beautifully, somewhat like some of the figures in Burnet's or Whiston's Theory of the Earth.

N.B. This experiment should be made in a closet, where the air is very still, or it will be apt to fail.

The light of the sun thrown strongly on both cork and shot by a looking-glass for a long time together, does not impair the repellency in the least. This difference between fire-light and sun-light is another thing that seems new and extraordinary to us.

We had for some time been of opinion, that the electrical fire was not created by friction, but collected, being really an element diffused among, and attracted by other matter, particularly by water and metals. We had even discovered and demonstrated its afflux to the electrical sphere, as well as its efflux, by means of little light windmill wheels made of stiff paper vanes, fixed obliquely, and turning freely on fine wire axes. Also by little wheels of the same matter, but formed like water-wheels. Of the disposition and application of which wheels, and the various phenomena resulting, I could, if I had time, fill you a sheet. The impossibility of electrising one's self (though standing on wax) by rubbing the tube, and drawing the fire from it; and the manner of doing it, by passing the tube near a person or thing standing on the floor, &c. had also occurred to us some months before Mr. Watson's ingenious Sequel came to hand, and these were some of the new things I intended to have communicated to you.—But now I need only mention some particulars not hinted in that piece, with our reasonings thereupon; though perhaps the latter might well enough be spared.

1. A person standing on wax, and rubbing the tube, and another person on wax drawing the fire, they will both of them (provided they do not stand so as to touch one another) appear to be electrised, to a person standing on the floor; that is, he will perceive a spark on approaching each of them with his knuckle.

2. But if the persons on wax touch one another during the exciting of the tube, neither of them will appear to be electrised.

3. If they touch one another after exciting the tube, and drawing the fire as aforesaid, there will be a stronger spark between them than was between either of them and the person on the floor.

4. After such strong spark, neither of them discover any electricity.

These appearances we attempt to account for thus: We suppose, as aforesaid, that electrical fire is a common element, of which every one of the three persons abovementioned has his equal share, before any operation is begun with the tube. A, who stands on wax and rubs the tube, collects the electrical fire from himself into the glass; and his communication with the common stock being cut off by the wax, his body is not again immediately supply'd. B, (who stands on wax likewise) passing his knuckle along near the tube, receives the fire which was collected by the glass from A; and his communication with the common stock being likewise cut off, he retains the additional quantity received.—To C, standing on the floor, both appear to be electrised, for he having only the middle quantity of electrical fire, receives a spark upon approaching B, who has an over quantity; but gives one to A, who has an under quantity. If A and B approach to touch each other, the spark is stronger, because the difference between them is greater: After such touch there is no spark between either of them and C, because the electrical fire in all is reduced to the original equality. If they touch while electrising, the equality is never destroy'd, the fire only circulating.

Hence have arisen some new terms among us; we say B, (and bodies like circumstanced) is electrised *positively*; A, *negatively*. Or rather, B, is electrised *plus*; A, *minus*. And we daily in our experiments electrise bodies *plus* or *minus*, as we think proper.—To electrise *plus* or *minus*, no more needs to be known than this, that the parts of the tube or sphere that are rubbed, do, in the instant of the friction, attract the electrical fire, and therefore take it from the thing rubbing; the same parts immediately, as the friction upon them ceases, are disposed to give the fire they have received, to any body that has less. Thus you may circumlate it, as Mr. Watson has shewn; you may also accumulate or subtract it, upon, or from any body, as you connect that body with the rubber or with the receiver, the communication with the common stock being cut off. We think that ingenious gentleman was deceived when he imagined (in his Sequel) that the electrical fire came down the wire from the ceiling to the gun barrel, thence to the sphere, and so electrised the machine and the man turning the wheel, &c. We suppose it was *driven off*, and not brought on through that wire; and that the machine and man, &c. were electrised *minus*; i.e., had less electrical fire in them than things in common.

As the vessel is just upon sailing, I cannot give you so large an account of American Electricity as I intended: I shall only mention a few particulars more.—We find granulated lead better to fill the phial with than water, being easily warmed, and keeping warm and dry in damp air.—We fire spirits with the wire of the phial.—We light candles, just blown out, by drawing a spark among the smoke between the wire and snuffers.—We represent lightning, by passing the wire in the dark, over a china plate that has gilt flowers, or applying it to gilt frames of looking-glasses, &c.—

We electrise a person twenty or more times running, with a touch of the finger on the wire, thus: He stands on wax. Give him the electrised bottle in his hand. Touch the wire with your finger, and then touch his hand or face; there are sparks every time.—We encrease the force of the electrical kiss vastly, thus: Let A and B stand on wax; or A on wax, and B on the floor; give one of them the electrised phial in hand; let the other take hold of the wire; there will be a small spark; but when their lips approach, they will be struck and shock'd. The same if another gentleman and lady, C and D, standing also on wax, and joining hands with A and B, salute or shake hands.

We suspend bv fine silk thread a counterfeit spider, made of a small piece of burnt cork, with legs of linen thread, and a grain or two of lead stuck in him, to give him more weight. Upon the table, over which he hangs, we stick a wire upright, as high as the phial and wire, four or five inches from the spider: then we animate him, by setting the electrified phial at the same distance on the other side of him; he will immediately fly to the wire of the phial, bend his legs in touching it; then spring off, and fly to the wire in the table: thence again to the wire of the phial, playing with his legs against both, in a very entertaining manner, appearing perfectly alive to persons unacquainted. He will continue this motion an hour or more in dry weather.—

We electrify, upon wax in the dark, a book that has a double line of gold round upon the covers, and then apply a knuckle to the gilding; the fire appears every where upon the gold like a flash of lightning: not upon the leather, nor if you touch the leather instead of the gold.

We rub our tubes with buckskin, and observe always to keep the same side to the tube, and never to sully the tube by handling; thus they work readily and easily, without the least fatigue, especially if kept in tight pasteboard cases, lined with flannel, and fitting close to the tube.[2] This I mention, because, the European papers on Electricity frequently speak of rubbing the tube as a fatiguing exercise. Our spheres are fixed on iron axes, which pass through them. At one end of the axis there is a small handle, with which you turn the sphere like a common grindstone. This we find very commodious, as the machine takes up but little room, is portable, and may be enclosed in a tight box, when not in use. 'Tis true, the sphere does not turn so swift as when the great wheel is used: but swiftness we think of little importance, since a few turns will change the phial, &c. sufficiently.

I am, &c.

B. FRANKLIN

[2] Our tubes are made here of green glass, 27 or 30 inches long, as big as can be grasped. Electricity is so much in vogue that above one hundred of them have been sold within these four months past. [Note to first edition.]

THE KITE EXPERIMENT

PETER COLLINSON, ESQ; F. R. S. LONDON.

Oct. 19, 1752.

Sɪʀ:

As frequent mention is made in public papers from Europe of the success of the Philadelphia experiment for drawing the electric fire from clouds by means of pointed rods of iron erected on high buildings, etc., it may be agreeable to the curious to be informed that the same experiment has succeeded in Philadelphia, though made in a different and more easy manner, which is as follows:

Make a small cross of two light strips of cedar, the arms so long as to reach the four corners of a large thin silk handkerchief when extended; tie the corners of the handkerchief to the extremities of the cross, so you have the body of a kite; which being properly accommodated with a tail, loop, and string, will rise in the air, like those made of paper; but this being of silk is fitter to bear the wet and wind of a thunder gust without tearing. To the top of the upright stick of the cross is to be fixed a very sharp pointed wire, rising a foot or more above the wood. To the end of the twine, next the hand, is to be tied a silk ribbon, and where the silk and twine join, a key may be fastened. This kite is to be raised when a thundergust appears to be coming on, and the person who holds the string must stand within a door or window, or under some cover, so that the silk ribbon may not be wet; and care must be taken that the twine does not touch the frame of the door or window. As soon as any of the thunder clouds come over the kite, the pointed wire will draw the electric fire from them, and the kite, with all the twine, will be electrified, and the loose filaments of the twine will stand out every way, and be attracted by an approaching finger. And when the rain has wet the kite and twine, so that it can conduct the electric fire freely, you will find it stream out plentifully from the key on the approach of your knuckle. At this key the phial may be charged; and from electric fire thus obtained, spirits may be kindled, and all the other electric experiments be performed, which are usually done by the help of a rubbed glass globe or tube, and thereby the sameness of the electric matter with that of lightning completely demonstrated.

B. FRANKLIN

LUIGI GALVANI

1 7 3 7 · 1 7 9 8

THE EXPERIMENTS OF Galvani, lecturer in anatomy at Bologna, furnished valuable data to the investigators who followed him. Although he was primarily a physiologist, there was an electric machine in his laboratory, which when in operation occasionally caused the legs of the frogs on which he was experimenting to twitch. This was not a new phenomenon; it had been noticed a hundred years earlier. But he became interested in the fact that the contractions occurred particularly when a metal instrument touched the nerves of the frog, while a spark was being drawn. During the investigation of this reaction, Galvani came on an entirely new fact; that muscle contraction could be caused if the frog was laid on a plate made of conducting material, and an instrument of another metal connected one of its nerves with the plate.

Galvani erroneously concluded that the cause of the electricity was in the animal itself; that "one of these electricities, to wit, the condensed or positive, is seated in the nerves, and the other in the muscles." He fought a losing battle trying to defend this theory, and died bitter and unreconciled to the correct explanation. Galvani's original paper was published in De Bononiensi Scientiarum et Artium Instituto atque Academia Commentarii (Commentaries on the Institute and Academy of Sciences and Arts at Bologna), Vol. 7, 1791, and is here taken from A Source Book in Physics, by William Francis Magie (McGraw-Hill Book Co., New York, 1935).

THE DISCOVERY OF
CURRENT ELECTRICITY

. . . The discovery was made in this way. I had dissected and prepared a frog as represented on the next page and while I was attending to something else, I laid it on a table on which stood an electrical machine at some distance from its conductor and separated from it by a considerable space. Now when one of the persons who were present touched accidentally and lightly the inner crural nerves *DD* of the frog with the point of a scalpel all the muscles of the legs seemed to contract again and again as if they were affected by powerful cramps. Another one who was there, who was helping us in electrical researches, thought that he had noticed that the action was excited when a spark was discharged from the conductor of the machine. Being astonished by this new phenomenon he called my attention to it, who at that time had something else in mind and was deep in thought. Whereupon I was inflamed with an incredible zeal and eagerness to test the same and to bring to light what was concealed in it. I therefore myself touched one or the other nerve with the point of the knife and at the same time one of those present drew a spark. The phenomenon was always the same. Without fail there occurred lively contractions in every muscle of the leg at the same instant as that in which the spark jumped, as if the prepared animal was affected by tetanus.

With the thought that these motions might arise from the contact with the point of the knife, which perhaps caused the excited condition, rather than by the spark, I touched the same nerves again in the same way in other frogs with the point of the knife, and indeed with greater pressure, yet so that no one during this time drew off a spark. Now no motions could be detected. I therefore came to the conclusion that perhaps to excite the phenomenon there were needed both the contact of a body and the electric spark.

Therefore I again pressed the blade of the knife on the nerve and kept it there at rest while the spark passed and while the machine

The apparatus used by Galvani, showing the static electric machine and the frog's legs. Notice the small hands which suggest the actual experiments. (From Commentaries on the Institute and Academy of Sciences and Arts at Bologna, 1791.)

was not in motion. The phenomenon only occurred while the sparks were passing.

We repeated the experiment, always using the same knife. But it was remarkable that when the spark passed the motions observed sometimes occurred and sometimes not.

Excited by the novelty of the phenomenon, we undertook to investigate the thing in one way and another and to follow it up experimentally, while still using one and the same scalpel, so that if possible we might discover the causes of this unexpected difference. And this new effort was not without results. We discovered that the whole phenomenon was to be ascribed to the different parts of the scalpel by which it was held by the fingers. The scalpel had a bone handle, and if this handle was held in the hand no contractions occurred when the spark passed; but they did occur if the finger rested on the metallic blade or on the iron rivet by which the blade was held in the handle.

Now since fairly dry bones have an electric nature but the metal blade and the iron rivet have a conducting or so called non-electric nature, we were led to assume that conditions were such that if we held the bone handle in the fingers the electric fluid which in some way or other was active in the frog would be kept from entering, but that it could enter if we touched the blade or the rivet which was connected with it.

Now to put the thing beyond all doubt we used instead of the scalpel sometimes a slender glass rod which had been wiped clean from dampness and dust, and sometimes an iron rod. With the glass rod we not only touched the nerves of the leg but rubbed them hard while the sparks were passing. But in vain; in spite of all our trouble the phenomenon never appeared, even when a number of powerful sparks were drawn from the conductor of the machine at a small distance from the animal. The phenomenon occurred however if we even lightly touched the same nerve with the iron rod and only little sparks passed.

The Force of Animal Electricity in Muscular Motion

After we had investigated the forces of atmospheric electricity during thunder storms our hearts burned with desire to investigate also the force of electricity in quiet times during the day.

Therefore, as I had casually noticed that the prepared frogs, which were hung by a brass hook passing through the spinal cord to the iron grating which enclosed a hanging garden of our house, showed the usual contractions not only when there was lightning but also when the sky was clear and fair, I thought that the origin of these contractions might be found in the changes which nevertheless were going on in the atmospheric electricity. Therefore I began, not without hope, carefully to investigate the action of these changes in the muscular motion and to set up experiments in one way and another. Thus I observed at different hours and indeed for days at a time suitably arranged animals, but scarcely ever did a motion of the muscles occur. Finally, tired of this useless waiting, I began to squeeze and press the hooks which were fastened in the spinal cord against the iron grating, in order to see whether such an artifice might excite the contraction of the muscles and whether instead of its depending on the condition of the atmosphere and its electricity any other change and alteration might have an influence. I quite often observed contractions, but none which depended upon the different conditions of the atmosphere and its electricity.

As I had observed these contractions only in the open air and as hitherto no researches had been undertaken in other places, there seemed to be little lacking to my argument and I might have referred such contractions to the atmospheric electricity which enters the animal and accumulates there and suddenly leaves it when the hook is brought in contact with the iron grating. So easy is it to deceive oneself in experimenting, and to think that we have seen and found that which we wish to see and find.

But when I transferred the animal to a closed room, had laid it on an iron plate, and began to press the hook which was in the spinal cord against the plate, behold, the same contractions, the same motions! I repeated the experiment by using other metals at other places and on other hours and days; with the same result, only that the contractions were different when different metals were used, being more lively for some and more sluggish for the others. At last it occurred to us to use other bodies which conduct electricity only a little or not at all, made of glass, rubber, resin, stone or wood and always dried, and with these nothing similar occurred, no muscular contractions and motions could be seen. Naturally such a result excited in us no slight astonishment and caused us to think that possibly the electricity was present in the animal itself. We were confirmed in this view by the assumption of a very fine nervous fluid which during the occurrence of the phenomenon flows from the nerves to the muscle like the electric current in the Leyden jar. . . .

To make the thing plainer I had with the greatest success laid the frog on a nonconducting plate, as on glass or on resin, and then using a curved rod, sometimes conducting and sometimes either altogether or partly non-conducting, I touched with one end of it the hook which entered the spinal cord and with the other end the muscles of the leg or the feet. In this experiment, when we used the conducting rod, we saw the contractions occur, but when we used the rod which was non-conducting, there were no contractions. The conducting rod was an iron wire, the hook was a brass wire. After these last discoveries it appeared to us that the contractions which, as has been said, occur in a frog laid on a metallic plate if the hook in the spinal cord is pressed against the plate, must come from a similar circuit in place of which, in a way, the metallic plate acts, and therefore it happens that the contractions will not occur in frogs which are laid on a non-conducting plate even when the same procedure is employed.

This opinion of ours has clearly explained a not unwelcome and accidentally observed phenomenon, if my judgment is correct. If the frog is held up in the fingers by one leg so that the hook that is fastened in the spinal cord touches a silver plate and the other free leg can come in contact with the plate, then if this leg touches the plate the muscles are repeatedly contracted, so that the leg is lifted, but soon, when it becomes quiet and falls down to the plate again, it again comes in contact with it and therefore is lifted again and in short it so proceeds to rise and fall that in a certain sense it seems like an electrical pendulum, to the greatest astonishment and delight of the observer. . . .

Before we end our discussion of the use of the curved rod and its forces we should not neglect to make clear its significance and, if I may say so, its necessity for such muscular contractions. These occur more clearly and more quickly not only with one but with two curved rods, if they are so applied and arranged that the end of one of them touches the muscle and at the end of the other the nerves in a similar way, and the two other ends are brought in contact with each other or if necessary are rubbed together. In this connection it is noticeable that the electricity which causes the contractions is not conducted away and dissipated by the contact of the hands with the two rods or by the repeated contacts of the rods with the parts of the animal's body. Furthermore we were fortunate enough to observe this peculiar and remarkable phenomenon, that the use of more than one metallic substance and the differences between them contribute much to the excitation, as also especially to the increase of the muscular contraction, far more indeed than when one and the same metal is used. Thus for example, if the whole rod was iron or the hook was iron and the conducting plate also, the contractions either did not occur or were very small. But if one of them was iron and the other brass, or better if it was silver (silver seems to us the best of all the metals for conducting animal electricity) there occur repeated and much greater and more prolonged contractions. The same thing occurs with one and the same arrangement of the non-conducting plate. If strips of different metals are laid in the same way on two points separate from each other, as for example, if you put a zinc strip at one place and a brass strip at the other, the contractions are usually much greater than when metal strips of the same sort are used, even when both places are brought in contact with silver. . . .

ALESSANDRO VOLTA

1 7 4 5 · 1 8 2 7

GALVANI'S GREAT experiment was immediately repeated by other scientists. Late in 1792 Dr. Alexander Monro (1733-1817), a Fellow of the Royal Society, known for his experiments in anatomical injections, heard through Dr. Black of Galvani's work. After a series of ten more experiments with dissected frogs on metal plates, he came to the conclusion that "there is no foundation for the opinion of Galvani and Galli that the nerve is electrified plus and the muscle minus, or that the electricity of one is positive and that of the other negative. We seem therefore to be led to the conclusion that the matter or fluid which is excited or put in motion by the application of the different metals to each other serves merely as a powerful stimulus to that energy or fluid which is lodged in the nerves."

It was left, however, for Alessandro Volta to make an apparatus for the production of electricity by simply putting dissimilar metals together. Volta, a native of Como in Italy, was professor of physics at the Universities of Como and Pavia. He first repeated Galvani's experiments. He then put tinfoil on the tip of his own tongue, and a silver coin beneath it; when the two were connected he noticed a strong sour taste. In a succession of similar experiments, he found that the further apart the two metals he used together stood in the following series—zinc, tin, lead, iron, copper, platinum, gold, silver, graphite, and charcoal—the stronger the electrical effect. He came to the conclusion that pairs of metals were "in a real sense the exciters of electricity, while the nerves themselves are passive."

The Voltaic pile and the crown of cups described below were in no sense, then, accidental discoveries, but part of a long development.

Volta also worked out a very sensitive straw electrometer, which won him the fellowship and Copley Medal of the Royal Society. His letter to Sir Joseph Banks, president of the Society, which we reproduce below, appeared in French in the Philosophical Transactions for 1800. The translation is by William Francis Magie, in A Source Book in Physics (McGraw-Hill Book Co., 1935).

THE FIRST ELECTRIC BATTERY

AFTER A LONG silence, which I do not attempt to excuse, I have
the pleasure of communicating to you, Sir, and through you to
the Royal Society, some striking results to which I have come in
carrying out my experiments on electricity excited by the simple
mutual contact of metals of different sorts, and even by the contact
of other conductors, also different among themselves, whether
liquids or containing some liquid, to which property they owe their
conducting power. The most important of these results, which includes practically all the others, is the construction of an apparatus
which, in the effects which it produces, that is, in the disturbances
which it produces in the arms etc., resembles Leyden jars, or better
still electric batteries feebly charged,[1] which act unceasingly or so
that their charge after each discharge reestablishes itself; which in
a word provides an unlimited charge or imposes perpetual action
or impulsion on the electric fluid; but which otherwise is essentially different from these, both because of this continued action
which is its property and because, instead of being made, as are
the ordinary jars and electric batteries, of one or more insulating
plates in thin layers of those bodies which are thought to be the
only electric bodies, coated with conductors or bodies called non-
electrics, this new apparatus is formed altogether of several of
these latter bodies, chosen even among the best conductors and
therefore the most remote, according to what has always been
believed, from the electric nature. Yes! the apparatus of which I

---

[1] Volta here refers to groups of condensers. These are commonly **discharged**
instantaneously, sometimes with a spark.

speak, and which will doubtless astonish you, is only an assemblage of a number of good conductors of different sorts arranged in a certain way. 30, 40, 60, pieces or more of copper, or better of silver, each in contact with a piece of tin, or what is much better, of zinc and an equal number of layers of water or some other liquid which is a better conductor than pure water, such as salt-water or lye and so forth, or pieces of cardboard or of leather, etc. well soaked with these liquids; when such layers are interposed between each couple or combination of the two different metals, such an alternative series of these three sorts of conductors always in the same order, constitutes my new instrument; which imitates, as I have said, the effects of Leyden jars or of electric batteries by giving the same disturbances as they; which in truth, are much inferior to these batteries when highly charged in the force and noise of their explosions, in the spark, in the distance through which the charge can pass, etc., and equal in effect only to a battery very feebly charged, but a battery nevertheless of an immense capacity; but which further infinitely surpasses the power of these batteries in that it does not need, as they do, to be charged in advance by means of an outside source; and in that it can give the disturbance every time that it is properly touched, no matter how often. . . .

I proceed to give a more detailed description of this apparatus and of some other analogous ones, as well as the most remarkable experiments made with them.

I provided myself with several dozen small round plates or discs of copper, of brass, or better of silver, an inch in diameter more or less (for example, coins) and an equal number of plates of tin, or which is much better, of zinc, approximately of the same shape and size; I say approximately because precision is not necessary, and in general the size as well as the shape of the metallic pieces is arbitrary: all that is necessary is that they may be arranged easily one above the other in a column. I further provided a sufficiently large number of discs of cardboard, of leather, or of some other spongy matter which can take up and retain much water, or the liquid with which they must be well soaked if the experiment is to succeed. These pieces, which I will call the moistened discs, I make a little smaller than the metallic discs or plates, so that when placed between them in the way that I shall soon describe, they do not protrude.

Now having in hand all these pieces in good condition, that is to say, the metallic discs clean and dry, and the other non-metallic ones well soaked in water or which is much better, in brine, and afterwards slightly wiped so that the liquid does not come out in drops, I have only to arrange them in the proper way; and this arrangement is simple and easy.

I place horizontally on a table or base one of the metallic plates, for example, one of the silver ones, and on this first plate I place a second plate of zinc; on this second plate I lay one of the moistened discs; then another plate of silver, followed immediately by another of zinc, on which I place again a moistened disc. I thus continue in the same way coupling a plate of silver with one of zinc, always in the same sense, that is to say, always silver below and zinc above or *vice versa*, according as I began, and inserting between these couples a moistened disc; I continue, I say, to form from several of these steps a column as high as can hold itself up without falling. . . .

[An account of the shocks that can be obtained from this instrument and details of the best method of experimenting with it are omitted.]

Coming back to the mechanical construction of my apparatus, which admits of several variations, I proceed to describe here not all those which I have thought out and constructed either on a large or small scale, but some only which are either more curious or more useful or which present some real advantage, such as being easier or quicker to construct, more certain in their effects or keeping in good condition longer. To begin with one of these which unites almost all of these advantages, which in its form differs the most from the columnar apparatus described before but which has the disadvantage of being a much larger apparatus, I present this new apparatus which I call the crown of cups in the next figure.

We set up a row of several cups or bowls made of any material whatever except the metals, cups of wood, of shell, of clay, or better of crystal (small drinking glasses or goblets are very suitable) half-full of pure water, or better of brine or of lye; and we join them all together in a sort of chain by means of metallic arms of which one

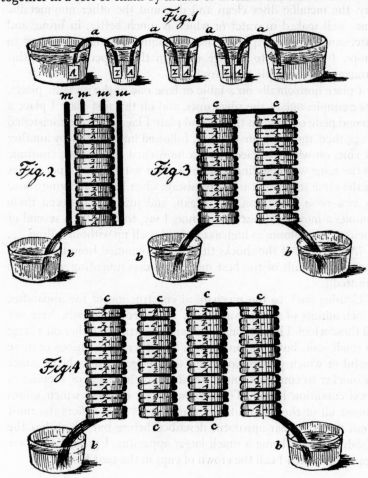

arm *Aa* or only the end *A* which is placed in one of the goblets is of red or yellow copper, or better of silvered copper, and the other Z, which is placed in the next goblet is of tin or better of zinc. I may observe here in passing that lye and the other alkaline liquids are preferable when one of the metals which is immersed in them is tin; brine is preferable when it is zinc. The two metals of which each arc is composed are soldered together somewhere above the part which is immersed in the liquid and which ought to touch it with a sufficiently large surface: for this purpose it is suitable that this part should be an inch square or very little less; the rest of the arc may be as much narrower as we please, and may even be a simple metallic wire. It may also be made of a third metal different from the two which are immersed in the liquid of the goblets; since the action on the electric fluid which results from all the contacts of several metals which are in immediate contact, the force with which this fluid is driven at the end, is the same absolutely or nearly as that which it would have received by the immediate contact of the first metal with the last without any of the intermediate metals, as I have verified by direct experiment, of which I shall have occasion to speak elsewhere.

Now then a train of 30, 40, 60 of these goblets joined up in this manner and arranged either in a straight line or in a curve or set round in any way forms the whole of this new apparatus, which fundamentally and in substance is the same as the other one of the column tried before; the essential feature, which consists in the immediate connection of the different metals which form each pair and the mediate connection of one couple with another by the intermediary of a damp conductor, appears in this apparatus as well as in the other.

[Other scientists immediately began to use the new means of creating a steady supply of electric current. A month following the publication of the above disclosure, Anthony Carlisle and William Nicholson decomposed water into oxygen and hydrogen by its means. For their experiment see p. 273.]

V

The Earth and Its Waters

AT FIRST GLANCE it seems somewhat strange that the study of the nature and history of our own earth should be among the last of the sciences to be developed, but there are two general reasons to be noted. One is that the common, ordinary things that everybody sees and takes for granted without question are not usually regarded as subjects for scientific inquiry, until some special circumstance leads to their examination. The second is that things which can be readily measured and classified become the material of science before things which cannot so readily be measured and classified; and the study of the earth presented problems whose solution had to await the development of complex instruments and techniques. The science of geology was, therefore, one of the latest to reach maturity.

There is so much to be known about our planet, its structure, its habits, and its attendant phenomena, that the subject has now been broken down into many sciences. Geology deals with the structure of the earth, astronomy its place and movement in the universe, meteorology its atmospheric changes, seismology its internal disturbances, and so on.

The earliest study of the earth was made by two vastly different types of men—the philosophers, who tried to find out how the earth came into being, when, and why; and the miners, who developed a practical knowledge of its outer skin while digging metals for their personal gain. From a wealth of available material, the selections which follow have been chosen with the idea of giving some idea of the way in which a few of the important problems necessarily included in any study of our earth were first approached. The excerpts from the writings of Leonardo da Vinci and Georgius Agricola offer early imaginative explanations of the manner in which rivers obtain the water which flows in them. Their theory of the upward rise of water through the earth was disproved a century later by Pierre Perrault, who made definite measurements, since confirmed, to show that ordinary rain and snow are more than sufficient to provide the water which fills streams and rivers.

Next come two discussions of the problem of the origin of the earth, written about a century apart. Leibnitz suggests that the existence of glassy rocks means that the earth originally must have been molten fluid. Buffon, going considerably further, attempts to divide the history of the earth, beginning with its incandescent stage, into seven geological eras. His is the first serious effort to estimate the length of geologic time.

With more space, we might have included specimens of the eighteenth century arguments between the "Plutonists" or "Vulcanists," who asserted that heat was the all-important force in rock formation, and the "Neptunists," who maintained staunchly that the earth's rocks were created chiefly by the physical or chemical action of water. The writers quoted here were, for the most part, inclined to take the middle ground, recognizing that certain types of rock formation could have been created by heat, such as the heat of a volcano, while at the same time appreciating the effects of surface erosion and of underground currents of water.

Jean Etienne Guettard (1715-1786) was a prominent figure in the debate. He made extensive investigations in the regions of extinct volcanos, and wrote a memoir on volcanic remains. Later, he made a special study of basalt, but failed to recognize its similarity to the volcanic rock he had earlier identified, and came instead to the conclusion that it was "a species of vitrifiable rock formed by crystallization in an aqueous fluid." Thus his early work inspired the Vulcanist school of geologists, while his later provided an important argument for the Neptunists. The Scot, James Hutton, from whom we quote, was a leader of the Plutonists, but he did not go so far as to deny that water, as well as heat, played a part in bringing about geologic transformations.

Finally, we have two studies of the movement of storms across the earth's surface. Benjamin Franklin observed that storms move in a direction opposed to the direction of the prevailing wind at the time, and attempted an explanation of this phenomenon. Hutton made a comprehensive attack on the whole problem of weather and the origin of storms, and in a general way anticipated the modern air-mass theory, which is of such value to aviation today.

We have not included the early, painstaking, but necessarily tedious and technical descriptions of types of rock and crystal, or the similar accounts of the discovery of rock stratification, and the demonstrations by this method of research that the island of England must originally have been connected with the Continent.

LEONARDO DA VINCI

1 4 5 2 · 1 5 1 9

HAD THE SCIENTIFIC work of Leonardo, the famous Florentine painter, been published during his lifetime or soon afterwards, many minor branches of science would have progressed faster than they did. Unfortunately, the bulk of his writings consisted of brief, random notes, often explanations of his drawings, which, after his death, disappeared from view, and were not published until comparatively recent times. His scientific influence was therefore restricted to the very limited number of people who knew him or saw his manuscripts while he was alive, and to those whom his paintings and drawings stimulated to give more careful attention to the study of anatomy.

Leonardo is popularly known as the painter of the "Mona Lisa" and "The Last Supper," but he was also an architect and engineer of genius, and an early student of geology. Among his technical drawings are sketches of airplane and parachute models, pumps, gears, flywheels, a boring machine with screw feed and adjustable chuck, spinning and weaving machines, most of which he never built.

The following selection from The Notebooks of Leonardo da Vinci, edited and translated by Edward MacCurdy (Reynal and Hitchcock, New York, 1938), shows how he attempted to keep his thinking scientifically clear and definite, though he still held the strange, ancient view of the earth's structure as being intrinsically the same as that of the human body. He was obviously more concerned to discover the immediate, concrete causes of things and the way they actually worked than to discuss philosophically the ultimate purpose of the universe or abstract ideas of "the good." It is interesting to note that he held a modern view of the origin of fossils, arguing that the presence of sea shells on the top of a mountain meant that the area had once been under water.

ON THE WATERS OF THE EARTH

MAN HAS BEEN called by the ancients a lesser world, and indeed the term is rightly applied, seeing that if man is compounded of earth, water, air, and fire, this body of the earth is the same; and as man has within himself bones as a stay and framework for the flesh, so the world has the rocks which are the supports of the earth; as man has within him a pool of blood wherein the lungs as he breathes expand and contract, so the body of the earth has its ocean, which also rises and falls every six hours with the breathing of the world; as from the said pool of blood proceed the veins which spread their branches through the human body, in just the same manner the ocean fills the body of the earth with an infinite number of veins of water. In this body of the earth there is lacking, however, the sinews, and these are absent because sinews are created for the purpose of movement, and as the world is perpetually stable within itself, no movement ever takes place there, and in the absence of any movement the sinews are not necessary; but in all other things man and the world show a great resemblance.

Of the springs of water on the tops of mountains

Clearly it would seem that the whole surface of the ocean, when not affected by tempest, is equally distant from the centre of the earth, and that the tops of the mountains are as much farther removed from this centre as they rise above the surface of the sea. Unless therefore the body of the earth resembled that of man it would not be possible that the water of the sea being so much lower than the mountains should have power in its nature to rise to the summit of the mountains. We must needs therefore believe

341

that the same cause that keeps the blood at the top of a man's head keeps water at the summit of mountains.

Of the heat that is in the world

Where there is life there is heat, and where there is vital heat there is movement of vapour. This is proved because one sees that the heat of the element of fire always draws to itself the damp vapours, the thick mists and dense clouds, which are given off by the seas and other lakes and rivers and marshy valleys. And drawing these little by little up to the cold region, there the first part halts, because the warm and moist cannot exist with cold and dryness; and this first part having halted receives the other parts, and so all the parts joining together one to another form thick and dark clouds.

And these are often swept away and carried by the winds from one region to another, until at last their density gives them such weight that they fall in thick rain; but if the heat of the sun is added to the power of the element of fire, the clouds are drawn up higher and come to more intense cold, and there become frozen and so produce hailstorms.

So the same heat which holds up so great a weight of water as is seen to fall in rain from the clouds sucks it up from below from the roots of the mountains and draws it up and confines it among the mountain summits, and there the water finds crevices, and so continuing, it issues forth and creates rivers. . . .

If heat is the cause of the movement of moisture, cold stops it. This has been already shown by the example of the cold region which stops the clouds drawn by the hot element. As for the proof that the heat draws the moisture it is shown as follows: heat a jug and set it in a vase with the mouth downwards, and place there some charcoal which has been lighted. You will see that the moisture, as it retires before the heat, will rise and fill the jug with water, and the air which was enclosed in this jug will escape through its opening.

Also if you take a wet cloth and hold it to the fire you will see the damp of the cloth leave its place, and that part of the moisture which has least substance will rise up, drawn by the proximity of the fire which from its nature rises towards the region of its element. In this way the sun draws up the moisture.

Explanation of the presence of water at the summits of the mountains

I say that it is just like the blood which the natural heat keeps in the veins at the top of the man, and when the man has died this blood becomes cold and is brought back into the low parts, and as the sun warms the man's head the amount of blood there increases, and it grows to such an excess there with the humours as to over-load the veins and frequently to cause pains in the head. It is the same with the springs which ramify through the body of the earth and by the natural heat which is spread through all the body that contains them, the water stays in the springs and is raised to the high summits of the mountains. And the water that passes through a pent-up channel within the body of the mountain, like a dead thing, will not emerge from its first low state, because it is not warmed by the vital heat of the first spring. Moreover the warmth of the element of fire, and by day the heat of the sun, have power to stir up the dampness of the low places and draw this to a height in the same way as it draws the clouds and calls up their moisture from the expanses of the sea.

Of the opinion held by some that the water of some seas is higher than the highest summits of the mountains and that the water was driven up to these summits: Water will not move from one spot to another unless to seek a lower level, and in the natural course of its current it will never be able to return to an elevation equal to that of the spot whence it first issued forth from the mountains and came into the light. That part of the sea which, by an error of imagination, you state to have been so high as to have flowed over the summits of the high mountains for so many centuries, would be consumed and poured out in the water that has issued from these same mountains. You can well imagine that during all the time that the Tigris and the Euphrates have flowed from the summits of the Armenian mountains, one may suppose the whole of the water of the ocean to have passed a great many times through their mouths.

Or do you not believe that the Nile has discharged more water into the sea than is at present contained in all the watery element? Surely this is the case. If then this water had fallen away from the body of the earth, the whole mechanism would long since have been without water. So therefore, one may conclude that the water passes from the rivers to the sea, and from the sea to the rivers, ever making the self-same round, and that all the sea and the rivers have passed through the mouth of the Nile an infinite number of times.

GEORGIUS AGRICOLA[1]

1 4 9 4 · 1 5 5 5

LIKE LEONARDO, Agricola compared the structure of the earth to the structure of the human body, and accepted the old Greek view that the four elements earth, air, fire, and water together compose our world. He had, however, a far more extensive knowledge of geological matters than Leonardo, for he spent most of his life studying German mines and minerals at first hand. He classified minerals according to their physical and chemical characteristics, describing over eighty in detail, twenty of which had not been described before.

The selections below are from his De ortu et causis subterraneum (On the Origin and Causes of Things Underground) included in the translation of his great work De re metallica (On Metals) by Herbert C. and Lou H. Hoover, 1912.

[1] On Agricola's interest in many kinds of knowledge, see below, p. 583.

HOW METALS ARE PRODUCED

I NOW COME to the *canales* in the earth. These are veins, veinlets, and what are called "seams in the rocks." These serve as vessels or receptacles for the material from which minerals are formed. The term *vena* is most frequently given to what is contained in the *canales*, but likewise the same name is applied to the *canales* themselves. The term vein is borrowed from that used for animals, for just as their veins are distributed through all parts of the body, and just as by means of the veins blood is diffused from the liver throughout the whole body, so also the veins traverse the whole globe, and more particularly the mountainous districts; and water runs and flows through them. With regard to veinlets or stringers and "seams in the rocks," which are the thinnest stringers, the following is the mode of their arrangement. Veins in the earth, just like the veins of an animal, have certain veinlets of their own, but in a contrary way. For the larger veins of animals pour blood into the veinlets, while in the earth the humours [fluids] are usually poured from the veinlets into the larger veins, and rarely flow from the larger into the smaller ones. As for the seams in the rocks we consider that they are produced by two methods: by the first, which is peculiar to themselves, they are formed at the same time as the rocks, for the heat bakes the refractory material into stone and the non-refractory material similarly heated exhales its humours and is made into "earth" generally friable. The other method is common also to veins and veinlets, when water is collected into one place it softens the rock by its liquid nature, and by its weight and pressure breaks and divides it. Now, if the rock is hard, it makes seams in the rocks and veinlets, and if it is not too hard it makes veins. However, if the rocks are not hard, seams and veinlets are created as well as veins. If these do not carry a very large quantity of water, or if they are pressed by a great volume of it, they soon discharge themselves into the nearest veins. . . .

. . . I must explain what it really is from which metals are produced. The best proof that there is water in their materials is the fact that they flow when melted, whereas they are again solidified by the cold of air or water. This, however, must be understood in the sense that there is more water in them and less "earth"; for it is not simply water that is their substance but water mixed with "earth." And such a proportion of "earth" is in the mixture as may obscure the transparency of the water, but not remove the brilliance which is frequently in unpolished things. Again, the purer the mixture, the more precious the metal which is made from it, and the greater its resistance to fire. But what proportion of "earth" is in each liquid from which a metal is made no mortal can ever ascertain, or still less explain, but the one God has known it, Who has given certain sure and fixed laws to nature for mixing and blending things together. It is a juice then, from which metals are formed; and this juice is created by various operations. Of these operations the first is a flow of water which softens the "earth" or carries the "earth" along with it, thus there is a mixture of "earth" and water, then the power of heat works upon the mixtures so as to produce that kind of a juice.

We have spoken of the substance of metals; we must now speak of their efficient cause. . . . We do not deny the statement of Albertus Magnus[1] that the mixture of "earth" and water is baked by subterranean heat to a certain denseness, but it is our opinion that the juice so obtained is afterward solidified by a cold so as to become a metal. . . . This view of Aristotle is the true one. For metals melt through the heat and somehow become softened; but those which have become softened through heat are again solidified

[1] Albertus Magnus (about 1193-1280), one of the most scientific medieval philosophers, who did much to revive the study of Aristotle to take the place of the more ignorant and superstitious writers of the centuries after Rome fell.

by the influence of cold, and, on the contrary, those which become softened by moisture are solidified by heat.

Construction and Destruction of Mountains

Hills and mountains are produced by two forces, one of which is the power of water, and the other the strength of the wind. There are three forces which loosen and demolish the mountains, for in this case, to the power of the water and the strength of the wind we must add the fire in the interior of the earth. Now we can plainly see that a great abundance of water produces mountains, for the torrents first of all, wash out the soft earth, next carry away the harder earth, and then roll down the rocks, and thus in a few years they excavate the plains or slopes to a considerable depth; this may be noticed in mountainous regions even by unskilled observers. By such excavation to a great depth through many ages, there rises an immense eminence on each side. When an eminence has thus arisen, the earth rolls down, loosened by constant rain and split away by frost, and the rocks, unless they are exceedingly firm, since their seams are similarly softened by the damp, roll down into the excavations below. This continues until the steep eminence is changed into a slope. Each side of the excavation is said to be a mountain, just as the bottom is called a valley. Moreover, streams, and to a far greater extent rivers, effect the same results by their rushing and washing; for this reason they are frequently seen flowing either between very high mountains which they have created, or close by the shore which borders them. . . .

Nor did the hollow places which now contain the seas all formerly exist, nor yet the mountains which check and break their advance, but in many parts there was a level plain, until the force of winds let loose upon it a tumultuous sea and a scathing tide. By a similar process the impact of water entirely overthrows and flattens out hills and mountains. But these changes of local conditions, numerous and important as they are, are not noticed by the common people to be taking place at the very moment when they are happening, because, through their antiquity, the time, place, and manner in which they began is far prior to human memory.

The wind produces hills and mountains in two ways: either when set loose and free from bonds, it violently moves and agitates the sand; or else when, after having been driven into the hidden recesses of the earth by cold, as into a prison, it struggles with a great effort to burst out. For hills and mountains are created in hot countries, whether they are situated by the sea coasts or in districts remote from the sea, by the force of winds; these no longer held in check by the valleys, but set free, heap up the sand and dust, which they gather from all sides, to one spot, and a mass arises and grows together. If time and space allow, it grows together and hardens, but if it be not allowed (and in truth this is more often the case), the same force again scatters the sand far and wide. . . .

Then, on the other hand, an earthquake either rends and tears away part of a mountain, or engulfs and devours the whole mountain in some fearful chasm. In this way it is recorded the Cybotus was destroyed, and it is believed that within the memory of man an island under the rule of Denmark disappeared. Historians tell us that Taygetus suffered a loss in this way, and that Therasia was swallowed up with the island of Thera. Thus it is clear that water and the powerful winds produce mountains, and also scatter and destroy them. Fire only consumes them, and does not produce at all, for part of the mountains—usually the inner part—takes fire.

PIERRE PERRAULT

1 6 1 1 - 1 6 8 0

BOTH OF THE preceding essays have suggested that rainfall does not provide enough water to keep the rivers flowing, but that inside the earth water is drawn uphill to issue forth from springs. This argument did not appeal to Perrault; he therefore made a calculation to show that, in the upper Seine valley, about five times more water falls in the form of rain than is necessary to keep the river flowing. This is one of the first uses of quantitative methods in geological theory.

Perrault was a French lawyer who studied geology and meteorology as a pastime. His book De l'Origine des Fontaines (On the Origin of Springs and Rivers) was originally published anonymously in Paris in the year 1674, and dedicated to Huygens.[1] A summary of the book appeared the next year in the Philosophical Transactions of the Royal Society of London, which reprinted the summary again in 1731 and in 1809. The translation here used is from A Source Book in Geology, by Kirtley F. Mather and Shirley L. Mason (McGraw-Hill Book Co., New York, 1935).

[1] On Huygens, see above, p. 136.

THE SOURCE OF WATER
IN SPRINGS AND RIVERS

I<small>F</small> <small>THE</small> <small>SPRINGS</small> and rivers are engendered, as Aristotle says, from air condensed and resolved into water in the caverns of the earth, that is to say, as Lydiat explains it, from vapor that exhales its humidity when it is heated: and if this humidity comes from rain which it absorbs, as Aristotle says in another place, there must then be sufficient rain to give the earth enough moisture to make the vapor which can supply water to the springs and rivers throughout the entire year. In this case according to his opinion, rain water must not only equal the greatness of the earth but greatly surpass it, since it is true that that water is subjected to the great waste which we have observed.

Concerning this idea, expressed in all ancient and modern philosophy, I believe there is greater probability in attributing the source of springs and rivers to rain and snow water than there is in attributing it solely to internal distillation in the earth; and that common sense will never prefer a medium as obscure as this distillation, whose consequences seem rather feeble, to a medium as apparent as the rains, whose consequences are so great and so well known. But as these reasons only make for the destruction of the contrary opinion, we must try to give other reasons which can establish what I maintain, and show that rain water is sufficient to make springs and rivers run throughout the entire year.

Although it is no more necessary for me to prove this affirmation than for those who make objection to prove their negative, one being as difficult as the other, I shall nevertheless attempt to do so, by making rough estimates of the quantity of rain relative to the basins of rivers. . . .

It is necessary for the success of our plan, to measure or estimate the water of some river as it flows from its source to the place where some stream enters it and to see if the rain water which falls around its course, being put in a reservoir, as Aristotle said, would be sufficient to make it run a whole year. I have chosen the Seine River and have examined it with sufficient precision in its course from its source to Aynay le Duc, where a stream enters and enlarges it. That is why I shall take it as the subject for the examination which I wish to make.

The course of this river from its source to Aynay le Duc is about three leagues, and the lands along its course extend to right and left about two leagues on each side, where there are other streams which go elsewhere; granting that those streams must have rain water for their subsistence as well as the Seine, I want to consider only half of this region of slopes and to say that the basin that the Seine occupies from its source to Aynay le Duc is three leagues long and two leagues wide, and consequently I make the following deductions.

If a reservoir of this length and breadth were made, it would be six square leagues in area, which reduced to *toises*, [a toise is about six feet] following the measurements previously accepted, would be 31,245,144 square *toises* of surface.

In this reservoir one must imagine that during a year there has fallen from the rain a height of 19⅓ *poulces* [inches], which is the height for an ordinary year, as we have observed. This height of 19⅓ *poulces* gives 224,899,942 hogsheads of water or thereabouts, following the measure on which we have agreed.

All this water thus collected must serve to keep this river running during a year, from its source to the place we have indicated, and must serve also to provide for all that it must lose for the nourishment of trees, plants, and herbs, and for evaporation, and for useless drainage into the river, which only enlarges it for a time and while it rains, and for wandering streams which may take another course than to this river because of irregular and contrary slopes, and other such wastes, losses, and impairments.

It would be difficult to ascertain exactly the measurement or estimation of the water of this small river, and to tell what quantity it contains. Nevertheless, as far as I can judge . . . the quantity of water flowing between the banks of this river from its source to Aynay le Duc during a year amounts only to the quantity of 36,453,600 hogsheads. But if I draw this quantity of water from 224,899,942 hogsheads, which are in this reservoir we have just imagined, there will remain 188,446,342 hogsheads, which amounts almost to five times more, and which serves to provide for the losses, diminution, and wastes which we have noticed. Therefore, only about the sixth part of the rain and snow water is necessary to make this river run continually throughout the year.

I well know that this deduction has no accuracy; but who could give one which would be precise? I believe, however, that it ought to be more satisfactory than a simple negative like Aristotle's, or than the premise of those who hold, without knowing why, that it does not rain enough to furnish the flow of rivers. At any rate, until someone makes more exact computations, by which he proves the contrary of what I have advanced, I shall remain convinced and shall content myself with this feeble light which gives me the observation that I have made, not having anything greater.

If then this water suffices for one river, it will suffice for all the other rivers of the world in proportion, considering especially the large margin for waste and the small area for the basin and course of the river which I allow. This is only a league on each side, for rivers are not usually closer to each other than two leagues. There is therefore some reason for saying that rain and snow water are adequate for all the rivers in the world.

I might say that there are regions where it rains very rarely, and others where it does not rain at all, which nevertheless contain fairly large streams. But the streams of these countries, where it rains only occasionally, are not continual; they are large only in winter and they dry up almost entirely in the summer. Because they are near high mountains, from which they come, abundant snow which falls on these mountains and which afterwards melts there can fill their beds as long as it lasts. When the supply is exhausted, they are left to the dryness of summer.

There are hardly any countries in the world where it never rains. The torrid zone, where this is more nearly true than anywhere else, is watered abundantly twice a year, possibly more than France is in the summer, and at least with greater abundance at certain times. But when we speak of regions where it never rains, we do not deny the possibility that there are large rivers there which may have their sources in other regions where it does rain, as, for example, the Nile, which flows through Egypt where it does not rain. There are countries in the world which do not produce wine, where not much of it could be produced, and business and commerce bring it from afar; similarly the great rivers make a kind of commerce of their waters to irrigate the provinces not watered ordinarily from heaven.

GOTTFRIED WILHELM LEIBNITZ

1 6 4 6 · 1 7 1 6

LEIBNITZ WAS a great philosopher and physicist, an international lawyer and diplomat, and the official historian of the House of Hanover. But one of his chief claims to fame was his invention of the integral calculus at the very time that Newton was perfecting his system of the differential calculus. The controversy as to whether or not he was indebted to Newton for his invention raged for many years, and exemplifies the undoubted fact that important scientific discoveries are every now and again made simultaneously and independently in different countries.

Leibnitz was a descendant of an old Slavic family which had settled in Saxony some generations earlier. As a youth he studied at the University of Leipzig, where he read widely in philosophy, including the so-called "natural philosophy," or science, of the day. At seventeen he presented a brilliant essay in philosophy and received his bachelor's degree. Three years later the University of Altdorf awarded him a doctor's degree and offered him a professorship in law. Later, in Paris, with the great Huygens as tutor, he developed his mathematical abilities, on both theoretical and practical levels. He invented a calculating machine, and made important contributions in the fields of optics, hydrostatics, and nautical science. He was elected a fellow of the Royal Society of London and of the French Academy of Sciences. Through his efforts, the Berlin Academy of Sciences was founded.

Among his voluminous writings is a work on the beginnings of the earth, Protogaea, published in 1680. He favored the so-called Plutonist theory, that fire formed the center of the earth, and from this he derived the idea that the earth was originally a molten mass. A secondary force, he thought, in shaping the earth, was the action of water on its crust. The selection below is quoted from the translation in A Source Book of Geology, by Kirtley F. Mather and Shirley L. Mason (McGraw-Hill Book Co., New York, 1935).

THE EARTH ORIGINALLY MOLTEN

IN AGREEMENT with these views, some savants [1] have developed an hypothesis that serves to explain more clearly the order of the world. They suggest that vast globes, self-luminous like the fixed stars or our sun, or projected from a luminous body, after reaching the last stages of ebullition, were covered with *scoriae* like bubbling foam. It is as if the spots by which the ancients suspected the sun could be altered and some day obscured, and which our optical instruments have allowed us to see, should increase in amount until they veiled the face of that orb. For the greater part they believe, in effect (as the sacred writers, in their way, tend to imply), that *there are raging fires at the center of the earth from which flames can break forth in eruption.*

Existing traces of the primitive aspect of nature support these conjectures, for *all scoria* resulting from fusion is *a sort of glass.* And the crust which covered the molten matter of the globe and which hardened from the fused condition would be like scoria, as happens with metals in the furnace. If then the great framework of the earth, the exposed rocks, the imperishable silicates, are almost entirely vitrified, does that not prove that they arose from a fusion of bodies, brought about by the powerful action of nature's fire on still soft material? And as the action of that fire infinitely surpasses that of our furnace, both in intensity and duration, is it a matter of astonishment that it led to a result that men cannot attain now? . . . It is everywhere true that the most simple and primitive material in the composition of the earth, that which represents most accurately the true nature of rock, is that which most resists fire, which melts [only] under an excessive heat, and finishes by vitrifying. . . .

[1] Descartes and his followers.

357

At the same time it is readily believed that at the origin of things, before the separation of the opaque material from the luminous, *when our globe was incandescent*, the fire drove the humidity into the air, acting like a distillation. That is to say, as a result of the lowering of the temperature, it was converted into aqueous vapors. These vapors, finding themselves in contact with the chilled surface of the earth, condensed to water. The water, working over the débris of the recent conflagration, took up the fixed salts, giving rise to *a sort of lixivium* [solution] which soon formed the sea. . . .

Finally it is credible that the consolidation of the crust of the globe, on cooling—as takes place with metals and other bodies which become more porous with fusion—has left *enormous bubbles*, accordant in grandeur with the planet; that is to say, *cavities*, enclosing water or air, were formed under its immense vaults. It is also probable that other parts stretched out in the form of beds and that, by the diversity of material and the [irregular] distribution of heat, *the masses were not equally compressed and have burst, here and there, so that certain portions have subsided to form the trough of valleys, whereas others, more solid, have remained upright like columns and for that reason constituted the mountains.*

To these causes would be added the action of the waters, which by their weight tended to furrow stream beds in the still soft surface. Then, the vaults of the earth breaking, either from the weight of the material or from the explosion of gases, the water would be forced from the depths of the abyss across the wreckage, and, joining that which was flowing naturally from the high places, would give rise to vast inundations which would leave abundant sediment at divers points. These sediments would harden, and, with repetition of the same conditions, [new] sedimentary beds would be superimposed. The face of the earth, still only slightly firm, having thus been exhausted or balanced, *a more stable state was finally produced*. These facts should make us understand *the double origin of solid bodies*, first by their chilling after igneous fusion, and then by new aggregations, after their solution in the waters.

BENJAMIN FRANKLIN[1]

1 7 0 6 · 1 7 9 0

ALL NATURAL phenomena interested Franklin—weather, wind, and waves no less than electricity. Wherever he went he observed nature, talked with those who battled natural forces, and reflected on his findings. The first letter below, telling how storms may move against the direction of the wind, shows the keen way his mind played over a few observed facts and led him to interesting generalizations. The letter on the flow of the Gulf Stream marks the beginning of the science of oceanography, so important to all navigators and ship-owners. Both letters are from the 1774 edition of Experiments and Observations on Electricity.

[1] For other works of Franklin see pp. 162, 314, 320. The best contemporary edition of Franklin's electrical experiments is that edited by I. Bernard Cohen, published by Harvard University Press, 1941.

HOW STORMS MOVE

Letter to Mr. Alexander Small

May 12, 1760

DEAR SIR,

Agreeable to your request, I send you my reasons for thinking that our northeast storms in North America begin first, in point of time, in the southwest parts: That is to say, the air in Georgia, the farthest of our colonies to the Southwest, begins to move southwesterly before the air of Carolina, which is the next colony northeastward; the air of Carolina has the same motion before the air of Virginia, which lies still more northeastward; and so on northeasterly through Pennsylvania, New-York, New-England, &c., quite to Newfoundland.

These northeast storms are generally very violent, continue sometimes two or three days, and often do considerable damage in the harbours along the coast. They are attended with thick clouds and rain.

What first gave me this idea, was the following circumstance. About twenty years ago, a few more or less, I cannot from my memory be certain, we were to have an eclipse of the moon at Philadelphia, on a Friday evening, about nine o'clock. I intended to observe it, but was prevented by a northeast storm, which came on about seven, with thick clouds as usual, that quite obscured the whole hemisphere. Yet when the post brought us the Boston newspaper, giving an account of the effects of the same storm in those parts, I found the beginning of the eclipse had been well observed there, though Boston lies N. E. of Philadelphia about 400 miles. This puzzled me because the storm began with us so soon as to prevent any observation, and being a N. E. storm, I imagined it must have begun rather sooner in places farther to the northeastward than it did at Philadelphia. I therefore mentioned it in a letter to my brother, who lived at Boston; and he informed me the storm did not begin with them till near eleven o'clock, so that they had a good observation of the eclipse: And upon comparing all the other accounts I received from the several colonies, of the time of beginning of the same storm, and, since that of other storms of the same kind, I found the beginning to be always later the farther northeastward. I have not my notes with me here in England, and cannot, from memory, say the proportion of time to distance, but I think it is about an hour to every hundred miles.

From thence I formed an idea of the cause of these storms, which I would explain by a familiar instance or two. Suppose a long canal of water stopp'd at the end by a gate. The water is quite at rest till the gate is open, then it begins to move out through the gate; the water next the gate is first in motion, and moves towards the gate; the water next to that first water moves next, and so on successively, till the water at the head of the canal is in motion, which is last of all. In this case all the water moves indeed towards the gate, but the successive times of beginning motion are the contrary, viz. from the gate backwards to the head of the canal. Again, suppose the air in a chamber at rest, no current through the room till you make a fire in the chimney. Immediately the air in the chimney, being rarefied by the fire, rises; the air next the chimney flows in to supply its place, moving towards the chimney; and, in consequence, the rest of the air successively, quite back to the door. Thus to produce our northeast storms, I suppose some great heat and rarefaction of the air in or about the Gulph of Mexico; the air thence rising has its place supplied by the next more northern, cooler, and therefore denser and heavier, air; that, being in motion, is followed by the next more northern air, &c. &c., in a successive current, to which current our coast and inland ridge of mountains give the direction of northeast, as they lie N. E. and S. W.

This I offer only as an hypothesis to account for this particular fact; and, perhaps, on farther examination, a better and truer may be found. I do not suppose all storms generated in the same manner. Our northwest thundergusts in America I know are not; but of them I have written my opinion fully in a paper which you have seen.

CHARTING THE GULF STREAM

Letter to Anthony Todd, 1769

DISCOURSING with Captain Folger, a very intelligent mariner of the Island of Nantucket, in New England, concerning the long passages made by some ships bound from England to New York, I received from him the following information, viz,

That the island in which he lives is inhabited chiefly by people concerned in the whale fishery, in which they employed near 150 sail of vessels; that the whales are found generally near the edges of the Gulph Stream, a strong current so called, which comes out of the Gulph of Florida, passing northeasterly along the coast of America, and then turning off most easterly, running at the rate of 4, 3½, 3, 2½ miles an hour. That the whaling business leading these people to cruise along the edges of the stream in quest of whales, they are become better acquainted with the course, breadth, strength, and extent of the same, than those navigators can well be who only cross it in their voyages to and from America, that they have opportunities of discovering the strength of it when their boats are out in the pursuit of this fish, and happen to get into the stream while the ship is out of it, or out of the stream while the ship is in it, for then they are separated very fast, and would soon lose sight of each other if care were not taken in crossing the stream to and fro. They frequently in the same meet and speak with ships bound from England to New York, Virginia, &c. who have passages of 8, 9, and 10 weeks and are still far from land, and not likely to be in with it for some time, being engaged in that part of the stream that sets directly against them, and it is supposed that their fear of Cape Sable Shoals, George's Banks, or Nantucket Shoals, hath induced them to keep so far to the southward as unavoidable to engage them in the said Gulph Stream, which occasions the length of their voyage, since in a calm it carries them directly back, and tho' they may have fair winds, yet the current being 60 or 70 miles a day, is so much subtracted from the way they make thro' the water. At my request Captain Folger hath been so obliging as to mark for me on a chart the dimensions, course and swiftness of the Stream from its first coming out of the Gulph when it is narrowest and strongest, until it turns away to go to the southward of the Western Islands, where it is broader and weaker, and to give me withall some written directions whereby ships bound from the banks of New-foundland to New York may avoid the said Stream; and yet be free of danger from the banks and shoals above mentioned. As I appre-hend that such chart and directions may be of use to our packets in shortning their voyages, I send them to you, that if their Lordships should think fit, so much of the chart as is contained within the red lines may be engraved, and printed, together with the remarks, at the charge of the office; or at least the manuscript copies may be made of the same for the use of the packets. The expence of the former would not much exceed the latter and would besides be of general service.

GEORGE LOUIS
LECLERC DE BUFFON

1 7 0 7 - 1 7 8 8

BUFFON WAS BORN in Montbard, France, of a family of means and culture. His father was councillor of the Burgundian Parlement at Dijon. In his youth Buffon became acquainted with a young Englishman, Lord Kingston, who happened then to be traveling on the Continent with a tutor. He joined the party in their travels through France and Italy, and finally accompanied them back to England, where he spent a year studying physics, mathematics, and botany. On his return to France, Buffon translated into French and published Newton's work on the calculus, Fluxions, and Hales' Vegetable Statics.[1] He was soon after elected to the French Academy of Sciences, and appointed keeper of the Jardin du Roi or King's Garden. Through his efforts, the Garden was reorganized for botanical research and became the Jardin des Plantes, the center of French biological studies.

Buffon had read Leibnitz, and like him, felt that all phenomena, biological as well as mechanical, could be explained as the operations of one universal, natural law. His Époques de la Nature, from which we quote below, describes seven geologic stages in the history of the earth. He differed from Leibnitz in believing that the earth was originally an offshoot from the sun, rather than always an independent star. The translation here used is taken from A Source Book in Geology, by Kirtley F. Mather and Shirley L. Mason (McGraw-Hill Book Co., New York, 1935).

[1] On Hales and his work in botany, see below, p. 405 ff.

EPOCHS OF
THE HISTORY OF THE EARTH

FIRST EPOCH. *When the earth and the planets took their form.* In the first days when the earth, molten and turning on herself, took her form and was raised at the equator on being lowered under the poles, the other planets, being in the same state of liquefaction and turning on themselves, took, like the earth, a form swollen on their equators and flattened under their poles. This swelling and this depression were proportional to the rapidity of their rotation. The globe Jupiter furnishes us proof of this. As it turns much more quickly than the earth, it is consequently more elevated at its equator, more lowered under its poles; observations show us that the two diameters of this planet differ more than a thirteenth while those of the earth differ but a 230th part. . . .

It has been seen by earlier experiments, that to warm a body to the point of fusion at least a fifteenth part of the time taken to cool it is necessary. Taking into consideration the great size of the earth and other planets, it would be necessary for them to have been stationed near the sun during many thousands of years to receive the degree of heat necessary for their liquefaction. But there is no evidence in the universe that any body, any planet, any comet remains stationary near the sun, even for an instant. On the contrary, the more the comets approach it (the sun) the more rapid is their movement; the time of their perihelium is extremely short and the fire of this star, while burning on the surface, has not time to penetrate the mass of the comets which approach it most closely.

Thus, all concurs to prove that it would not suffice that the earth and planets, like certain comets, have passed in the vicinity of the sun for their liquefaction to have taken place there. We ought, then, to assume that the matter of the planets has previously belonged to the body of the sun itself and been separated from it, as we have said, by a single and the same impulse. . . .

Let us consider the state and aspect of our universe in its first youth: all the planets, newly consolidated at the surface, were still liquid in the interior, and shot out a very bright light. They were like little suns detached from the great one, which excelled them in nothing but volume, and they diffused light and heat in the same way. This time of incandescence lasted until the planet had been consolidated clear to the center, that is to say, about 2936 years for the earth, 644 years for the moon, 2127 years for Mercury, 1130 years for Mars, 3596 years for Venus, 5140 years for Saturn, and 9433 years for Jupiter.

The satellites of these two great planets as well as the rings which surround Saturn, which are all in the plane of the equator of their principal planet, were projected during the time of liquefaction by the centrifugal force of these great planets which turn on themselves with a prodigious rapidity. . . .

I ought to reply to a criticism that has already been made concerning the overlong duration of time. "Why throw us," I have been asked, "into a space as vague as a duration of 168,000 years? According to your picture, the earth is 75,000 years old, and the existing nature ought to continue another 93,000 years. Is it easy, is it even possible, to form an idea of all or of the parts of a series of centuries as long as that?" My only reply is to present the evidence and my deductions from the works of nature. I shall therefore give the details and the dates in the epochs which are going to follow this. It will be seen that, far from having increased the duration of time unnecessarily, I may have shortened it far too much.

To render this opinion more comprehensible, let us give an example. Let us calculate how much time is necessary for the construction of a hill of clay six thousand feet high. The successive deposits of the waters have formed all the beds of the hill from bottom to top. But we can judge the successive and daily deposits of the waters by the laminae of the shales: they are so thin that one can count a dozen in a *ligne* [one twelfth of an inch] of thickness. Suppose then that each tide deposits sediment of a twelfth of a *ligne* of thickness—that is to say, of a sixth of a *ligne* every day—the deposit will grow one *ligne* in six days . . . and consequently above five inches in a year. Even this time appears too short if it is compared with what takes place before our eyes on certain shores of the sea where muds and clays are being deposited, as on the coast of Normandy. There the increase of the deposit is not discernible and is much less than five inches in a year. . . .

Second Epoch. *When matter, being consolidated, formed the interior rock of the globe as well as the great vitreous masses at its surface.* During this epoch, and even for a long time afterward, as long as the heat was excessive, there was a separation and forcing out of all the volatile substances, such as water, air, and other substances that the great heat drove off. These could only exist in a region more temperate than the surface of the earth was then. All the volatile materials gathered about the globe in the form of atmosphere, while the molten matter, on being consolidated, formed the interior rock of the globe and the nucleus of those great mountains which are composed of vitreous materials. Thus, the first disposition of the great chains of mountains belongs to this second epoch, whereas the formation of the limestone mountains which have existed only since the establishment of the waters, inasmuch as their composition presupposes the existence of shells and other substances that the sea raises and nourishes, were formed many centuries later. As long as the surface of the globe had not been cooled to the point of allowing the water to remain there without being driven off in vapor, all our seas were in the atmosphere. They were not able to fall and establish themselves upon the earth before the moment when the surface was sufficiently cooled to reject the water no longer by too strong a bubbling. This time of the establishment of the waters on the face of the globe preceded by only a few centuries the moment when one could touch this surface without burning oneself. Thus, counting 75,000 years since the formation of the earth and half that time for its cooling to the point of being able to touch it, perhaps 25,000 of the first years passed before the water, hitherto rejected into the atmosphere, was able to establish itself permanently on the surface of the globe. . . .

During these first 37,000 years, all the great veins and the great lodes of mines where minerals occur, were formed by sublimation. The metallic substances were separated from the other vitreous matter by the long and constant heat which sublimated them and pushed them from the interior of the mass of the globe into all the eminences of its surface, where the contraction of material caused by rapid cooling left fissures and cavities which were encrusted and sometimes filled by the metallic substances we find there today. The same distinction must be made in the origin of mines that we have shown for the origin of vitreous and calcareous matter; the former have been produced by the action of fire, the latter by the medium of water. In the metal mines, the principal vein, or, if one wishes, the primordial mass, has been produced by fusion and sublimation, that is to say, by the action of fire. The other mines that are regarded as secondary and parasite veins, have been produced later, by means of water. . . .

But let us return to our principal topic, the topography of the globe before the descent of the waters. We have but few indices still remaining as to the first form of its surface. The highest mountains composed of vitreous matter are the sole vestiges of this ancient state. They were then even higher than they are today, for, since that time and even after the establishment of the waters, the movements of the sea, the rains, the winds, the frosts, the currents of water, and the fall of the torrents, in short, all the destructive activity of the elements of air and water and the vibrations due to subterranean movements, have not ceased bringing them down, trenching through them, and even overturning the less solid parts. We cannot doubt that the valleys which are at the foot of the mountains were once much deeper than they are today.

Third Epoch. *When the waters covered our continents*. At a time thirty or thirty-five thousand years after the formation of the planet the earth found itself sufficiently cooled to receive the waters without rejecting them as vapor. The chaos of the atmosphere was slowly dissipated. Not only the water, but all the volatile matter that the excessive heat had held suspended there, fell in its proper order. It filled all the depths, it covered all the plains, all the spaces it found between the eminences on the surface of the globe, and even surmounted all of those that were not excessively high. There is definite proof that the seas have covered the continent of Europe to 1500 fathom [1] above the level of the present sea, because shells and other marine products are found in the Alps and in the Pyrenees to that height. There are similar proofs for the continents of Asia, Africa and even America, where the mountains are higher than in Europe. Marine shells have been found at more than 2000 fathoms above the level of the southern sea.

It is certain that in these early days the diameter of the earth was two leagues greater, as it was enveloped in water to an elevation of 2000 fathoms. The surface of the earth in general was much higher than it is today; and during a long period of time, the seas covered it entirely, except perhaps for some very high lands and the summits of tall mountains which may have projected above this universal sea, which reached at least to that height where shells cease to appear. From this we should infer that the animals to which these remains belonged could be regarded as the first inhabitants of the globe. Judging by the immense quantity of their remains and detritus, this population was innumerable, because these same remains and detritus have formed all the beds of limestone, marble, chalk, and tufa that compose our hills and stretch over great areas in all parts of the earth.

But in the beginning of this sojourn of the waters on the surface of the globe, did they not have a degree of heat which our fish and

[1] A fathom is six feet.

our shell fish existing at present would be unable to support? And ought we not to presume that the first inhabitants of a still boiling sea would be different from those which it offers us today? Such great heat could agree only with shell fish and fish of another sort; and consequently it is in the earlier part of this epoch, that is to say, from thirty to forty thousand years after the formation of the earth, that one might expect the existence of lost species, living analogues of which are not to be found. These first species, now annihilated, subsisted during the ten or fifteen thousand years that followed the time when the waters were first established.

The time of the formation of the clays followed immediately that of the establishment of the waters. The time of the formation of the first shell fish ought to be placed some centuries later; and the time of transport of their remains followed almost immediately. There is no more interval than that which Nature has put between the birth and the death of these shell animals. The action of the water would constantly convert the vitreous sands into clays. As its movement transported them from place to place, it would carry along at the same time the shells and other debris of marine creatures. Depositing it all as sediments, it formed the beds of clay where today we find these relics, the most ancient mementos of organized Nature.

The formation of shales, slates, coals, and bituminous material date from almost the same time. These are ordinarily found at rather great depth in the clays. They seem to have preceded the deposition of the last clay beds, for below 130 feet of clay with beds containing belemnites, horns of Ammon, and other debris of the most ancient shells, I have found carbonaceous and inflammable material. And it is known that most coal mines are more or less covered by beds of argillaceous earth.

Moreover, it is certain that the two northern continents were not yet separated and even that their separation did not take place until a long time after life had appeared in our northern climates, because elephants have existed at the same time in Siberia and in

Canada. This proves incontrovertibly the continuity of Asia or of Europe with America. On the other hand, it seems equally certain that Africa was separated from southern America from the first, because in this part of the new world not a single animal of the old continent has been found nor any remains which could indicate that they previously existed there.

During the long space of time that the sea sojourned over our lands, the sediments and the deposits of the waters formed the horizontal beds of the earth, the lower ones of clay and the upper of limestone. It was in the sea itself that the petrification of marble and of stones took place. These materials, being soft at first, were deposited successively, one on the other, as the waters brought them and let them fall in the form of sediments. Then they were hardened gradually by the force of the affinity of their constituent parts, and finally they formed all the mass of calcareous rocks which are composed of horizontal or evenly inclined beds, like all other materials deposited by the waters.

Fourth Epoch. *When the waters withdrew and the volcanos became active.* . . . In this time when the lands were raised above the waters, they were covered with great trees and vegetation of all kinds. The world-wide sea was populated throughout with fish and shell fish. It was also the universal receptacle for all that which broke away from the lands which rose above it. The fragments of primitive vitreous and vegetable material were carried down from the heights of the land into the depths of the sea, on the bottom of which they formed the first beds of vitreous sand, clay, schist, and slate as well as the ores of coal, of salt, and of bitumens which later were spread throughout all the seas. The quantity of vegetable products and remains in these first lands is too great to be described. When we reduce the surface of all the elevated lands then above the sea to a hundredth or even a two hundredth part of the surface of the globe, that is to say, 130,000 square leagues, it is easy to imagine how much this vast terrain could produce in the way of trees and plants during several thousands of years, how their remains accumulated, and in what enormous quantity they were transported and deposited under the waters, where they formed the great volume of coal in all the mines found in so many places. It is the same for the salt mines, those of granular iron, pyrites, and all other substances in the composition of which acid enters and which could not be formed until after the fall of the waters. These materials have been carried down and deposited in the low places and in the fissures of the rock of the globe where, finding substances already sublimated by the great heat of the earth, they formed the essential material for the alimentation of the volcanos to come. I say "to come," for there was no volcano in activity before the establishment of the waters. They could not begin activity, or at least a permanent activity, until after a lowering of the waters. One ought to distinguish terrestrial volcanos from marine volcanos; the latter only make explosions, momentary so to speak, because at the instant the fire is started by the effervescence of the combustible and pyrite-bearing stones, it is immediately extinguished by the water which covers it. The land volcanos have, on the contrary, a lasting activity and one proportionate to the quantity of material they contain. These materials need a certain quantity of water to enter into effervescence, and it is only then, by the shock of a great volume of fire against a great volume of water, that they can produce their violent eruptions. It is for this reason that all the volcanos at present in activity are in the islands or near the seacoast and that one can count a hundred times more extinguished ones than active ones; for, as the waters withdraw too far from the foot of the volcanos, their eruptions gradually diminish and finally cease. . . .

Up to the time of the activity of the volcanos there existed on the globe only three sorts of materials: first, the vitreous products from the primitive fire; second, the limestones formed by the medium of water; third, all substances produced by the remains of animals and plants. But the fire of the volcanos has given birth to materials of a fourth sort, which often resemble the other three. The fourth class is that of materials raised and thrown out by the volcanos. Some of this appears to be a mixture of the first with other materials, and other portions appear to have undergone a second action of the fire which has given them a new character.

Fifth Epoch. *When the elephants and other animals of the south inhabited the lands of the north.* All the living creatures which exist today have been able to exist in the same way since the temperature of the earth became similar to that of the present. But for a long time the northern countries of the globe enjoyed the same degree of heat that the southern countries enjoy today and in the time when these countries of the north enjoyed this temperature, the lands toward the south were still burning and remained as deserts. . . .

Elephants lived, reproduced, and multiplied during many centuries in Siberia and in the north of Russia. Then they occupied the lands between the fortieth and fiftieth parallel, where they subsisted even longer than in their native country. They lived for a still longer time in the country of the fortieth and thirtieth parallels, and so forth, because the gradual cooling of the globe has always been slower in the regions approaching the equator, due as much to the greater thickness of the globe as to the greater heat of the sun.

But this regular migration that the first and greatest animals of our continent have undergone seems to have encountered obstacles in the other continents. It is certain that armament and skeletons of elephants have been found, and it is probable that more will be found in Canada, in the country of the Illinois, in Mexico, and in other places of northern America, but we have as yet no observation that would show the same fact for the countries of southern America.

Sixth Epoch. *When the separation of the continents was effected.* The time of the separation of the continents is certainly subsequent to the time when the elephants inhabited the lands of the north, since their species existed equally in America, in Europe, and in Asia. . . .

If Europe is today separated from Greenland, it is probably because there was a considerable subsidence between the lands of Greenland and those of Norway and the point of Scotland, in which region the Orkneys, the islands of Shetland, those of Faroé, of Iceland, and of Hola appear to be only the higher portions of submerged land. If the continent of Asia is no longer contiguous to that of America toward the north, it is without doubt a consequence of a very similar change. . . .

We further imagine that not only has Greenland been joined to Norway and Scotland, but also that Canada could have been joined to Spain by the banks of Newfoundland, the Azores, and other islands and shallows which are found in this portion of the sea. . . . The submergence of this land is perhaps more modern than that of the continent of Iceland, since tradition appears to record it. The history of Atlantis,[2] reported by Diodorus and Plato, could only be applied to a very great land which stretched far to the west of Spain. . . .

Seventh Epoch. *When the power of man was added to that of nature.* The first men, witnesses of the convulsive movements of the earth, still occurring frequently, having only the mountains as asylums against floods and often driven from these same asylums by the fire of volcanos, trembling on an earth which trembled under their feet, naked of spirit and of body, exposed to the injuries of all the elements, victims of the fury of ferocious animals whose prey they were, all equally impressed with the sentiment of melancholy terror, did they not seek promptly to unite, first to defend themselves by their number, then to work together to make dwellings and gain protection? They began by sharpening those hard stones, those jades and "fire flints" in the form of hatchets that have been considered as fallen from the clouds and formed by thunder, whereas they really are the first relics of the art of man in the state of pure Nature. . . .

[2] Atlantis was a legendary island lying northwest of Africa which, according to Plato, the historian Diodorus, and others, was once inhabited by a highly civilized people but which was swallowed up by the sea in a terrible earthquake.

JAMES HUTTON

1 7 2 6 · 1 7 9 7

THE NEW METHODS of weather forecasting are today so accurate that they have raised the weather man to an important place in the councils of war and made him an indispensable factor in peace-time economics and travel. These modern techniques are based on observation of the movement of great masses of cold air from the poles and of warm air from the equator.

A little-known paper by James Hutton, "The Theory of Rain," from which we quote here, and which lay almost unseen for a century and a half, contained the first statement of some of the basic principles of this "air mass" theory. It appeared in 1788 in The Transactions of the Royal Society of Edinburgh, Vol. 1.

James Hutton was born in Edinburgh. He studied medicine at the Universities of Edinburgh, Paris, and Leyden, obtaining from the last institution the degree of Doctor of Medicine in 1749. He never, however, practiced his profession. For sixteen years he was a farmer, but, in 1768, he rented his farm and returned to live in Edinburgh. Here he devoted himself to the study of physics, metaphysics, and geology. He is best known for his book, The Theory of the Earth, in which, like Leibnitz, he emphasized the action of heat in geologic formation, and gave secondary place to the action of water and wind.

THE THEORY OF RAIN

THERE IS AN atmospherical appearance which is not explained by the known laws of heat and cold. It is the breath of animals becoming visible, in being expired into an atmosphere which is cold or moist; and the transformation of transparent steam into the state of mist, when mixed with air which is of a colder temperature. Natural philosophers have certainly considered these appearances as being explained in the general law by which heat and cold are communicated among contiguous bodies, otherwise they would have endeavored to point out this particular law, which seems to depart from a more general rule, or does not follow the natural course of things observed on other occasions. The subject of this paper is to investigate a certain rule which, in the case now mentioned, may be discovered as directing the action and effects of heat and cold; and to form a theory of rain upon that investigated rule, concerning the evaporation and condensation of water.

The air, inspired by an animal, may be considered as a menstruum [solvent] dissolving water upon the warm and humid surface of the lungs, and as thus becoming saturated with humidity in this degree of heat. When this solution is again cooled, then, according to the known laws of condensation, water must be separated from the menstruum, and become visible by reflecting light. In like manner, water may be rendered an invisible elastic fluid by means of heat alone; and this fluid, in being cooled, will be condensed into water, and appear visible. But it is now to be shown that, when breath or steam becomes visible, in mixing with the atmosphere, this effect is not produced in consequence of the general principles of heat and cold: That, for the explanation of this appearance, there is required the knowledge of a particular law; and that the effects of heat or cold, in relation to air and vapor, proceed not always in ratios which are equally increasing or diminishing. . . .

If the solution of water in air increases with heat in an equal rate, no mixture can be made of portions, in different degrees of heat, that will produce either super or undersaturation; but the mixture, like the constituent portions, will be always saturated without superfluity.

If the solution of water in air increases with heat in a decreasing rate, the mixture of two saturated portions, in different degrees of heat, will produce no condensation of humidity, but, on the contrary, will be capable of dissolving more aqueous substance.

If, on the other hand, the solution of water in air increases with heat in an increasing rate, the mixture of two saturated portions, in different degrees of heat, will produce a condensation of humidity, as being supersaturated in the medium temperature of heat.

This last case properly applies to the phenomena of breath and steam, which have been rendered visible in mixing with air that is colder than themselves; and it explains the various appearances that may occur, in mixing together several portions of air, more or less saturated with humidity, and in different temperatures of heat and cold: for it is not every mixture of the atmospheric fluid, in different temperatures, that should, according to this theory, form a visible condensation; this effect requiring, in that atmosphere, a sufficient degree of saturation with humidity. Neither is it necessary, for this effect, that the two portions to be mixed should each be saturated with humidity up to the temperature in which it is then found; it is sufficient that the difference in the temperatures of those portions to be mixed should more than compensate the defect in point of saturation. But, if a mixture shall be made of two portions of the atmosphere, both fully saturated with humidity, then, however small may be the difference of their temperatures, there is reason to believe that a condensation, proportionate to this difference, will take place.

Having thus explained the atmospherical appearance of visible mist, produced in the mixture of invisible fluids, we may now apply this rule of condensation as a principle for the theory of rain.

Rain is the distillation of water, which had been first dissolved in the atmosphere, and then condensed from that state of vapor or solution. It is the explanation of this condensation that must form the theory of rain. So far, therefore, as the condensation of aqueous vapor has been explained, and so far as the evaporation of water from the surface of the globe is understood, we have a theory for the general appearance of rain.

Water, indeed, is condensed in a cloud equally as in rain, and yet clouds may subsist without rain. But it is evident that, without condensation of aqueous vapor in the atmosphere, no rain could be produced; and that, however different causes may influence water condensed in the atmosphere, and operate variously, in either retaining it longer in a suspended state, or bringing it sooner to the ground, the condensation of the water is properly the cause of rain. We may now endeavor to confirm this theory of rain, in having again recourse to natural appearances.

The most convincing experiment, in confirmation of the theory, would be to have rain or snow produced by a mixture of portions of the atmosphere, properly conditioned for the condensation of the contained vapor. But such an experiment as this we also have. M. de Maupertuis, [1] in his *Discours sur la mesure de la terre* [Discourse on the Size of the Earth], says, That, at Tornea, upon the opening of a door, the external air immediately converts the warm vapor of the chamber into snow, which then appears in what he calls "de gros tourbillons blancs" [great, white whirlwinds]. A similar appearance happened at St. Petersburgh, anno 1773. I have it from Professor Robinson, who saw it. It was in a crowded assembly; the company suffering the closeness of the room, a gentleman broke

[1] Pierre de Maupertuis (1698-1759), a French astronomer and mathematician, was sent by Louis XV as head of an expedition to Lapland to measure a degree of longitude in that region. The town of Tornea lies at the head of the Gulf of Bothnia.

a window for relief. The cold air rushing in formed a visible cir-
cumgiration of a snowy substance.

The law of nature, on which this theory of rain is founded, may
be now considered in relation to its final cause; or how far it may
appear to be conceived in wisdom for the purpose of this world, as
affording a proper climate for plants and animals.

Had the law respecting aqueous evaporation in the atmosphere
been conceived in any other manner than that which has been now
found established in nature, the summer's heat, which is the cause
of vegetation, could never have been attended, as at present, with
refreshing showers of rain. By the circulation of the fluid atmosphere, the heat of torrid regions is carried away, and the cold of
frigid regions is brought to temper the excessive heat that is
excited upon the surface of the earth in the summer solstice; but if
no condensation of humidity in the atmosphere could be produced
by the mixture of its parts, however saturated with aqueous vapor,
and in different degrees of heat, the natural cold of the polar regions,
and the contingent cold of snows, accumulated during winter upon
the higher countries, however transported to warmer regions, would
be altogether ineffectual for the purpose of forming clouds and
condensing rain.

The present system of the atmosphere is so calculated as that
every mixture of different portions of that fluid, unequal in their
degrees of heat, and saturated with humidity, must procure a condensation of water. This system, therefore, of the atmosphere, with
this particular law in relation to heat and cold, is calculated to
produce rain, by the continual mixture of its parts, which are in
different temperatures.

In this system, we shall see that the cold regions of the polar
circles are not useless and inactive in the operations of this world.
In like manner, the frozen regions of the Alpine situations of the
Continent serve a purpose in the constitution of this earth, by preserving, in the accumulated snows, a store of the winter cold for
the summer season; and thus preparing cold portions of the

atmosphere to be mixed with the warmer portions, saturated with humidity, and ready to produce rain.

While the atmosphere is thus tempered, by transporting the heat and cold in distant regions, the regions of the earth most distant from the sea may be supplied with showers of rain at every season of the year, or at any season, according to the arrival of those streams of the atmosphere which are in the proper conditions for producing, by their mixture, a medium degree of heat, and a supersaturation or condensation of aqueous vapor. This wise system of things, or this useful purpose in the economy of the world, could not have been accomplished without that particular law of nature respecting aqueous condensation; for, if the mixing together of the atmospheric streams produced no condensation, the summer hemisphere of the globe would be parched with drought, and the winter hemisphere deluged with rain.

To see this, let us consider the summer hemisphere of the globe, warmed by the influence of the ascending sun. From the laws of hydrostatics, it will appear that there should be formed, on this occasion, two opposite currents in the atmosphere above this half of the globe, the one moving along the surface of the earth, from the polar region toward the equator, the other flowing above, in a contrary direction. This circulation, therefore, being supposed, let us see what follows, according to the actual constitution of things. On the one hand, the evaporation of the winter's moisture from the surface of the continent, warmed by the summer sun, must tend to saturate with humidity the polar atmosphere, as it acquires an evaporating power from its increasing heat; on the other hand, the progress of the upper current, from the tropic towards the pole, in having its degree of heat diminished by the general cooling cause, will naturally bring the mass to a point of saturation with the aqueous vapor which it had received. In this state of things, the two opposite currents in the atmosphere, while separate, might pass on without condensing humidity sufficient to produce rain; but the moment that sufficient portions of those saturated streams shall mix, not only cloud, but showers will be produced; because the sudden formation of a mean degree of heat, in the mixture of two portions in different temperatures, must condense a quantity of vapor sufficient to form rain.

Rain having fallen in a place, in consequence of the mixture in the atmosphere above, will naturally be followed by clearness in the sky and sunshine, which is so necessary for warming the surface of the earth, and for giving health and vigor to growing plants.

But, without the particular law now investigated, respecting evaporation and condensation of vapor, neither rain nor dew could be produced upon the summer hemisphere of the globe, nor perhaps ever in tropical latitudes; evaporation would everywhere take place, more or less; the general tendency would be to saturate the atmosphere with water, or fill it with vapor in its greatest heat; and the mixture of the different parts of the atmosphere would only conduce to temper the saturation, without producing any condensation of vapor in the mean degrees of heat. But when, in consequence of the declining sun, the influence of the general cooling cause should prevail, the atmosphere would gradually become clouded, and be darkened. This cloudiness would increase to a general distillation of the condensed vapor; and this distillation would be uniformly continued, until the returning summer should change the state of condensation to that of evaporation. . . .

We may now proceed to consider the natural appearances which generally attend rain in this island, with a view to recommend the theory, in showing that such mixtures actually take place.

1. If the mixing together of different streams of the atmosphere be the cause of rain, calmness or steady breezes should be the attendants of fair weather; but this, in general, is the case. The converse of this is also true; for partial showers never happen without wind, although general rains, or such as are produced in the higher regions of the atmosphere, may be attended with a calm or fall without disturbance, in the place of our observation. Now, the truth of the proposition is manifested in this, that, by people

who reason from the immediate observation alone, wind is attributed to the shower as an effect, when it may more truly be considered as standing in the relation of a cause.

2. When, in calm weather, rain begins, it is reasonable to expect that this should be followed by wind; and, in like manner, if in windy weather it begins to rain, it may be reasonable to expect that the wind should calm, after a certain period, with the rain. These undoubtedly are the general appearances; and these appearances are explained upon this principle, that wind is the cause of rain, and that, in the opposition of winds, a calm may be produced.

3. During a calm and clear sky, showers never happen; but with squalls of wind, sudden showers appear. In calm weather, before it rains, the heaven is all overclouded, and the rain becomes general, equable, and not in spots: But, when attended with wind, the rain is unsteady; one while, the spot around us is involved in the thickest cloud and heavy rain; another while, it is under the clearest sky; and these alternate operations in the atmosphere of thickening and clearing continue during the squally weather.

4. These facts are from my own observation; and they necessarily imply the mixture of hot and cold streams of air for the production of rain. But sometimes this operation is a thing visible in itself; for when, by means of the motion of the clouds, the atmosphere is perceived to be moved in opposite directions, here, it is evident, nothing is required besides the proper conditions in those mixing streams for the condensation of rain. Now, I have had it from experienced seamen, men of great knowledge and observation, that, in our Channel, they had often occasion to remark this opposition in the winds, or the clouds going against the wind, as being a sure mark of heavy rain to follow.

5. The changes in the temperature of our atmosphere attend the alterations of rain and fair weather no less evidently than those changes happen in consequence of changes in the streams of wind. If the wind has blown from the southern and warmer regions, replete with humidity, it brings warmer weather, and this may con-

tinue to be fair; but, when rain succeeds, it is generally found that a change of wind succeeds the rain, and then the air becomes more cold. In like manner, if a cold north wind prevails, it may continue fair; but, when rain succeeds, there is commonly a change in the wind, and also in the temperature of the atmosphere. And, in general, as many alterations as shall happen in the prevalencies of those different winds or streams of hot and cold atmosphere, so many repetitions have we of the rain.

Upon the coast of Hudson's Bay, while the thermometer is at 90 degrees, with calmness and a sky perfectly serene, it is common for a sudden gust of wind to come from the northwest, with such violence as to threaten oversetting everything; and along with the blast, there comes a shower of snow or hail. This lasts only a short space of time; it clears up, grows calm and serene, as before; but the temperature of the air has much changed; from 90 the thermometer will fall to 50 degrees for a short space of time, and then it gradually rises to the ordinary heat. This observation, which I have from my friend, Mr. Graeme, a gentleman of great accuracy, who lived long in that country, points out clearly the agitation of the atmosphere as being the cause of rain, and not its consequence. It also demonstrates the sudden mixture, in the atmosphere, of air which for the season is extremely cold, compared with the general temperature of the atmosphere upon this continent.

But in the application of these general rules to particular cases of observation, it must always be considered that though intestine commotion, or mixture of the atmosphere, be necessarily required in order to produce rain, it is not every mixture or commotion in the atmosphere that will be followed by this effect; for though mixture of the atmosphere be a necessary condition in the cause of rain, it is not the only condition; and, therefore, the same appearances, in relation to the winds, and to the different temperatures of the atmosphere, may be observed, while rain, as the effect, may either follow or not, according as the third condition may or may not take place: That is, that the mixed atmosphere be sufficiently saturated with vapor or humidity; which is a thing that cannot perhaps be made a subject of our observation.

6. Rain happens in the hottest weather, and in every degree of temperature, down to the freezing point; it requires, therefore, much attention to observe the changes of temperature in the atmosphere that usually attend the production of rain, in all this range of the thermometer from 80 to 32 degrees. But, about the freezing point, the effects of heat and cold are so manifest, in the fluidity and congelation of water, that a person can hardly avoid making observations which will tend to confirm the theory.

When, after settled frost, it begins to snow, the cold is always found to relent, and the thermometer to rise to the freezing point or nearly, however low it may have been before. But after the snow has fallen, and the sky becomes clear, the cold increases, until it again resumes its former intensity, or even proceeds to a greater degree. This is an appearance which is easily explained in the theory; and it is an appearance which every person who can make an observation has it frequently in his power to verify.

7. The climate which we inhabit has, for character, temperance in extreme; our winters and our summers differ but little from each other in their mean temperatures. There is, in this island, but little steady determination for the wind, which, in general, is extremely variable. The variable nature of our winds cannot be the effect of the temperance of our climate; but the temperance of our climate may, in some measure, be produced in consequence of the variable nature of our winds. So far as this is the case, that the mixture of different streams of the atmosphere temperates the heat and cold of our air, this operation should be attended with proportionate condensation of aqueous vapor. Here the theory is brought to the test of observation. But, before deciding the point in question, let us understand what it is which, in observation, should be decisive with respect to the theory.

It is not the quantity of rain which falls during the year, nor in any portion of it, that affords a principle by which to form a judgment in relation to the present question; for it is the continuance of rain, and not the quantity, that is the object of enquiry. The number of days and hours, throughout the year, in which it rains, is no doubt a proper subject for our observation, in order to form an estimate with regard to the point in question; but it is not itself that point in question. The point is the condensation of aqueous vapor in the atmosphere; and though no rain can fall without the condensation of aqueous vapor, there may be much condensation of that vapor, without rain, as a testimony of that event. Thus we are led to direct our observation to other phenomena besides rain; appearances which may be equally conclusive, in relation to the point to be decided, with rain itself. Now these appearances, in which the condensation of aqueous vapor is equally demonstrated with that of rain, are no other than cloudiness in our atmosphere.

The question respecting the theory being now brought to this issue with regard to observation, it may be demanded what is the proportion of serene sky and cloudiness in the atmosphere that properly belongs to this climate? Here is a question proposed that requires extreme exactness in its answer. I believe everybody, from their recollection, will allow that, for one day or hour of clear sunshine, there are two or three of cloudiness in the atmosphere; and this is sufficient for determining the question, whether or not the condensation of aqueous vapor be prevalent in the climate of this island.

8. Cloudiness in the sky being a demonstration of the aqueous condensation in the atmosphere, in like manner as is the case with rain, this appearance may now be examined with regard to the temperature of the air, in relation to heat and cold, that commonly attends on this occasion. Let us begin with summer; and suppose the weather to be warm; that is, precisely in the natural temperature of the season. There is no question with regard to the effect of a clear sky or continued sunshine: Heat is certainly the effect of sunshine; and this heat is accumulated in the earth, *caeteris paribus* [other things being equal], in proportion to the intensity of the light

and the duration of the illumination. The question now to be examined is this, what should be the effect of condensation of aqueous vapor in the atmosphere at this season, and in this summer temperature; that is to say, whether should heat or cold be the consequence of this operation?

Nothing is so easy as to answer this question. We suppose the atmosphere in the mean temperature of the summer season, and that a condensation of aqueous vapor is produced by the admixture of a current of atmosphere in a different temperature. Now, as this effect may be produced by the admixture of air either hotter or colder than our atmosphere, which is supposed to be quite serene, the effect must be a change of the temperature of our atmosphere, either to a greater or a less degree of heat than its mean temperature for the season, according as the supervening atmosphere, producing cloudiness in our sky, shall be either hotter or colder, in its temperature, than that in which we had been involved immediately before.

From this conclusion, we will now draw a practical observation, which may be of some utility in trying the theory and explaining appearances. If the heat of the atmosphere be, at any time, above its mean temperature for the season, and a change shall happen from a serene sky to cloudiness, we have reason to expect that the extreme heat will be temperated, and the atmosphere consequently cooled. But if the temperature of our atmosphere be below its mean heat for the season, then, from the change of clearness for a cloudy sky, we have reason to look for a change from cold to hot.

From this also we have a proper explanation of a general appearance, with regard to the serenity of the sky, in every climate, and and in the opposite seasons of summer and winter; for this serene sky, or clear atmosphere, is perfectly consistent with the two extremities of temperature; that is, with that of heat upon the one hand, and of cold upon the other. It is only a mixture of those two extremes, that is to say, of hot and cold atmosphere, which produces, at the same time, cloudiness to the sight and temperance in relation to the sense of heat and cold. Thus will be explained a common observation with regard to the weather of this country, that the air is always cold, below its mean temperature for the season, when the sky is clear. The country people allege that it is then frost, even in the midst of summer. They probably find hoar-frost early in the morning, especially in the higher parts of the country; and surely the making of ice in Bengal justifies that observation.

9. The formation of hail is evidently upon the same principle as that of snow. The one is, therefore, equally with the other, explained by the theory. There are, however, peculiarities in the production of hail, which do not take place in that of snow; but these peculiar circumstances are to us, perhaps, unknown; and as there is nothing in the appearance of hail that is in any respect inconsistent with the theory, the confounding of snow and hail brings no error into our science, nor affects the doctrine with the least uncertainty. Hail is evidently formed by the collection of smaller molecules, which ultimately are of the nature of snow; and it is probably by means of electrical attraction that this collection is performed.

10. There is one appearance more that often attends rain and, therefore, should be considered; this is thunder, which so frequently accompanies violent and sudden rain. But as we are ignorant of any principle upon which electricity should be the cause of condensing aqueous vapor in the atmosphere, this is not the place for examining what may be the effects of electricity with regard to aqueous vapor condensed from its elastic state, farther than that it is most reasonable, and also consistent with appearances, to suppose a more sudden attraction of the condensed particles of water than what happens upon other occasions, where even a degree of electrical repulsion may preserve them from immediate contact, and protract the fall of rain by suspending the condensed vapor in form of mist.

VI

How Plants Grow

DURING THE Middle Ages, plants were studied largely for their actual or supposed medicinal virtues. Books about plants were written by herbalists, who were more interested in descriptions of the uses of herbs than in the study of how the plants themselves grew. A typical "herbal" would give the names of a few hundred or thousand specimens in from two to five languages, describe the superficial appearance and habitat of each, state its medicinal value, and how to gather and prepare it for use. The herbals were usually illustrated with hundreds of plates, but in the earlier books these were so crude and formalized that it would be difficult to recognize the plant from the picture. Very often both the pictures and the text were taken from still older works of different periods.

Ancient remedies popular in the Middle Ages were: the peony for lunacy, heliotrope for snakebite, ivy for dropsy, pennyroyal and wormwood for seasickness. Often herbs were classified according to the old pattern of the Greek physician Galen, as either hot or cold, dry or moist, and the ailments for which each might be used were listed accordingly, a "dry" herb, for example, for a "moist" ailment.

In the middle of the sixteenth century a few European universities introduced the study of botany for its own sake, quite apart from the cultivation of plants for healing. The universities of Padua and Pisa were among the first to take this step. But even after the establishment of the Chelsea Physic Garden in London by the great Apothecaries Company in 1676, it was still expected that the garden should yield a stock of "physic plants or simples" for the members.

An effort to recover all the medicinal plants known to the Greeks led to some extensive comparative studies of plants in European countries. Usually, however, each new investigator merely added his findings to an already existing list. It was difficult then for a reader to tell whether he could depend on any one description as reliable or not. William Turner, an English scholar and churchman whose hobby was botany, performed a valuable service in the several volumes he wrote on the subject between 1538 and 1564 by putting emphasis on first-hand observation. He boasted that he made no mention of old authors. "I would not be," he said, "like unto a cryer that cryeth a lost horse in the market and telleth all the marks and tokens that it hath, and yet neither saw the horse, neither could know the horse if he saw it. I went into Italy and into divers parts of Germany to know and see the herbes myself, and to know by practice their powers and working, not trusting only to the old herbwives and apothecaries, as many physicians have done of late years."

Clusius of Antwerp (1525-1609) gave first-hand accounts of the rarer flora of France, Spain, Portugal, Austria, and Hungary, and wrote also on the flora of the Levant and India. Pietro Andrea Mattioli (1501-1577) identified by his own observations many of the Italian plants mentioned by the ancients. Kaspar Bauhin (1560-1624) of Basle, a student of Fabricius ab Aquapendente at Padua, [1] pronounced the existing systems of naming plants a hopeless confusion. He introduced a two-name system (still in use as modified later by Linnaeus), and in a great work on botanical synonyms assigned class names to 6000 varieties. He showed how plants should be named and described so that they could be accurately recognized, and worked out a natural method of classification.

Andrea Cesalpini (1519-1603), on the other hand, classified plants by their fruits, taking that single part of the plant as the most convenient basis for his system of organization. This was an "artificial" rather than a "natural" system, for the latter would be based on the characteristics

[1] See below, p. 485.

of the plant as a whole. Linnaeus choose another single feature of the plant, its reproductive organs, as a basis for his artificial classification pattern, and although he looked to find a better natural basis, his work continues to be the foundation for the system in common use today.

Up to the year 1600 most of the attention of botanists had been spent on the collection and classification of plants, rather than on the study of plant growth. From that point on three new influences began to affect the course of botanical study. The invention of the microscope made possible observation of the minute details of plant anatomy. The growing interest in animal physiology led to more interest in the physiology of plants. The development of chemistry brought about studies of the chemical side of vegetable life.

Van Helmont and Priestley, from whom we quote below, were interested chiefly in chemistry; their experiments were concerned with the nature of "elements," the word "element" meaning something less definite and tangible than it does today. Grew and Malpighi worked on plant anatomy and cell structure. Hales and Ingenhousz concentrated more on physiological problems: how do plants grow, what is their food, and how do they utilize it? Linnaeus himself belonged in the encyclopedic tradition of the herbalists; but with his genius for organization he brought order into their random patterns of classification. He took the flower stamens and pistils, the reproductive mechanism of plants, as the basis for his system of classification, and therefore developed a special interest in the sex of plants.

JOHANN BAPTISTA VAN HELMONT

1 5 7 7 · 1 6 4 4

A CAREFUL quantitative study, from which the wrong conclusions were drawn, is the subject of the first selection in this section. In order to prove that "all salt, clay, and indeed all tangible bodies are really and materially the product of water only, and may be reduced again to water by nature or art," van Helmont, first, produced a liquid by a distillation of wood, and argued that the escaping gases too could be reduced to "water" by condensation.[1] But in order to make his demonstration complete, he felt it necessary to show also that water could be turned into wood. The passage below is his account of this second experiment, and his conclusions.

Van Helmont was born in 1577 of a noble family in Brussels. He studied classics at the University of Louvain, visited London, and returned to devote himself to the medical care of the poor. His work brought him into contact with the medicinal chemistry of Paracelsus,[2] which started him off on chemical researches of his own, particularly with gases. He was, incidentally, the first to employ the word gas. The term, however, did not become popular until Lavoisier reintroduced it. The selection which follows is from the Oriatrike, or Physick Refined, published in Latin in 1648, and translated into English by K. J. Chandler, in 1662.

[1] For another discussion of this same question, see Boyle's *Sceptical Chymist,* above, pp. 248 to 257.
[2] See above, p. 211.

IS WOOD MADE OF WATER?

ALL EARTH, CLAY, and every body that may be touched, is truly and materially the offspring of water onely, and is reduced again into water, by nature and art. . . . Water always remains whole as it is; or without any dividing of the three beginnings,[1] it is transformed and goes into fruits whither the Seedes do call and withdraw it. . . . For an Element should cease to be a simple body if it is to be separated into anything before or more simple than itself. But nothing in corporeall things is granted to be before, or more simple than an element.

But I have learned by this handicraft-operation, that all Vegetables do immediately and materially proceed out of the Element of water onely. For I took an Earthen vessel in which I put two hundred pounds of Earth that had been dried in a Furnace, which I moystened with Rainwater, and I implanted therein the Trunk, or Stem, of a Willow Tree, weighing five pounds; and at length, five years being finished, the Tree sprung from thence did weigh one hundred and sixty-nine pounds, and about three ounces: But I moystened the Earthen vessel with Rainwater, or distilled water (alwayes when there was need) . . . and least the dust should be co-mingled with the Earth, I covered the lip or mouth of the Vessel, with an Iron Plate covered with Tin, and easily passable with many holes, I computed not the weight of the leaves that fell off, in the four Autumnes. At length, I again dried the Earth of the Vessel, and there were found the same two hundred pounds, wanting about two ounces. Therefore one hundred and sixty-four pounds of

---

[1] According to Paracelsus, there were three elemental substances or "beginnings,"—salt, sulphur, and mercury, from which all other solid matter was derived.

Wood, Barks, and Roots arose out of water onely. . . . Fire indeed destroyeth simple but it generates nothing. . . . Therefore Wood, since it is wholly of *water*, the ashes . . . shall be of water.

NEHEMIAH GREW

1 6 4 1 · 1 7 1 2

THE HISTORY of science is full of accounts of bitter rivalries and disputes among men working in the same field. We rarely hear of such pleasant mutual respect and cooperation as existed between the Italian, Malpighi, and the Englishman, Grew, in the field of vegetable anatomy.

Nehemiah Grew, the son of an anti-Royalist clergyman, took his bachelor's degree at Cambridge in 1661. In 1664 he started his study of vegetable anatomy, with little technical background but with the firm conviction that "both plants and animals came at first out of the same hand, and were therefore the contrivances of the same wisdom." His first paper on the subject was read at a meeting of the Royal Society of London in 1670, and printed at the order of the Society in 1671. That same year Marcello Malpighi (1628-1694), the founder of microscopic anatomy, sent the results of ten years of his own investigations in the anatomy of plants to the Royal Society, where they also were read. Grew spoke enthusiastically of the work of the brilliant Italian, and would modestly have retired from further studies in this area. He was, that same year, taking his degree as Doctor of Medicine at Leyden.

However, the members of the Society urged him to continue his botanical studies, and appointed him Curator to the Royal Society for the Anatomy of Plants. Malpighi, for his part, had Grew's work translated into Latin. "These two scientists," says Nordenskiöld in his History of Biology, "improved vegetable anatomy so far that it was to take more than a century before any important addition could be made to their work. Through them biology acquired its knowledge of organized matter as being something peculiar in its structure; the idea of tissue was established . . . also the simple elements of the tissues—the cells—were observed and described."

When the value of his work became recognized, Grew lived quietly in London, dividing his time between medicine, his botanical researches, and his duties as Secretary of the Royal Society, a position he shared jointly with Robert Hooke.

His major work, The Anatomy of Plants, dealing with the various parts and functions of plants, was published in English in the year 1682. In his introduction he said "that even a Plant lives partly upon Aer." He failed, however, to discover the part that leaves play in the assimilation of air. The function of leaves, he thought, was to afford protection to the plant, purify the sap, and hold supplies of sap. The chapter on the leaves of flowers, quoted below, together with the illustrations, shows something of his scrupulous methods of description and organization.

THE ANATOMY OF PLANTS

To His Most Sacred Majesty Charles II, King of Britain, &c.

May it please Your Majesty,

THE DEDICATION of one Part of the following Anatomy having been very graciously received by Your Majesty, I am now emboldened most humbly to present the Whole into Your Royal Hands.

By which Your Majesty will find, That there are Terrae Incognitae in philosophy, as well as Geography. And for so much as lies here, it comes to pass, I know not how, even in this Inquisitive Age, That I am the first, who have given a Map of the Country.

Your Majesty will here see, That there are those things within a Plant, little less admirable, than within an Animal. That a Plant, as well as an Animal, is composed of several Organical Parts; some whereof may be called its Bowels. That every Plant hath Bowels of divers kinds, conteining divers kinds of Liquors. That even a Plant lives partly upon Aer; for the reception whereof, it hath those Parts which are answerable to Lungs. So that a Plant is, as it were, an Animal in Quires; as an Animal is a Plant, or rather several Plants, bound up into one Volume.

Again, that all the said Organs, Bowels, or other Parts, are as artificially made; and for their Place and Number, as punctually set together; as all the Mathematick Lines of a Flower or Face. That the Staple of the Stuff is so exquisitely fine, that no Silkworm is able to draw any thing near so small a Thred. So that one who walks about with the meanest Stick, holds a Piece of Natures Handicraft, which far surpasses the most elaborate Woof or Needle-Work in the World.

397

That by all these Means, the Ascent of the Sap, the Distribution of the Aer, the Confection of several sorts of Liquors, as Lympha's, Milks, Oyls, Balsames; with other parts of Vegetation, are all contrived and brought about in a Mechanical way.

In sum, Your Majesty will find, that we are come ashore into a new World, whereof we see no end.

It may be, that some will say, into another Utopia. Yet not I, but Nature speaketh these things: the only true Pallas, wherewith it is treasonable for the most curiously handed Arachne [1] to compare. In whose Name, I, the meanest of her Pupils, do in all humility crave your Majesties Gracious Patronage. Whereof I cannot doubt, since Your Majesty hath been pleased to be the Founder, and to style Your Self the Patron of that Society, of which I have the honour to be a Member. Your Majesty deeming it to be a more Noble Design, To enlarge the Territories of Knowledge, than those of Dominion; and the Highest Pitch of Human Glory, not to rule, in any sort, over many; but to be a Good Prince over Wise Men, I am

Your Majesties most humble and
Most obedient Subject
Nehemiah Grew

Of the Foliature

1. The Leaves of the Flower are folded up in such Sort as is most agreeable to their own shape, and that of their enclosed Attire: [2] whereof I have given instances in the Fifth Book. I shall here add some further Remarques.

2. The Leaves of the Flower of Blataria, although of different Size and Shape, are so lapped one over another, as to make an Equilateral Pentangle.

---

[1] Arachne was a maiden who in Greek legend challenged the great goddess Pallas Athene to a contest in fine weaving. As a punishment she was changed into a spider.

[2] Old botanists gave the name "attire" to the parts of a flower enclosed with the corolla, such as the stamens, or the florets of a compound flower.

3. The Spiral Fold, which is proper to the Flower, and never seen in the Green Leaves, as it is itself immediately visible on the Surface, so by cutting off the top of the Flower before it is expanded, seems also to make a Helix; [3] as in Periwinkle, the larger Convolvulus, &c.

4. In some flowers, where the Attire is lofty or spreading, as in Holioak, together with the Spiral Fold, the Leaves are all at the top tacked down a little; thereby making a blunter cone, and so a more ample Pyramid for the inclosed Attire.

5. In Poppy, although the Leaves are extraordinary broad, yet being but few, and inclosing a small Attire, they could not be reduced to any regular Fold, without leaving such a vacuity, as by being filled with Aer, might be prejudicial to the Seed. For which reason, they are cramb'd up within the Empalement by hundreds of little Wrinkles or Puckers, as if Three or Four fine Cambrick Handkerchiefs were thrust into ones Pocket. . . .

8. Of the Hairs upon Flowers and their Use to the Attire, I have also spoken in the First Book. I shall here add, That they are likewise of Use to the Leaves themselves, that is, for their closer and faster Conjunction. For of some Flowers it is observable, That they are all over smooth, saving on their Edges, which are bordered with Fringes of Hair; as of Spanish Broome, Dulcamara, and others: In which, the Hairs on the Edge of one Leaf are so complicated, or at least indented, with those of another, that all the Leaves seem to be but one piece. Nature seeing it fit, by this means to tie them together, lest they should be expanded before it be due time.

9. Many Flowers instead of Hairs are beset round about with a great Number of small Parts, not ending in a Poynt, but having a Head. Sometimes oval, as in Snap-Dragon, like the Horns of a Butterfly, or a Plummers Sodering-Iron. But usually Globular, as in Deadly Nightshade, like so many little Mushrooms sprouting out of the Flower.

[3] That is, a coil or spiral.

10. Out of these Heads, doth sometimes issue a Gummy or Balsamick Juyce. From whence proceeds that Clamminess of some Flowers, whereby, being handled they stick to our Fingers, as do those of Blattaria, and of Marigold; and those of Colus Jovis, where the said Heads are so soft and succulent, that they resemble so many little Drops of Balsame. The Clamminess which is felt upon fresh Carduus may perhaps proceed from the like Cause.

11. The Number of the Leaves of the Flower hath been noted by the Learned Sir Thomas Brown, to be usually Five. And this Nature so far affecteth, that many times where the Leaves of the same Flower are of a different Size, yet they keep to this Number, as in Blattaria.

12. I also add, That even those Flowers, which are not properly parted into Leaves have yet their Tops usually divided into Five great Scallops; as those of Toad-Flax, Snap-Dragon, Coded-Arsmart, Clary, Broom, and others. And when the Flower hath more than Five, even many times Five Leaves, yet the top of each Leaf is indented into Five Parts, as in Scorzonera, Cichory, and all the Intybous Kind, with many others. . . .

14. The number of the Leaves, as hath been said, is commonly Five. Yet some Flowers have fewer, and some more, and that with constancy, in divers numbers, from One to One and Twenty, perhaps in all so far. The Flower of Acanthus Syriacus, is in a manner one single Leaf, that of Monks-Rubarb, Three-Leav'd; of Poppy, Crosswort, Radish, and many others, Four-Leav'd; the greater Number of Flowers, Five-Leav'd of White Hellebore, Tulip, Onion, and most Plants with Bulbous Roots, Six-Leav'd; of French Marigold, commonly Eight-Leav'd; of Flower de luce, Nine-Leav'd; of Chickweed, Ladies-Mantle, Ten-Leav'd; of St. James Wort, Thirteen-Leav'd; and I think Febrifuge, Cotula, Ageratum, Corn-Marigold, with others, and of Chamomile, Buphthalmum, and some few more, the Leaves are commonly One and Twenty. In that of St. James's Wort, the Number is so constant that there is scarce one Flower in Forty, wherein the Leaves are more or fewer than

Thirteen. Divers of which Numbers seem also to have some relation to the Number 5. For 9 is Twice; 13, Thrice; and 25, Five times 5 running into itself.

15. The Constituent Parts of the Flower are the same as those of the Leaf, sc. the Parenchyma or Pulp, and the Vessels. But in the Basis on Bottom of the Flower, the Parenchyma is commonly much more spongy and dry, than in the Leaves; conteining, after the Flower is open'd, little or no Sap, but only a dry and warm Aer. Which standing continually under the Seed, hastens the Maturation or due Exiccation thereof: as we used to dry Maulted Barly over a warm Kiln.

16. The Vessels of the Flower are both for Sap and for Aer, as well as in other Parts. And for both of them sometimes, even in the Skin of the Flower; as may be argued from its being stained with divers Colours; produced as hath formerly been shewed, by the mixed Tinctures of the said Vessels. These Colours, in many Flowers, as Tulips, as they are in the Skin itself, so therein only; the Pulp of the Leaf being white.

17. The Lignons or Sap-Vessels are fewer, and the Aer-Vessels smaller in the Flower than in the Leaf. And therefore it is very difficult to observe the latter by Glasses;[1] especially the Proportion which they hold to the other Parts. But if you break the Leaves of some Flowers with very great gentleness, they may hereby be Unroaved [separated] or drawn out, as in the Green Leaves, to some visible length; and their different Number in divers Flowers may be discerned.

18. The use of the Flower or of the Foliature whereof we are speaking is various; as hath formerly been shewed. I now only add, That one Use hereof seemeth to be for the Separation of the more Volatile and stronger Sulphur of the Plant. That so the Seed, which lyeth within or next it, may be so much the milder, and the Principles thereof more fixed and concentred. And this, both for its

[1] That is, microscopes.

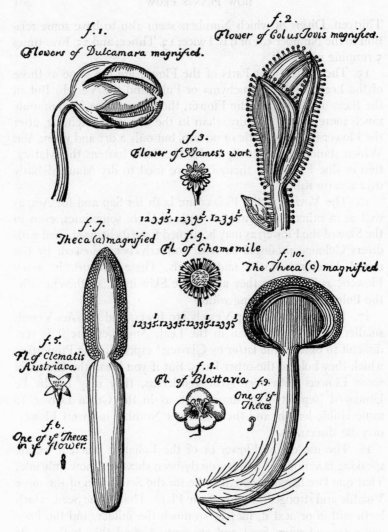

f. 1.
Flowers of Dulcamara magnified.

f. 2.
Flower of Colus Jovis magnified.

f. 3.
Flower of St James's wort.

f. 7.
Theca (a) magnified

12395. 12395. 12395

f. 9.
Fl. of Chamemile

f. 10.
The Theca (c) magnified

12395. 12395. 12395. 12395

f. 5.
Fl. of Clematis
Austriaca

f. 8.
Fl. of Blattaria *f. 9.*
One of ye
Theca

f. 6.
One of ye Thecæ
in ye flower.

The petals of flowers, from *The Anatomy of Plants*
by Nehemiah Grew, 1682.

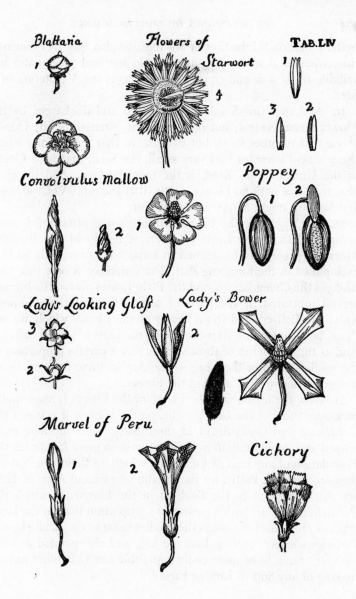

Blattaria

1

2

Flowers of

Starwort

4

TAB. LIV

1

3   2

Convolvulus mallow

2   1

Poppey

1   2

Lady's Looking Glass

3

2

Lady's Bower

2

Marvel of Peru

1   2

Cichory

better Duration till the time of Sowing; and also, that its Fermentation, when it is sow'n, may not be too hot and precipitate; but suitable to so slow and equal a motion, as is the Vegetation of a Seed.

19. And that this Sulphur is separated and discharged by the Flower seems evident, not only from the Strength of the Odour, above that of other Parts; but likewise, in that many times where there is no Flower, or that very small, the Seed, that is its Cover, in the Umbelliferous Kind, is the more odorous. And therefore also, the Vine hath no Flower, partly, that the most Volatile Spirit and Sulphur might all run into the Fruit.

20. The Figure of the Flower, although it is often much more complex than of the Leaf: yet there is no doubt but that the Measure hereof may be defined in some way, answerable to that exemplified in the foregoing Part. The difference is only this, that whereas the Green Leaves, and the Plain Leaves also of the Flower, are all measured by the parts of several Circles: those Flowers which are Bellyed, and those Leaves of the Flower which are not Plain, but Convex, are all measured by the parts of several Spheres. And as the Diametres of those Circles bear a certain proportion to the midle stemm of the Leaf; so the Aex of these Spheres, to an imaginary one in the Centre of the Flower.

21. Now the reason why the Figure of the Flower is more multiplex than those of the Leaf may be, partly, because it is under the Command and Government of those Salts which are here more refined and depurate than in the Leaf; and so more free to lay the Foundation of any kind of Figure, for which, of their own Nature, they are adapted. Partly, for that as the nitrous and Alkaline Salts are chiefly regnant in the Leaf; so in the Flower, in which the Parenchymous Part hath a greater (a) proportion than in the Leaf; it is most reasonable to assign the Predominion to the Acid; (b) the Particles whereof, both as they are less, and also pointed at both ends, (c) seem to be more easily applicable one to another for the making of any Sort of Line or Figure.

STEPHEN HALES

1 6 7 7 · 1 7 6 1

THE INTRODUCTION of strict quantitative methods and rigorous scientific thinking into the whole study of biology was the contribution of a gentle and pious Anglican clergyman.

Stephen Hales studied theology at Cambridge, took holy orders, and devoted himself assiduously to parish matters, prison reform, and other works of charity. At Cambridge, however, he had also studied physics, chemistry, and botany; and these formed the background for his scientific avocations, which though to him of secondary importance, assured him a notable place in biological history.

Hales was the first man to bring the exact methods of physics, systematically and on a large scale, to the study of living things. Some of the methods he invented to determine the pressure exerted by sap in plants are in common use today in the study of agriculture. Like Newton, he sought to find the mechanical laws governing the processes he examined, and avoided merely hypothetical explanations.

He sprinkled potted plants with measured quantities of water and weighed the plants daily, to find the water consumption. He measured the surfaces of leaves and stems, to calculate the ratio between the surface area of the plant and the amount of water absorbed. By similar means he calculated the quantity of water that various plants absorbed from the earth by their roots, and the speed with which sap circulated through the plants. He maintained that plants absorbed air through their leaves rather than through their roots, as former biologists had believed. It was perhaps no more than an inspired guess, but he held the view that leaves convert a part of the air into

solid substances, and that light, penetrating the leaves, helps the
digestive processes. But he spoke half a century before much was
definitely known about the chemistry of the air.

For his scientific work Hales was awarded the Copley medal of
the Royal Society and was appointed one of the eight foreign members of the French Academy. His Vegetable Statics, published in
1727, from which the following excerpts are taken, was translated
into French, German, Dutch, and Italian.

THE PRESSURE OF SAP IN PLANTS

The Introduction

THE FARTHER researches we make into this admirable scene of things, the more beauty and harmony we see in them: And the stronger and clearer convictions they give us, of the being, power and wisdom of the divine Architect, who has made all things to concur with a wonderful conformity, in carrying on, by various and innumerable combinations of matter, such a circulation of causes and effects, as was necessary to the great ends of nature.

And since we are assured that the all-wise Creator has observed the most exact proportions, *of number, weight and measure,* in the make of all things; the most likely way therefore, to get any insight into the nature of those parts of the creation, which come within our observation, must in all reason be to number, weigh, and measure. And we have much encouragement to pursue this method of searching into the nature of things, from the great success that has attended any attempts of this kind.

Thus, in relation to those Planets which revolve about our Sun, the great Philosopher of our age [1] has, by numbering and measuring, discovered the exact proportions that are observed in their periodical revolutions and distances from their common centres of motion and gravity: And that God has not only *comprehended the dust of the earth in a measure, and weighed the mountains in scales, and the hills in a balance* (Isai. xl. 12), but that he also holds the vast revolving Globes, of this our solar System, most exactly poised on their common centre of gravity.

And if we reflect upon the discoveries that have been made in the

[1] Sir Isaac Newton.

animal economy, we shall find that the most considerable and rational accounts of it have been chiefly owing to the statical examination of their fluids, viz, by inquiring what quantity of fluids, and solids dissolved into fluids, the animal daily takes in for its support and nourishment: And with what force and different rapidities those fluids are carried about in their proper channels, according to the different secretions that are to be made from them: And in what proportion the recrementitious [excremental] fluid is conveyed away, to make room for fresh supplies; and what portion of this recrement nature allots to be carried off by the several kinds of emunctories [cleansing organs] and excretory ducts.

And since in vegetables, their growth and the preservation of their vegetable life is promoted and maintained, as in animals, by the very plentiful and regular motion of their fluids, which are the vehicles ordained by nature to carry proper nutriment to every part; it is therefore reasonable to hope that in them also, by the same method of inquiry, considerable discoveries may in time be made, there being, in many respects, a great analogy between plants and animals.

The Force of Sap in Vegetables

. . . . I was endeavouring by several ways to stop the bleeding of an old stem of a Vine, which was cut too near the bleeding season, which I feared might kill it. Having, after other means proved ineffectual, tied a piece of bladder over the transverse cut of the Stem, I found the force of the Sap did greatly extend the bladder; whence I concluded, that if a long glass tube were fixed there in the same manner as I had before done to the Arteries of several living Animals, I should thereby obtain the real ascending force of the Sap in that Stem, which succeeded according to my expectation: and hence it is that I have been insensibly led on to make farther and farther researches by variety of Experiments.

As the Art of Physick [medicine] has of late years been much improved by a greater knowledge of the animal economy; so doubtless a farther insight into the vegetable economy must needs proportionately improve our skill in Agriculture and Gardening, which gives me reason to hope that inquiries of this kind will be acceptable to many who are intent upon improving those innocent, delightful, and beneficial Arts: Since they cannot be insensible that the most rational ground for Success in this laudable Pursuit must arise from a greater insight into the nature of Plants.

Finding by many Experiments in the fifth chapter, that the Air is plentifully inspired by Vegetables, not only at their roots, but also thro' several parts of their trunks and branches; this put me upon making a more particular inquiry into the nature of the Air, and to discover, if possible, wherein its great importance to the life and support of Vegetables might consist; on which account I was obliged to delay the Publication of the rest of these Experiments, which were read two years since before the Royal Society, till I had made some progress in this inquiry: An account of which I have given in the sixth chapter.

Experiment XLVI

In *August*, I cut off the bark, for an inch round, of a young thriving Oak-branch, on the North-west side of the tree. The leaves of this and another branch, which had the bark cut at the same time, fell early, viz, about the latter end of *October*, when the leaves of all the other branches of the same tree, except those at the very top of the tree, continued on all the winter.

This is a further proof that less sap goes to branches which have the bark cut off than to others.

The 19th of *April* following, the buds of this branch were 5 or 7 days forwarder than those of other branches of the same tree; the reason of which may probably be because less fresh crude sap coming to this branch than the others, and the perspirations in all branches being, *caeteris paribus*, [other things being equal] nearly equal, the lesser quantity of sap in this branch must sooner be inspissated [thickened] into a glutinous substance, fit for new productions, than the sap of other branches that abounded with a greater plenty of fresh thin sap.

The same is the reason why Apples, Pears, and many other fruits, which have some of their great sap-vessels eaten asunder by insects bred in them, are ripe many days before the rest of the fruit on the same trees; as also that fruit which is gathered some time before it is ripe will ripen sooner than if it had hung on the tree, tho' it will not be so good; because in these cases the worm-eaten fruit is deprived of part of its nourishment, and the green-gathered fruit of all.

And for the same reason some fruits are sooner ripe towards the tops of the trees than the other fruit on the same tree; viz, not only because they are more exposed to the sun; but also, because being at a greater distance from the root, they have somewhat less nourishment.

And this is, doubtless, one reason why plants and fruits are forwarder in dry, sandy, or gravelly soils than in moister soils; viz, not only because those soils are warmer, on account of their driness; but also, because less plenty of moisture is conveyed up the plants; which plenty of moisture, tho' it promotes their growth, yet retards their coming to maturity. And for the same reason, the uncovering the roots of trees for some time will make the fruit be considerably the forwarder.

And on the other hand, where trees abound with too great a plenty of fresh-drawn sap, as is the case of trees whose roots are planted too deep in cold moist earth, as also of too luxuriant Peach and other wall trees; or, which comes almost to the same, where the sap cannot be perspired off in a due proportion; as in orchards, where trees stand too near each other, so as to hinder perspiration, whereby the sap is kept in too thin and crude a state; in all these cases little or no fruit is produced.

Hence also, in moderately dry summers, *caeteris paribus*, there is usually greatest plenty of fruit; because the sap in the bearing twigs and buds is more digested, and brought to a better consistence for shooting out with vigour and firmness than it is in cool moist summers: And this observation has been verified in the years 1723, 1724, and 1725.

But to return to the subject of the motion of the sap: When the sap has first passed thro' that thick and fine strainer, the bark of the root, we then find it in greatest quantities in the most lax part, between the bark and wood, and *that* the same thro' the whole tree. And if, in the early spring, the Oak and several other trees were to be examined near the top and bottom, when the sap first begins to move, so as to make the bark easily run or peel off, I believe it would be found that the lower bark is first moistened; whereas the bark of the top branches ought first to be moistened, if the sap descends by the bark: As to the Vine, I am pretty well assured that the lower bark is first moistened.

We see in many of the foregoing experiments what quantities of moisture trees do daily imbibe and perspire. Now the celerity of the sap must be very great, if that quantity of moisture must, most of it, ascend to the top of the tree, then descend, and ascend again, before it is carried off by perspiration.

The defect of a circulation in vegetables seems in some measure to be supplied by the much greater quantity of liquor which the vegetable takes in, than the animal, whereby its motion is accelerated; for by Experiment I, we find the sun-flower, bulk for bulk, imbibes and perspires seventeen times more fresh liquor than a man, every 24 hours.

Besides, nature's great aim in vegetables being only that the vegetable life be carried on and maintained, there was no occasion to give its sap the rapid motion which was necessary for the blood of animals.

In animals, it is the heart which sets the blood in motion, and makes it continually circulate, but in vegetables we can discover no other cause of the sap's motion but the strong attraction of the capillary sap-vessels, assisted by the brisk undulations and vibrations caused by the sun's warmth, whereby the sap is carried up to the top of the tallest trees, and is there perspired off thro' the leaves:

But when the surface of the tree is greatly diminished by the loss of its leaves, then also the perspiration and motion of the sap is proportionably diminished, as is plain from many of the foregoing experiments: So that the ascending velocity of the sap is principally accelerated by the plentiful perspiration of the leaves, thereby making room for the fine capillary vessels to exert their vastly attracting power, which perspiration is effected by the brisk rarefying vibrations of warmth: A power that does not seem to be any ways well adapted to make the sap descend from the tops of vegetables by different vessels to the root. . . .

The instances of the Jessamine tree and of the Passion tree have been looked upon as strong proofs of the circulation of the sap, because their branches, which were far below the inoculated Bud, were gilded: But we have many visible proofs in the Vine and other bleeding trees of the sap's receding back and pushing forwards alternately, at different times of the day and night. And there is great reason to think that the sap of all other trees has such an alternate, receding and progressive motion, occasioned by the alternacies of day and night, warm and cool, moist and dry.

For the sap in all vegetables does probably recede in some measure from the tops of branches, as the sun leaves them; because its rarefying power then ceasing, the greatly rarefied sap, and air mixt with it, will condense and take up less room than they did, and the dew and rain will then be strongly imbibed by the leaves, as is probable from Exper. 42 and several others; whereby the body and branches of the vegetable, which have been much exhausted by the great evaporation of the day, may at night imbibe sap and dew from the leaves; for by several Experiments in the first chapter, plants were found to increase considerably in weight in dewy and moist nights. And by other experiments on the Vine in the third chapter, it was found that the trunk and branches of Vines were always in an imbibing state, caused by the great perspiration of the leaves, except in the bleeding season; but when at night that perspiring power ceases, then the contrary imbibing power will prevail, and draw the sap and dew from the leaves, as well as moisture from the roots.

And we have a farther proof of this in Experiment 12, where, by fixing mercurial gages to the stems of several trees which do not bleed, it is found that they are always in a strongly imbibing state, by drawing up the mercury several inches. Whence it is easy to conceive how some of the particles of the gilded Bud in the inoculated Jessamine may be absorbed by it, and thereby communicate their gilding Miasma to the sap of other branches; especially when some months after the inoculation, the stock of the inoculated Jessamine is cut off a little above the Bud; whereby the stock, which was the counteracting part to the stem, being taken away, the stem attracts more vigorously from the Bud.

Another argument for the circulation of the sap, is that some sorts of graffs will infect and canker the stocks they are grafted on. But by Exper. 12, and 37, where mercurial gages were fixed to fresh cut stems of trees, it is evident that those stems were in a strongly imbibing state; and consequently the cankered stocks might very likely draw sap from the graff, as well as the graff alternately from the stock; just in the same manner as leaves and branches do from each other, in the vicissitudes of day and night. And this imbibing power of the stock is so great, where only some of the branches of a tree are grafted, that the remaining branches of the stock will, by their strong attraction, starve those graffs; for which reason it is usual to cut off the greatest part of the branches of the stock, leaving only a few small ones to draw up the sap.

The instance of the Ilex grafted upon the *English* Oak, seems to afford a very considerable argument against a circulation. For, if there were a free uniform circulation of the sap thro' the Oak and Ilex, why should the leaves of the Oak fall in winter, and not those of the Ilex?

Another argument against an uniform circulation of the sap in trees, as in animals, may be drawn from Exper. 37. where it was found by the three mercurial gages fix'd to the same Vine, that while some of its branches changed their state of protruding [discharging] sap into a state of imbibing, others continued protruding sap, one nine, and the other thirteen days longer.

In the second Vol. of Mr. *Lowthorp's Abridgment of the Philos. Transact.*, p. 708, is recited an Experiment of Mr. *Brotherton's*; viz, A young Hazel n (Fig. 27) was cut into the body at x z with a deep gash; the parts of the body below at z, and above at x, were cleft upwards and downwards, and the splinters x z by wedges were kept off from touching each other, or the rest of the body. The following year, the upper splinter x was grown very much, but the lower splinter x did not grow; but the rest of the body grew, as if there had been no gash made: I have not yet succeeded in making this Experiment, the wind having broken at x z all the trees I prepared for it. But if there was a Bud at x which shot out leaves, and none at z, then, by Experiment 41, 'tis plain that those leaves might draw much nourishment thro' x, and thereby make it grow; and I believe, if, vice versa, there were a leaf-bearing Bud at z, and none at x, that then the splinter z would grow more than x.

The reason of my conjecture I ground upon this Experiment, viz, I chose two thriving shoots of a dwarf *Pear-tree*, 1 1 a a, Fig. 28, 29. At three quarters of an inch distance, I took half an inch breadth of bark off each of them, in several places, viz, 2, 4, 6, 8, and at 10, 12, 14. Every one of the remaining ringlets of bark had a leaf-bearing bud which produced leaves the following summer, except the ringlet 13, which had no such Bud. The ringlet 9 and 11 of a a grew and swelled at their bottoms till *August*, but the ringlet 13 did not increase at all, and in *August* the whole shoot a a withered and died; but the shoot 1 1 lives and thrives well, each of its ringlets swelling much at the bottom: Which swellings at their bottoms must be attributed to some other cause than the stoppage of the sap in its return downwards, because in the shoot 1 1, its return downwards is intercepted three several times by cutting away the bark at 2, 4, 6. The larger and more thriving the leaf-bearing Bud

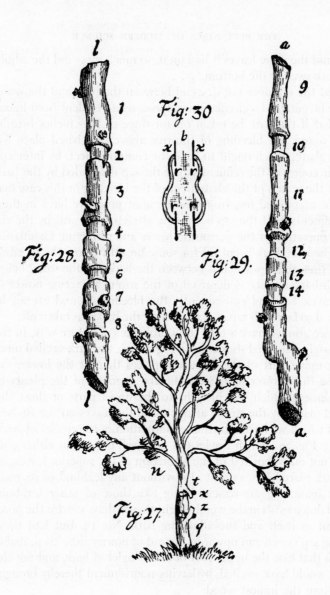

Fig: 30.

Fig: 28. *Fig: 29.*

Fig: 27.

was, and the more leaves it had on it, so much more did the adjoining bark swell at the bottom. . . .

That the sap does not descend between the bark and the wood, as the favourers of a circulation suppose, seems evident from hence; viz, that if the bark be taken off for three or four inches breadth quite round, the bleeding of the tree above that bared place will much abate, which ought to have the contrary effect, by intercepting the course of the refluent sap, if the sap descended by the bark.

But the reason of the abatement of the bleeding in this case may well be accounted for, from the manifest proof we have in these Experiments, that the sap is strongly attracted upwards by the vigorous operation of the perspiring leaves and attracting Capillaries. But when the bark is cut off for some breadth below the bleeding place, then the sap which is between the bark and the wood below that disbarked place is deprived of the strong attracting power of the leaves, &c., and consequently the bleeding wound cannot be supplied so fast with sap as it was before the bark was taken off.

Hence also we have a hint for a probable conjecture why, in the alternately disbarked sticks, 11 aa, Fig. 28, 29, the bark swelled more at the upper part of the disbarked places than at the lower; viz, because those lower parts were thereby deprived of the plenty of nourishment which was brought to the upper parts of those disbarked places by the strong attraction of the leaves on the Buds 7, &c., of which we have a further confirmation in the ringlet of bark, No. 13. Fig. 29., which ringlet did not swell or grow at either end, being not only deprived of the attraction of the superior leaves, by the bark placed No. 12, but also without any leaf-bud of its own, whose branching sap-vessels, being like those of other leaf-buds rooted downwards in the wood, might thence draw sap, for the nourishment of itself and the adjoining bark, No. 13. But had these rooting sap vessels run upwards, instead of downwards, 'tis probable that in that case the upper part of each ringlet of bark, and not the lower, would have swelled, by having nourishment thereby brought to it from the inmost wood.

We may hence also see the reason why, when a tree is unfruitful, it is brought to bear fruit by the taking ringlets of bark off from its branches; viz. because thereby a less quantity of sap arising, it is better digested and prepared for the nourishment of the fruit; which, from the greater quantity of oil that is usually found in the seeds and their containing vessels than in other parts of plants, shews that more sulphur and air is requisite for their production than there is for the production of wood and leaves.

But the most considerable objection against this progressive motion of the sap, without a circulation, arises from hence, viz. that it is too precipitate a course for a due digestion of the sap, in order to nutrition. Whereas in animals nature has provided that many parts of the blood shall run a long course, before they are either applied to nutrition, or discharged from the animal.

But when we consider that the great work of nutrition, in vegetables as well as animals (I mean, after the nutriment is got into the veins and arteries of animals), is chiefly carried on in the fine capillary vessels, where nature selects and combines, as shall best suit her different purposes, the several mutually attracting nutritious particles, which were hitherto kept disjoined by the motion of their fluid vehicle; we shall find that nature has made an abundant provision for this work in the structure of vegetables; all whose composition is made up of nothing else but innumerable fine capillary vessels, and glandulous portions or vesicles.

Upon the whole, I think we have, from these experiments and observations, sufficient ground to believe that there is no circulation of the sap in vegetables; notwithstanding many ingenious persons have been induced to think there was, from several curious observations and experiments, which evidently prove that the sap does in some measure recede from the top towards the lower parts of plants, whence they were with good probability of reason induced to think that the sap circulated.

The likeliest method effectually and convincingly to determine this difficulty, whether the sap circulates or not, would be by ocular inspection, if that could be attained. And I see no reason we have to despair of it, since by the great quantities imbibed and perspired, we have good ground to think that the progressive motion of the sap is considerable in the largest sap-vessels of the transparent stems of leaves. And if our eyes, assisted with microscopes, could come at this desirable sight, I make no doubt but that we should see the sap, which was progressive in the heat of day, would on the coming on of the cool evening and the falling dew, be retrograde in the same vessels.

LINNAEUS

1 7 0 7 · 1 7 7 8

KARL VON LINNÉ, commonly known as Linnaeus, introduced and promoted the use of a logical and concise system for naming plants, to replace the chaotic and confusing descriptions in common use in his time. With a passion for order, Linnaeus took the facts accumulated by his predecessors, paying careful attention to give each one his proper credit, and therewith laid the foundations of a system by which a careful observer can determine the correct classification of any plant by simply observing the flower.

Linnaeus inherited a love for horticulture and botany from his father, a Swedish peasant, who had by great personal toil and sacrifice educated himself for the ministry. In school the son showed a remarkable gift for natural science and mathematics. He went on to study medicine at Upsala, living there at first in great want, until his ability and personal charm became known. He was then awarded a number of money grants, and, while still an undergraduate, was permitted to lecture on botany, attracting large audiences.

Since no degree of Doctor of Medicine was offered in Sweden at the time, Linnaeus later journeyed to Holland, where a small university granted him the degree in a couple of weeks. He stayed on in Holland for three years, during which time he wrote several treatises on botany; then, after visits to England and France, he returned to Sweden with an international reputation, to be speedily appointed professor of botany at Upsala. He helped found and was the first principal of the Swedish Academy of Science.

Linnaeus had read in the published letter of a German physician, Rudolf Camerarius (1665-1721), De Sexu Plantarum (On Sex in

Plants), 1694, of the experimental discovery of the function of the stamens and pistils in the reproduction of plants. An early work of his own was a Dissertation on the Sexes of Plants. Later he took the arrangement and number of these easily observed, physical features as the basis for the artificial classification pattern which has ever since been known by his name.

The following selection from A Dissertation on the Sexes of Plants is taken from the translation by James Edward Smith, published in 1786. Our second selection, in which Linnaeus discusses some of the problems that arise in naming plants, is from his Critica Botanica, published in 1737, and translated for the Ray Society by Sir Arthur Hort, in 1938.

A DISSERTATION

ON THE SEXES OF PLANTS

᪥

ALTHOUGH THE earliest observers of nature could not possibly be ignorant of the sexes of plants, it has been left for the philosophers of the present age to demonstrate them. And so abundant are the proofs of this phenomenon, that not a single vegetable can be found which does not offer them to our consideration.

The Arabians, from time immemorial, have derived their principal sustenance from the *Phoenix,* or date-bearing palm, the Persians from their turpentine tree, and the inhabitants of the Archipelago from the fig; the people of Chios have likewise cultivated mastich from the most remote ages. As it has all along been the practice of these nations to promote the action of the male trees on the female by the same means which they use at this day, they must certainly have been acquainted with that sexual difference in plants upon which the success of this practice depends. It is altogether impossible that they should have been ignorant of a circumstance, which, in these trees, at least, is so apparent. If, however, we duly consider the fate of botanical science, we shall soon see why the doctrine in question has not been long ago universally understood and received. . . .

The organs common in general to all plants are, 1st, the root, with its capillary vessels, extracting nourishment from the ground; 2nd, the leaves, which may be called the limbs, and which, like the feet and wings of animals, are organs of motion; for being themselves shaken by the external air, they shake and exercise the plant; 3rd, the trunk, containing the medullary substance, which is nourished by the bark, and for the most part multiplied into several compound plants; 4th, the fructification, which is the true body of the plant, set at liberty by a metamorphosis, and consists only of the organs of generation; it is often defended by a calyx, and furnished with petals, by means of which it in a manner flutters in the air.

Many flowers have no calyx, as several of the lily tribe, the *Hippusis*, etc.; many want the corolla, as grasses, and the plants called *apetalous*; but there are none destitute of stamina and pistilla, those important organs destined to the formation of fruit. We therefore infer from experience that the stamina are the male organs of generation, and the pistilla the female; and, as many flowers are furnished with both at once, it follows that such flowers are hermaphrodites. Nor is this so wonderful, as that there should be any plants in which the different sexes are in distinct individuals; for plants being immovably fixed to one spot, cannot, like animals, travel in search of a mate. There exists, however, in some plants, a real difference of sex. From seeds of the same mother, some individuals will be produced whose flowers exhibit stamina without pistilla, and may therefore be properly called males; while the rest, being furnished with pistilla, without stamina, are therefore denominated females: and so uniformly does this take place that no vegetable was ever found to produce female flowers without flowers furnished with stamina being produced, either on the same individual, or on another plant of the same species, and vice versa.

As all seed-vessels are destined to produce seeds, so are the stamina to bear the *pollen*, or fecundating powder. All seeds contain within their membranes a certain medullary substance, which swells when dipped into warm water. All pollen, likewise, contains in its membrane an elastic substance, which, although very subtile, and almost invisible, by means of warm water often explodes with great vehemence. While plants are in flower, the pollen falls from their antherae, and is dispersed abroad, as seeds are dislodged from their situation when the fruit is ripe. At the same time that the pollen is scattered, the pistillium presents its stigma, which is then in its highest vigor, and, for a portion of the day, at least, is moistened with a fine dew. The stamina either surround this stigma, or, if the flowers are of the drooping kind, they are bent towards one side, so that the pollen can easily find access to the stigma, where it not only adheres by means of the dew of that part, but the moisture occasions its bursting, by which means its contents are discharged. What issues from it, being mixed with the fluid of the stigma, is conveyed to the rudiments of the seed.

Many evident instances of this present themselves to our notice; but I have nowhere seen it more manifest than in the Jacobean lily (Amaryllis formosissima), the pistillium of which, when sufficient heat is given the plant to make it flower in perfection, is bent downwards, and from its stigma issues a drop of limpid fluid, so large that one would think it in danger of dropping to the ground. It is, however, gradually reabsorbed into the style about three or four o'clock, and becomes invisible till about ten the next morning, when it appears again; by noon it attains its largest dimensions; and in the afternoon, by a gentle and scarcely perceptible decrease, it returns to its source. If we shake the antherate over the stigma, so that the pollen may fall on this limpid drop, we see the fluid soon after become turbid, and assume a yellow color; and we perceive little rivulets, or opaque streaks, running from the stigma towards the rudiments of the seed. Some time afterwards, when the drop has totally disappeared, the pollen may be observed adhering to the stigma, but of an irregular figure, having lost its original form.

No one, therefore, can assent to what Morland and others have asserted, that the pollen passes into the stigma, pervades the style, and enters the tender rudiments of the seed, as Leeuwenhoek supposed his worms to enter the ova. A most evident proof of the falsehood of this opinion may be obtained from any species of Mirabilis (Marvel of Peru), whose pollen is so very large that it almost exceeds the style itself in thickness, and, falling on the stigma, adheres firmly to it; that organ sucking and exhausting the pollen, as a cuttle-fish devours everything that comes within its grasp. One evening, in the month of August, I removed all the stamina from three flowers of the *Mirabilis longiflora*, at the same time destroying all the rest of the flowers which were expanded; I sprinkled these three flowers with the pollen of *Mirabilis Jalappa*; the seed buds swelled, but did not ripen. Another evening I performed a similar experiment, only sprinkling the flowers with the pollen of the same species; all these flowers produced ripe seeds.

Some writers have believed that the stamina are parts of the fructification, which serve only to discharge an impure or excrementitious matter, and by no means formed for so important a work as generation. But it is very evident that these authors have not sufficiently examined the subject; for as, in many vegetables, some flowers are furnished with stamina only and others only with pistilla, it is altogether impossible that stamina situated at so very great a distance from the fruit, as on a different branch, or perhaps on a separate plant, should serve to convey any impurities from the embryo.

No physiologist could demonstrate, *a priori*, the necessity of the masculine fluid to the rendering the eggs of animals prolific; but experience has established it beyond a doubt. We therefore judge, *a posteriori* principally, of the same effect in plants.

In the month of January, 1760, the *Antholyza Cunonia* flowered in a pot in my parlor, but produced no fruit, the air of the room not being sufficiently agitated to waft the pollen to the stigma. One day, about noon, seeing the stigma very moist, I plucked off one of the antherae, by means of a fine pair of forceps, and gently rubbed it on one of the expanded stigmata. The spike of flowers remained eight or ten days longer; when I observed, in gathering the branch for my herbarium, that the fruit of that flower only, on which the experiment had been made, had swelled to the size of a bean. I then dissected this fruit, and discovered that one of the three cells contained seeds in considerable number, the other two being entirely withered.

In the month of April, I sowed the seeds of hemp (*Cannabis*) in two different pots. The young plants came up so plentifully that each pot contained thirty or forty. I placed each by the light of a window, but in different and remote apartments. The hemp grew extremely well in both pots. In one of them I permitted the male and female plants to remain together, to flower and bear fruit, which ripened in July, and being macerated in water, and committed to the earth, sprung up in twelve days. From the other, however, I removed all the male plants, as soon as they were old enough for me to distinguish them from the females. The remaining females grew very well, and presented their long pistilla in great abundance, these flowers continuing a very long time, as if in expectation of their mates; while the plants in the other pot had already ripened their fruit, their pistilla having, quite in a different manner, faded as soon as the males had discharged all their pollen.

It was certainly a beautiful and truly admirable spectacle, to see the unimpregnated females preserve their pistilla so long green and flourishing, not permitting them to begin to fade till they had been for a very considerable time exposed, in vain, to the access of the male pollen. Afterwards, when these virgin plants began to decay through age, I examined all their calyces in the presence of several botanists, and found them large and flourishing, although every one of the seed buds was brown, compressed, membranaceous, and dry, not exhibiting any appearance of cotyledons or pulp. Hence I am perfectly convinced that the circumstance which the authors have recorded, of the female hemp having produced seeds, although deprived of the male, could only have happened by means of pollen brought by the wind from some distant place. No experiment can be more easily performed than the above; none more satisfactory in demonstrating the generation of plants.

The *Clutia tenella* [probably *pulchella*] was in like manner kept growing in my window through the months of June and July. The male plant was in one pot, the female in another. The latter abounded with fruit, not one of its flowers proving abortive. I removed the two pots into different windows of the same apartment; still all the female flowers continued to become fruitful. At length I took away the male entirely, leaving the female alone, and cutting off all the flowers which it had already borne. Every day new ones appeared from the axilla of every leaf; each remained eight or ten days, after which their foot-stalks turning yellow, they fell barren to the ground. A botanical friend, who had amused himself with observing this phenomenon with me, persuaded me to bring, from the stove [hothouse] in the garden, a single male flower, which he placed over one of the female ones, then in perfection, tieing a piece of red silk around its pistillum. The next day the male flower was taken away, and this single seed bud remained, and bore fruit. Afterwards I took another male flower out of the same stove, and with a pair of slender forceps pinched off one of its antherae, which I afterwards gently scratched with a feather, so that a very small portion of its pollen was discharged upon one of the three stigmata of a female flower, the two other stigmata being covered with paper. This fruit likewise attained its due size, and, on being cut transversely, exhibited one cell filled with a large seed, and the other two empty. The rest of the flowers, being unimpregnated, faded, and fell off. This experiment may be performed with as little trouble as the former.

The *Datisca cannabina* came up in my garden from seed ten years ago, and has every year been plentifully increased by means of its perennial root. Flowers in great number have been produced by it; but, being all female, they proved abortive. Being desirous of procuring male plants, I obtained more seeds from Paris. Some more plants were raised; but these likewise, to my great mortification, all proved females, and bore flowers, but no fruit. In the year 1757, I received another parcel of seeds. From these I obtained a few male plants, which flowered in 1758. These were planted at a great distance from the females; and when their flowers were just ready to emit their pollen, holding a paper under them, I gently shook the spike or panicle with my finger, till the paper was almost covered with the yellow powder. I carried this to the females, which were flowering in another part of the garden, and placed it over them.

The cold nights of the year in which this experiment was made destroyed these Datiscas, with many other plants, much earlier than usual. Nevertheless, when I examined the flowers of those plants, which I had sprinkled with the fertilizing powder, I found the seeds of their due magnitude; while in the more remote Datiscas, which had not been impregnated with pollen, no traces of seeds were visible.

Several species of *Momordica*, cultivated with us, like other Italian vegetables, in close stoves, have frequently borne female flowers; which, although at first very vigorous, after a short time have constantly faded, and turned yellow, without perfecting any seed, till I instructed the gardener, as soon as he observed a female flower, to gather a male one, and place it above the female. By this contrivance we are so certain of obtaining fruit, that we dare pledge ourselves to make any female flowers fertile that shall be fixed on.

The *Jatropha urens* has flowered every year in my hothouse; but the female flowers, coming before the males, in a week's time dropped their petals, and faded before the latter were opened; from which cause no fruit has been produced, but the germina themselves have fallen off. We have therefore never had any fruit of the Jatropha till the year 1752, when the male flowers were in vigor on a tall tree at the same time that the females began to appear on a small Jatropha which was growing in a garden pot. I placed this pot under the other tree, by which means the female flowers bore seeds, which grew on being sown. I have frequently since amused myself with taking the male flowers from one plant, and scattering them over the female flowers of another, and have always found the seeds of the latter impregnated by it.

Two years ago I placed a piece of paper under some of these male flowers, and afterwards folded up the pollen which had fallen upon it, preserving it so folded up, if I remember right, four or six weeks, at the end of which time, another branch of the same Jatropha was in flower. I then took the pollen, which I had so long preserved in paper, and strewed it over three female flowers, the only ones at the time expanded. These three females proved fruitful, while all the rest, which grew in the same bunch, fell off abortive.

The interior petals of the *Ornithogalum*, commonly but improperly called *Canadense*, cohere so closely together that they only just admit the air to the germen, and will scarcely permit the pollen of another flower to pass; this plant produced every day new flowers and fruit, the fructification never failing in any instance; I therefore, with the utmost care, extracted the antherae from one of the flowers with a hooked needle, and, as I hoped, this single flower proved barren. This experiment was repeated about a week after with the same success. . . .

To relate more experiments would only be to fatigue the reader unnecessarily. All nature proclaims the truth I have endeavored to inculcate, and every flower bears witness to it. Any person may make the experiment for himself, with any plant he pleases, only taking care to place the pot in which it is growing in the window of a room sufficiently out of the reach of other flowers; and I will venture to promise him that he will obtain no perfect fruit, unless pollen has access to the pistillum.

Logan's experiments on the Mays are perfectly satisfactory; and manifestly show that the pollen does not enter the style, or arrive at the germen, but that it is exhausted by the genital fluid of the pistillum. And, as in animals no conception can take place unless the genital fluid of the female be discharged at the same moment as the impregnating liquor of the male, so in plants, generation fails unless the stigma be moist with prolific dew.

Husbandmen all know, by long experience, that if the rain falls while rye is in flower, by coagulating the pollen of its antherae, it occasions the emptiness of many husks in the ear.

Gardeners remark the same thing every year in fruit trees. Their blossoms produce no fruit if they have unfortunately been exposed to long-continued rains.

Aquatic plants rise above the water at the time of flowering, and afterwards again subside, for no other reason than that the pollen may safely reach the stigma.

The white Water-lily (*Nymphaea alba*) raises itself every morning out of the water, and opens its flowers, so that by noon at least three inches of its flowerstalk may be seen above the surface. In the evening it is closely shut up and withdrawn again; for about four o'clock in the afternoon the flower closes, and remains all night under water; which was observed full two thousand years since, even as long ago as the time of Theophrastus,[1] who has described this circumstance in the *Nymphaea Lotus*, a plant so much resembling our white water lily that they are only distinguished from each other by the leaves of the *Lotus* being indented. Theophrastus gives the following account of this vegetable, in his *History of Plants*, book iv, chap. 10. "It is said to withdraw its flowers into the Euphrates, which continue to descend till midnight, to so great a depth that at daybreak they are out of the reach of the hand; after which it rises again, and in the course of the morning appears above water, and expands its flowers, rising higher and higher, till it is a considerable height above the surface." The very same thing may be observed in our *Nymphaea alba*.

Many flowers close themselves in the evening, and before rain, lest the pollen should be coagulated; but after the discharge of the pollen they always remain open. Such of them as do not shut up incline their flowers downward in those circumstances, and several flowers, which come forth in the moisture of spring, droop perpetually. The manner in which the Parnassia and Saxifrage move their antherae to the stigma is well-known. The common Rue, a plant everywhere to be met with, moves one of its antherae every day to the stigma, till all of them in their turns have deposited their pollen there.

The Neapolitan star-flower (*Ornithogalum nutans*) has six broad

[1] Theophrastus (c. 372-287 B.C.) was a Greek philosopher and scientist, pupil of Aristotle and his successor as head of the Lyceum. He wrote two authoritative works on botany.

stamina, which stand close together in the form of a bell, the three external ones being but half the length of the others; so that it seems impossible for their antherae ever to convey their pollen to the stigma; but nature, by an admirable contrivance, bends the summits of these external stamina inwards between the other filaments, so that they are enabled to accomplish their purpose.

The Plantain tree (*Musa*) bears two kinds of hermaphrodite flowers, some having imperfect antherae, others only the rudiments of stigmata: as the last-mentioned kind appear after the others, they cannot impregnate them, consequently no seeds are produced in our gardens, and scarcely ever on the plants cultivated in India. An event happened this year, which I have long wished for; two plantain trees flowering with me so fortunately that one of them brought forth its first female blossoms at the time that the male ones began to appear on the other. I eagerly ran to collect antherae from the first plant, in order to scatter them over the newly-expanded females, in hopes of obtaining seed from them, which no botanist has yet been able to do. But when I came to examine the antherae, I found even the largest of them absolutely empty, and void of pollen, consequently unfit for impregnating the females; the seeds of this plant, therefore, can never be perfected in our gardens. I do not doubt, however, that real male plants of this species may be found in its native country, bearing flowers without fruit, which the gardeners have neglected; while the females in this country produce imperfect fruit, without seeds, like the female fig; and, like that tree, are easily increased by suckers. The fruit, therefore, of the plantain-tree scarcely attains anything like its due size, the larger seed-buds only ripening, without containing anything in them.

The day would sooner fail me than examples. A female date-bearing palm flowered many years at Berlin, without producing any seeds. But the Berlin people taking care to have some of the blossoms of a male tree, which was then flowering at Leipsic, sent to them by the post, they obtained fruit by that means; and some dates, the offspring of this impregnation, being planted in my garden, sprung up, and to this day continue to grow vigorously. Kaemp-fer formerly told us how necessary it was found by oriental people, who live upon the produce of palm-trees, and are true *Lotophagi* [Lotus-eaters], to plant some male trees among the females, if they hoped for any fruit; hence it is the practice of those who make war in that part of the world to cut down all the male palms, that a famine may afflict their proprietors; sometimes even the inhabitants themselves destroy the male trees, when they dread an invasion, that their enemies may find no sustenance in the country.

Leaving these instances and innumerable others which are so well known to botanists that they would by no means bear the appearance of novelty, and can only be doubted by those persons who have neither observed nature nor will take the trouble to study her, I pass on to a fresh subject, concerning which much new light is wanted: I mean *hybrid,* or mule vegetables, the existence and origin of which we shall now consider.

I shall enumerate three or four real mule plants, to whose origin I have been an eye-witness.

1. *Veronica spuria,* described in *Amaenitates Acad.* vol iii, p. 35, came from the impregnation of *Veronica maritima* by *Verbena officinalis;* it is easily propagated by cuttings, and agrees perfectly with its mother in fructification, and with its father in leaves.

2. *Delphinium hybridum* sprung up in a part of the garden where *Delphinium elatum,* and *Aconitum Napellus* grew together; it re-sembles its mother as much in its internal parts, that is in the fructi-fication, as it does its father (the *Aconitum*) in outward structure, or leaves; and, owing its origin to plants so nearly allied to each other, it propagates itself by seed; some of which I now send with this dissertation.

3. *Hieracium Taraxici,* gathered in 1753 upon our mountains by Dr. Solander, in its thick, brown, woolly calyx; in its stem being hairy towards the top, and in its bracteae, as well as in every part of its fructification, resembles so perfectly its mother, *Hieracium alpinum,* that an inexperienced person might mistake one for the

other; but in the smoothness of its leaves, in their indentations and whole structure, it so manifestly agrees with its father, *Leontodon Taraxacum* (dandelion) that there can be no doubt of its origin.

4. *Tragopogon hybridum* attracted my notice the autumn before last, in a part of the garden where I had planted *Tragopogon pratense*, and *Tragopogon porrifolium*; but winter coming on destroyed its seeds. Last year, while the *Tragopogon pratense* was in flower, I rubbed off its pollen early in the morning, and about eight o'clock sprinkled its stigmata with some pollen of the *Tragopogon porrifolium*, marking the calyces by tieing a thread round them. I afterwards gathered the seeds when ripe, and sowed them that autumn in another place; they grew and produced this year, 1759, purple flowers yellow at the base, seeds of which I now send. I doubt whether any experiment demonstrates the generation of plants more certainly than this.

There can be no doubt that these are all new species produced by hybrid generation. And hence we learn that a mule offspring is the exact image of its mother in its medullary substance, internal nature, or fructification, but resembles its father in leaves. This is a foundation upon which naturalists may build much. For it seems probable that many plants, which now appear different species of the same genus, may in the beginning have been but one plant, having arisen merely from hybrid generation. Many of those Geraniums which grow at the Cape of Good Hope, and have never been found wild anywhere but in the south parts of Africa, and which, as they are distinguished from all other Geraniums by their single-leaved calyx, many-flowered foot-stalk, irregular corolla, seven fertile stamina, and three mutilated ones, and by their naked seeds furnished with downy awns; so they agree together in all these characters, although very various in their roots, stems, and leaves; these Geraniums, I say, would almost induce a botanist to believe that the species of one genus in vegetables are only so many different plants as there have been different associations with the flowers of one species, and consequently a genus is nothing else than a number of plants sprung from the same mother by different fathers. But whether all these species be the offspring of time; whether, in the beginning of all things, the Creator limited the number of future species, I dare not presume to determine. I am, however, convinced this mode of multiplying plants does not interfere with the system or general scheme of nature; as I daily observe that insects, which live upon one species of a particular genus, are contented with another of the same genus.

A person who has once seen the *Achyranthes aspera*, and remarked its spike, the parts of its flower, its small and peculiarly formed *nectaria*, as well as its calyces bent backwards as the fruit ripens, would think it very easy at any time to distinguish these flowers from all others in the universe; but when he finds the flowers of *Achyranthes indica* agreeing with them even in their minutest parts, and at the same time observes the large, thick, obtuse, undulated leaves of the last-mentioned plant, he will think he sees *Achyranthes aspera* masked in the foliage of the *Xanthium strumarium*. But I forbear to mention any more instances.

Here is a new employment for botanists, to attempt the production of new species of vegetables, by scattering the pollen of various plants over various widowed females. And if these remarks should meet with a favorable reception, I shall be the more induced to dedicate what remains of my life to such experiments, which recommend themselves by being at the same time agreeable and useful. I am persuaded by many considerations that those numerous and most valuable varieties of plants which are used for culinary purposes have been produced in this manner, as the several kinds of cabbages, lettuces, etc.; and I apprehend this is the reason of their not being changed by a difference of soil. Hence I cannot give my assent to the opinion of those who imagine all varieties to have been occasioned by change of soil; for if this were the case, the plants would return to their original form, if removed again to the original situation.

That the sexes of plants admit of a proof *a priori* from experiments appears therefore from hybrid productions.

GENERIC NAMES

210. THE CLASSIFICATION being made, let Nomenclature, the other of the two foundations of Botany, forthwith bestow names.

We have laid down the twofold foundation of Botany, the Classification and the Nomenclature of plants, in undertaking either of which the botanist must use judgment.

If anyone should distinguish precisely all the plants in the world according to the characters stamped on them, and yet bestow no names on the plants themselves, he would be keeping his learning entirely to himself. Even a rustic knows plants, and so maybe does a brute beast, but neither can make anyone else the wiser: hence in the words of Isidorus,[1] "If you know not the names, the knowledge of things too is wasted."

Wherefore the botanist is distinguished from the layman by the fact that the former is able to give a name which fits one particular plant and not another, and which can be understood by anyone all the world over.

The names bestowed on plants by the ancient Greeks and Romans I commend, but I shudder at the sight of most of those given by modern authorities: for these are for the most part a mere chaos of confusion, whose mother was barbarity, whose father dogmatism, and whose nurse prejudice. Now is there anything surprising in this? For what novice was ever well versed in nomenclature? Who has ever given for the naming of plants principles, conclusive arguments or examples? Those who in recent times have made the attempt have forthwith experienced shipwreck: they have avoided sundry rocks, but have often fallen victims to Scylla in their desire to escape Charybdis.

[1] Isidore of Seville (about 560-636), a Spanish bishop who lived under the Gothic conquerors of Spain, was author of an encyclopedia of strangely assorted knowledge, which he called *Etymologies*, because it was in the form of a series of definitions of the names of things.

Tournefort[2] has been the chief chooser of names, Ruppius has chosen a certain number, Dillenius has proceeded with greater caution than the rest. But both these botanists and others would have rejected far more names, had not men advanced in years been too scrupulous about parting with names which had become familiar to them, and which they defended as they would their own hearths and homes. Yet a beginning must sometime be made, even though one risks one's reputation over the attempt: for the assent of one wise man counts for more with me than the idle reproaches of a hundred laymen.

There is no spell to bind me before the publication of Sherard's *Pinax*[3]: after its appearance Threlkeld[4] has threatened with anathema anyone who should change the names of plants. To that anathema I indeed would subscribe, if only he would in the meanwhile provide suitable names. But, as so far this has not been done, I need feel no scruple in putting forward suggestions of my own and submitting them to the criticism of others.

Only when plants have been classified under genera, and not before, should names be assigned to them. Hence no names that have been assigned to plants must be adopted if they do not fit the genera—neither those assigned by the ancients, nor the official names, nor any other accepted names which include different genera under a single designation: *Where a single genus is concerned, there shall be but one name!*

211. It is only real botanists who have the power of assigning true names to plants. By a botanist I mean one who understands how to observe the genera of Nature. I judge unworthy of the name of botanist the meddlesome person who is indifferent to genera.

Again, the foundation of all classification of plants depends on Genera and Species: let those things which agree in genus or species

[2] Tournefort, Ruppius, and Dillenius were all European botanists of the generation before Linnaeus.

[3] A manuscript in five volumes, still unpublished.

[4] Threlkeld, *Synopsis Stirpium Hibernicarium*, preface.

come under the same generic or specific name: and let the converse of this rule hold. Therefore it follows that no one can assign true names to plants unless he be a botanist and understands the genera and the known species.

Further, it is required of the botanist that he should use judgment in assigning names, and not merely assign the first that occur to his mind. We see from the examples cited how absurd, foolish and ridiculous are the names assigned by the Commentators, when these studies had lately been revived and the science had not yet been developed: and so we ought to learn wisdom from the example of others (a).

We reject all the names assigned to plants by anyone, unless they have been either invented by the Systematists or confirmed by them. For none of those given by the ancients are of this kind: if any of their names are good, it is only by accident.

Nor is there any need for one to be afraid about assigning a new name to a plant which has been already named by some collector: for the name which he gave is bound to be untrue in so far as he did not understand genera—unless by pure accident he hit on a suitable name, or some more learned person taught him about the plant.

We exclude all new names given in memory of botanists by anyone who was not himself a real botanist: for in truth he who desires a name given by himself to be permanent must observe the plant's character (b).

We do reverence to the omnipotence of the Creator, and to His sublime mysteries as discerned in plants: but we do not admit those names which have a religious significance (c):

a. *Names given by the ancients.*

Pater	noster	*Cyperus*
Bonus	Henricus	*Chenopodium*
Malus	Henricus	*Squamaria*
Noli	me tangere	*Impatiens*
Morsus	Diaboli	*Scabiosa*

Morsus	Ranae	*Hydrocharis*
Viscera	Diaboli	*Cuscuta*
Fuga	Daemonum	*Hypericum*
Surge	& ambula	*Gentiana*
Filius	ante patrem	*Tussilago*
Regina	prati	*Filipendula*
Gratia	Dei	*Gratiola*
Mater	violarum	*Cheiranthus*
Mater	Herbarum	*Artemisia*
Arbor	tristis	*Nyctanthes*
Arbor	vitae	*Thuya*
Fel	terrae	*Gentiana*
Podagra	lini	*Cuscuta*
Herba	impia	*Gnaphalium*
Herba	furum	*Cannabis*
Herba	inferni	*Cuscuta*
Herba	casta	*Mimosa*
Lacryma	Jobi	*Coix*
Flos	passionis	*Passiflora*
Chaerophyllo	accedens	*Aphanes*
Cicutariae quodammodo	similis	*Aphanes*
Sol	indianus	*Aphanes*
Barba	jovis	*Aphanes*
Barba	caprae	*Helianthus*

b. *Names given in recent times.*

Bontiana	*Pt.*	
Breyniana	*Pt.*	
Ruyschiana	*Pt.*	
Drakena	*Clus.*	*Dorstenia*

c. *Religious names.*

Oculus	Christi	*Aster*
Palma	Christi	*Orchis*

Spina	Christi	*Rhamnus*
Lancea	Christi	*Lycopus*
Labrum	Veneris	*Dipsacus*
Umbilicus	Veneris	*Saxifraga*
Speculum	Veneris	*Campanula*
Pecten	Veneris	*Scandix*
Calceus	Veneris	*Cypripedium*
Barba	Jovis	
Chirothecae	S. Mariae	*Aquilegia*
Claves	S. Mariae	*Calceolus*
Chlamys	S. Mariae	*Petasites*
Lacryma	S. Mariae	*Coix*
Lac	S. Mariae	*Carduus*
Poma	S. Mariae	*Punica*
Stramen	S. Mariae	*Galium*
Stragulum lecti	S. Mariae	*Thymus*

212. All names used in mentioning a plant are either understood, as those of Class and Order, or explicitly given, as those which denote genera, species and varieties.

That the whole System of Botany is comprised under five appropriate divisions, namely, Classes, Orders, Genera, Species, Varieties, we have said in par. 155, and we now proceed to give proof of this in the Philosophy of Botany. There will, I hope, be no one to deny that to all of these divisions appropriate names should be assigned, though in the case of Orders (which were called by Tournefort Sections) this has hitherto not been the practice.

I will quote an example from Zoology, in which I have divided all animals into six classes, namely, into Quadrupeds, Birds, Amphibia, Fish, Insects, and Worms (Compare my *Systema Naturae*). If a duck should come before me for examination and I pronounce that it is a Bird, that is the same thing as though I had said that it was an Animal with two feet and the same number of wings, and furnished with feathers and down. If an ignorant person requires a further description of the thing before us, I should add that it is of the Goose Order; from which single word he should know that it is a broad-footed, aquatic, swimming bird. And so names of a scientific terminology are necessary to secure readiness, brevity, and conciseness. I would have botanists observe in this paragraph that these names should be made suitable and be carefully devised.

In naming some particular species it is not necessary also to enumerate the names of the Class and Order, as these are easily retained in the memory, in which the Genera are marshalled as in a phalanx; wherefore let us give only the generic name with whatever follows it. For instance, *Tetra cauda bifurcata* [the black cock] sounds better than *Avis gallinacea Tetra cauda bifurcata* [Bird of the goose order, black cock], in which the two first words, given in accordance with the principles of the System represent facts already known. Nor should the names of Classes and natural Orders in Botany be included in the name of the plant, so long as their number remains small; about any names that might be substituted, discussion would be endless.

Accordingly, as to making true names suitable to this fivefold classification of the System, it has seemed good to give the following advice:

213. All those plants which belong to one genus must be designated by the same generic name.

All those plants which agree in their method of fruiting should be united in one genus. That all those which are comprised in the same genus should be designated by the same name is the primary rule on which, as foundation, rests the whole superstructure of botanical science, so that if this foundation is removed, the superstructure cannot but collapse entirely. Not a single exception occurs to qualify this rule, not a single saving clause: like an axiom it abides in naked absoluteness.

That peerless botanist Tournefort, since he wished to retain the names, did not proceed to segregate the species placed under the same genus and call some by one name, some by another: on the contrary, he broke up the natural genera, so as to retain the names as he himself states. Thus *Meum* (which is an equivocal name) remained, though it seemed to him that without question that plant should be referred to *Faeniculum*: and in like manner he retained the names *Limon, Aurantium, Malus* and *Cydonia*. And so I conclude that the man who does not introduce a natural genus [where required] makes the same mistake as he who should give several generic names to plants belonging to the same genus. The latter would be laughed at by everyone, but the former would at least escape the ridicule of ordinary people.

JOSEPH PRIESTLEY

1 7 3 3 · 1 8 0 4

IN THE LONG LIST of writings left by Priestley, there are more religious titles than scientific ones, but it is for his work in chemistry and physiology and for his histories of the sciences of light and electricity that he is known today. His income as a Unitarian minister was so slender that Josiah Wedgwood, the celebrated potter, and Erasmus Darwin, grandfather of Charles Darwin, supplemented his salary with gifts, so that he might continue his valuable scientific work without fear of want.

Priestley sympathized with the doctrines of the French Revolution so warmly that he published an answer to Burke's attack upon it. Enraged by his attitude, an English mob in 1791 looted his house and burned his chapel to the ground. All his papers and apparatus, the fruit of years of labor, were destroyed. The French, on the other hand, invested him with citizenship in their Republic, and chose him a member of the French National Convention, an honor which he declined. Bitter and disappointed at the later violent turn of events in France, he emigrated in 1794 to Pennsylvania, where he died ten years later.

As a scientist, Priestley was particularly interested in various kinds of "air." Although he did not call them by these names, he isolated nitric oxide, hydrogen chloride, ammonia, sulphur dioxide, and oxygen. His discussion of these things is, however, often difficult to read today because he used the language of certain faulty theories of his time. But in the course of his researches into the problems of what kind of air would support life, and how air that had been vitiated could be purified in the ordinary course of nature, he performed a number of interesting experiments. These finally led him to the experiment with the mouse and the sprig of mint, so important for plant as well as for animal physiology.

The following account is taken from Volume III of Priestley's Experiments and Observations on Different Kinds of Air (Birmingham, 1790).

OF THE RESTORATION OF AIR
INFECTED BY ANIMAL RESPIRATION

THAT CANDLES WILL burn only a certain time in a given quantity of air is a fact not better known than it is that animals can live only a certain time in it; but the cause of the death of the animal is not better known than that of the extinction of flame in the same circumstances; and when once any quantity of air has been rendered noxious by animals breathing in it as long as they could, I do not know that any methods have been discovered of rendering it fit for breathing again. It is evident, however, that there must be some provision in nature for this purpose, as well as for that of rendering the air fit for sustaining flame; for without it the whole mass of the atmosphere would, in time, become unfit for the purpose of animal life; and yet there is no reason to think that it is, at present, at all less fit for respiration than it has ever been. I flatter myself, however, that I have hit upon one of the methods employed by nature for this great purpose. How many others there may be, I cannot tell.

When animals die upon being put into air in which other animals have died, after breathing in it as long as they could, it is plain that the cause of their death is not the want of any *pabulum vitae* [food of life], which has been supposed to be contained in the air, but on account of the air being impregnated with something stimulating to their lungs; for they almost always die in convulsions, and are sometimes affected so suddenly that they are irrecoverable after a single inspiration, though they may be withdrawn immediately and every method has been taken to bring them to life again. They are affected in the same manner when they are killed in any other kind of noxious air that I have tried, viz, fixed air, inflammable air [hydrogen],[1] air filled with the fumes of sulphur, infected with putrid matter, in which a mixture of iron filings and sulphur has stood, or in which charcoal has been burned, or metals calcined, or in nitrous air, &c.

As it is known that *convulsions* weaken and exhaust the vital powers, much more than the most vigorous *voluntary* action of the muscles, perhaps these universal convulsions may exhaust the whole of what we may call the *vis vitae* [vital force] at once; at least the lungs may be rendered absolutely incapable of action, till the animal be suffocated, or be irrecoverable for want of respiration. . . .

The discovery of the provision in nature for restoring air which has been injured by the respiration of animals, having long appeared to me to be one of the most important problems in natural philosophy, I have tried a great variety of schemes in order to effect it. In these, my guide has generally been to consider the influences to which the atmosphere is, in fact, exposed; and, as some of my unsuccessful trials may be of use to those who are disposed to take pains in the farther investigation of this subject, I shall mention the principal of them.

The noxious effluvium with which air is loaded by animal respiration is not absorbed by standing, without agitation, in fresh or salt water. I have kept it many months in fresh water, when, instead of being meliorated, it has seemed to become even more deadly, so as to require more time to restore it by the methods which will be explained hereafter, than air which has been lately made noxious. I have even spent several hours in pouring this air from one glass vessel into another, in water sometimes as cold, and sometimes as warm, as my hands could bear it, and have sometimes also wiped the vessels many times, during the course of the experiment, in order to take off that part of the noxious matter which might adhere to the glass vessels, and which evidently gave them an offensive

1 See above, p. 259 and p. 270 f.

smell; but all these methods were generally without any sensible effect. The *motion*, also, which the air received in these circumstances, it is very evident, was of no use for this purpose. I had not then thought of the simple, but most effectual method of agitating air in water, by putting it into a tall jar and shaking it with my hand.

This kind of air is not restored by being exposed to the *light*, or any other influence to which it is exposed, when confined in a thin phial in the open air for some months. Among other experiments, I tried a great variety of different *effluvia*, which are continually exhaling into the air, especially of those substances which are known to resist putrefaction; but I could not by these means effect any melioration of the noxious quality of this kind of air.

Having read, in the Memoirs of the Imperial Society, of a plague not affecting a particular village in which there was a large sulphur-work, I immediately fumigated a quantity of this kind of air; or (which will hereafter appear to be the very same thing) air tainted with putrefaction, with the fumes of burning sulphur, but without any effect.

I once imagined that the *nitrous acid* in the air might be the general restorative which I was in quest of; and the conjecture was favoured by finding that candles would burn in air extracted from saltpetre. I therefore spent a good deal of time in attempting, by a burning glass and other means, to impregnate this noxious air with some effluvium of saltpetre, and, with the same view, introduced into it the fumes of the smoking spirit of nitre; but both these methods were altogether ineffectual.

In order to try the effect of *heat*, I put a quantity of air in which mice had died into a bladder tied to the end of the stem of a tobacco pipe, at the other end of which was another bladder, out of which the air was carefully pressed. I then put the middle part of the stem into a chafing-dish of hot coals, strongly urged with a pair of bellows; and, pressing the bladders alternately, I made the air pass several times through the heated part of the pipe. I have also made this kind of air very hot, standing in water before the fire. But neither of these methods were of any use. *Rarefraction* and *condensation* by instruments were also tried, but in vain.

Thinking it possible that the *earth* might imbibe the noxious quality of the air, and thence supply the roots of plants with such putrescent matter as is known to be nutritive to them, I kept a quantity of air in which mice had died in a phial, one half of which was filled with fine garden-mould; but, though it stood two months in these circumstances, it was not the better for it.

I once imagined that, since several kinds of air cannot be long separated from common air, by being confined in bladders, in bottles well corked, or even closed with ground stoppers, the affinity between this noxious air and the common air might be so great, that they would mix through a body of water interposed between them; the water continually receiving from the one and giving to the other, especially as water receives some kind of impregnation from, I believe, every kind of air to which it is contiguous; but I have seen no reason to conclude that a mixture of any kind of air with the common air can be produced in this manner.

I have kept air in which mice have died, air in which candles have burned out, and inflammable air, separated from the common air by the slightest partition of water that I could well make, so that it might not evaporate in a day or two, if I should happen not to attend to them; but I found no change in them after a month or six weeks. The inflammable air was still inflammable, mice died instantly in the air in which other mice had died before, and candles would not burn where they had burned out before.

Since air tainted with animal or vegetable putrefaction is the same thing with air rendered noxious by animal respiration, I shall now recite the observations which I have made upon this kind of air, before I treat of the method of restoring them.

That these two kinds of air are, in fact, the same thing, I conclude from their having several remarkable common properties, and from their differing in nothing that I have been able to observe. They equally extinguish flame, they are equally noxious to animals, they are equally, and in the same way, offensive to the smell, they equally precipitate lime in lime water, and they are restored by the same means. . . .

When air has been freshly and strongly tainted with putrefaction, so as to smell through the water, sprigs of mint have presently died upon being put into it, their leaves turning black; but if they do not die presently, they thrive in a most surprising manner. In no other circumstances have I ever seen vegetation so vigorous as in this kind of air, which is immediately fatal to animal life. Though these plants have been crowded in jars filled with this air, every leaf has been full of life; fresh shoots have branched out in various directions, and have grown much faster than other similar plants, growing in the same exposure in common air. This observation led me to conclude that plants, instead of affecting the air in the same manner with animal respiration, reverse the effects of breathing, and tend to keep the atmosphere sweet and wholesome, when it is become noxious in consequence of animals either living and breathing, or dying and putrefying in it.

In order to ascertain this, I took a quantity of air, made thoroughly noxious by mice breathing and dying in it, and divided it into two parts; one of which I put into a phial immersed in water; and into the other (which was contained in a glass jar, standing in water) I put a sprig of mint. This was about the beginning of August, 1771; and after eight or nine days, I found that a mouse lived perfectly well in that part of the air in which the sprig of mint had grown, but died the moment it was put into the other part of the same original quantity of air; and which I had kept in the very same exposure, but without any plant growing in it.

This experiment I have several times repeated; sometimes using air in which animals had breathed and died; and at other times using air tainted with vegetable or animal putrefaction; and generally with the same success. . . .

The air on which I made the first experiments was rendered exceedingly noxious by mice dying in it, on the 20th of June. Into a jar nearly filled with one part of this air, I put a sprig of mint, while I kept another part of it in a phial, in the same exposure; and on the 27th of the same month, and not before, I made a trial of them by introducing a mouse into a glass vessel, containing two ounce measures and a half, filled with each kind of air; and I noted the following facts:

When the vessel was filled with the air in which the mint had grown, a very large mouse lived five minutes in it, before it began to shew any sign of uneasiness. I then took it out and found it to be as strong and vigorous as when it was first put in; whereas in that air which had been kept in the phial only, without a plant growing in it, a younger mouse continued not longer than two or three seconds, and was taken out quite dead. It never breathed after, and was immediately motionless. After half an hour, in which time the larger mouse (which I had kept alive, that the experiment might be made on both the kinds of air with the very same animal) would have been sufficiently recruited, supposing it to have received any injury by the former experiment, it was put into the same vessel of air; but though it was withdrawn again after being in it hardly one second, it was recovered with difficulty, not being able to stir from the place for near a minute. After two days, I put the same mouse into an equal quantity of common air, and observed that it continued seven minutes without any sign of uneasiness; and being very uneasy after three minutes longer, I took it out. Upon the whole, I concluded that the restored air wanted about one fourth of being as wholesome as common air. The same thing also appeared when I applied the test of nitrous air.

In the seven days in which the mint was growing in this jar of noxious air, three old shoots had extended themselves about three inches, and several new ones had made their appearance in the same time. Dr. Franklin[2] and Sir John Pringle happened to be with me when the plant had been three or four days in this state, and

[2] Benjamin Franklin.

took notice of its vigorous vegetation and remarkably healthy appearance in that confinement. . . .

These proofs of a partial restoration of air by plants in a state of vegetation, though in a confined and unnatural situation, cannot but render it highly probable that the injury which is continually done to the atmosphere by the respiration of such a number of animals, and the putrefaction of such masses of both vegetable and animal matter, is, in part at least, repaired by the vegetable creation. And, notwithstanding the prodigious mass of air that is corrupted daily by the above-mentioned causes; yet, if we consider the immense profusion of vegetables upon the face of the earth, growing in places suited to their nature, and consequently at full liberty to exert all their powers both inhaling and exhaling, it can hardly be thought but that it may be a sufficient counterbalance to it, and that the remedy is adequate to the evil.

Dr. Franklin, who, as I have already observed, saw some of my plants in a very flourishing state in highly noxious air, was pleased to express very great satisfaction with the result of the experiments. In his answer to the letter in which I informed him of it, he says,

"That the vegetable creation should restore the air which is spoiled by the animal part of it, looks like a rational system, and seems to be of a piece with the rest. Thus fire purifies water all the world over. It purifies it by distillation, when it raises it in vapours and lets it fall in rain; and farther still, by filtration, when, keeping it fluid, it suffers that rain to percolate the earth. We knew before that putrid animal substances were converted into sweet vegetables, when mixed with the earth and applied as manure; and now, it seems, that the same putrid substances, mixed with the air, have a similar effect. The strong thriving state of your mint in putrid air seems to shew that the air is mended by taking something from it, and not by adding to it." He adds, "I hope this will give some check to the rage of destroying trees that grow near houses, which has accompanied our late improvements in gardening, from an opinion of their being unwholesome. I am certain, from long observation, that there is nothing unhealthy in the air of woods; for we Americans have everywhere our country habitations in the midst of woods, and no people on earth enjoy better health, or are more prolific." ...

I shall be happy, if the mention of this fact should excite an attention to things of this nature. Trifling as they seem to be, they have, in a philosophical view, the greatest dignity and importance; serving to explain some of the most striking phenomena in nature, respecting the general plan and constitution of the system, and the relation that one part of it bears to another.

JAN INGENHOUSZ

1 7 3 0 · 1 7 9 9

A Dutch physician read the passages from Priestley, just quoted, on the purification of air by plants, and in three months performed five hundred experiments to find out more about the action of leaves in sunlight on the purification of air. Ingenhousz showed that the purifying action of leaves depended on the presence of the light of the sun, rather than on its heat.

In a long series of experiments, not described here, Ingenhousz went on to show that all flowers, leaves, fruit, and roots give off bad air constantly at night or in the dark, while even offensive smelling plants purify the air in sunlight. In other words, he recognized that two independent types of activity were present; the breathing out of plants, and the assimilation of carbon dioxide in the presence of sunlight.

Ingenhousz was born in Breda, in the Netherlands, studied and practiced medicine there, and was particularly known for his skill in inoculation for smallpox, an operation which required a high degree of dexterity. After a three-year visit to England, he went to live in Vienna, where he was appointed physician to the Emperor Joseph II. In 1779 he returned to England and there spent most of the rest of his life. He was chosen a Fellow of the Royal Society, and made frequent contributions to the Philosophical Transactions.

The following selection, containing some of the conclusions derived from his experiments, is taken from his Experiments upon Vegetables, discovering Their Great Power of Purifying the Common Air in the Sun-Shine, and of Injuring it in the Shade and at Night, published in London in 1779.

451

THE BREATHING OF PLANTS

I WAS NOT LONG engaged in this enquiry before I saw a most important scene opened to my view: I observed, that plants not only have a faculty to correct bad air in six or ten days, by growing in it, as the experiments of Dr Priestley indicate, but that they perform this important office in a compleat manner in a few hours; that this wonderful operation is by no means owing to the vegetation of the plant, but to the influence of the light of the sun upon the plant. I found that plants have, moreover, a most surprising faculty of elaborating the air which they contain and undoubtedly absorb continually from the common atmosphere into real and fine dephlogisticated air;[1] that they pour down continually, if I may so express myself, a shower of this depurated air, which, diffusing itself through the common mass of the atmosphere, contributes to render it more fit for animal life; that this operation is far from being carried on constantly, but begins only after the sun has for some time made his appearance above the horizon, and has, by his influence, prepared the plants to begin anew their beneficial operation upon the air, and thus upon the animal creation, which was stopt during the darkness of the night; that this operation of the plants is more or less brisk in proportion to the clearness of the day, and the exposition of the plants more or less adapted to receive the direct influence of that great luminary; that plants shaded by high buildings, or growing under a dark shade of other plants, do not perform this office, but, on the contrary, throw out an air hurtful to animals, and even contaminate the air which surrounds them; that this operation of plants diminishes towards the close

[1] Oxygen was supposed in the late eighteenth century to be air from which phlogiston, the fire principle, had been removed. See above, p. 267.

ot the day, and ceases entirely at sun-set, except in a few plants, which continue this duty somewhat longer than others; that this office is not performed by the whole plant, but only by the leaves and the green stalks that support them; that acrid, ill-scented, and even the most poisonous plants perform this office in common with the mildest and the most salutary; that the most part of leaves pour out the greatest quantity of this dephlogisticated air from their under surface, principally those of lofty trees; that young leaves, not yet come to their full perfection, yield dephlogisticated air less in quantity, and of an inferior quality than what is produced by full-grown and old leaves; that some plants elaborate dephlogisticated air better than others; that some of the aquatic plants seem to excell in this operation; that all plants contaminate the surrounding air by night, and even in the day-time in shaded places; that, however, some of those which are inferior to none in yielding beneficial air in the sun-shine, surpass others in the power of infecting the circumambient air in the dark, even to such a degree, that in a few hours they render a great body of good air so noxious, that an animal placed in it loses its life in a few seconds; that all flowers render the surrounding air highly noxious, equally by night and by day; that the roots removed from the ground do the same, some few, however, excepted; but that in general fruits have the same deleterious quality at all times, though principally in the dark, and many to such an astonishing degree, that even some of those fruits which are the most delicious, as, for instance, peaches, contaminate so much the common air as would endanger us to lose our lives, if we were shut up in a room in which a great deal of such fruits are stored up; that the sun by itself has no power to mend air without the concurrence of plants, but, on the contrary, is apt to contaminate it. . . .

ON THE NATURE OF PLANTS

Section I

*Some general remarks on the nature of the leaves of plants, and
their use*

It seems to be more than probable, that the leaves, with which
the most part of plants are furnished during the summer in temperate climates, and perpetually in hot countries, are destined to
more than one purpose. Such a great apparatus, which nature dis-
plays as soon as the sun begins to afford a certain degree of warmth
upon the surface of the earth, can scarcely be considered as solely
destined either to ornament, to nourishment of the plant, to its
growth, to ripen its fruit, or for any other peculiar and single use.
It seems probable that they are used to the growth of the tree; for,
by depriving the tree of all its leaves, it is in danger of decay. By
taking a considerable part of the leaves from a fruit tree, the fruit
is less perfect; and by taking them all away, the fruit decays and
falls before its maturity. It is also probable that the tree receives
some advantage from the leaves, absorbing, by their means, moisture
from the air, from rain, and from dew; for it has been found a
considerable advantage to the growth of a tree, to water the stem
and the leaves now and then. . . .

As soon as the sun begins to diffuse its warmth over the surface
of the earth in the spring, and to promote that general tendency
to corruption which all dead bodies of the animal and vegetable
kingdom and many other substances are so liable to, the trees display in a few days the most wonderful scene that can be imagined.
Contracted as they were in that state of stupor and inactivity in
which they remain during the winter, exposing to the air no other
surface than that of their trunk and branches, as if they wanted
to have as little to do as possible with the external air, they all at
once increase, perhaps more than a thousand times, their surface
by displaying those kind of numberless fans which we call leaves.

Some of them produce their leaves a long while before any flowers appear upon them; others a good while after the flowers are formed, and the fructification is already in an advanced state; and keep their leaves in the best condition, and even push out continually new ones, long after the whole fructification is finished; which seems to indicate, that the chief use of these fans is not to assist the fructification and propagation of their species. These fans, when compleated, seem to compose or arrange themselves in such a manner as to expose their upper and varnished surface to the direct influence of the sun, and to hide as much as they can their under surface from the direct influence of this luminary. It seems as if they required rather the light of the sun than the influence of its heat, as their polished surfaces must reflect some of the rays of the sun, and thus moderate the degree of heat.

It will, perhaps, appear probable that one of the great laboratories of nature for cleansing and purifying the air of our atmosphere is placed in the substance of the leaves, and put in action by the influence of the light; and that the air thus purified, but in this state grown useless or noxious to the plant, is thrown out for the greatest part by the excretory ducts, placed chiefly, at least in far the most part of plants, on the under side of the leaf.

Is there not some probability that the under part of the leaves may have been chiefly destined for this purpose; because in this way the dephlogisticated air [oxygen], gushing continually out of this surface, is inclined to fall rather downwards, as a beneficial shower for the use of the animals who all breathe in a region of the air inferior to the leaves of trees? Does not this conjecture get some weight, if we consider that dephlogisticated air is in reality specifically heavier than common air, and thus tends rather to fall downwards?

If we add to these reflexions another of no less importance, viz, that most sorts of foul air are specifically lighter than common air, we shall be inclined to believe that the difference of the specificial gravity of that beneficial air of which I treat, and that which is become hurtful to our constitution by corruption, breathing, and other causes, indicates one of those special blessings designed by the hand of God: for by this arrangement we get soon rid, in a great measure, of that air which is become hurtful to us, as it rises soon up out of our reach;[1] whereas the dephlogisticated air, being heavier than common air, is rather inclined to settle on the surface of the earth among the animal creation.

But, as animals spoil equally as much air in the winter as in the summer by the act of respiration, it might seem somewhat surprizing, that his great laboratory ceases entirely by the decay of the leaves. Is this defect supplied by some other means equally powerful? Though we are very far from being able to trace all the active causes which contribute their share in keeping up the wholesomeness of our atmosphere, yet we have already traced some of them, and therefore must not despair of discovering some more. The shaking of foul air in water will in great measure correct it. Water itself has a power of yielding dephlogisticated air, as Dr. Priestley discovered. Plants have a power to correct bad air, and to improve good air. Winds will blow away the noxious particles of the air, and bring on air corrected by the waters of the seas, lakes, rivers, and forests. All these causes exist equally in the winter as in the summer, or at least nearly so. The influence of the vegetable creation alone ceases in the winter: but the loss of this influence is, perhaps, more than amply counterbalanced by the diminution of the general promoting cause of corruption, viz. heat. Everybody knows, that warm weather hastens in a great degree putrefaction. . . .

Section II

On the manner in which the dephlogisticated air [oxygen] is obtained from the leaves of plants

As the leaves of plants yield dephlogisticated air only in the clear day-light, or in the sun-shine, and begin their operation only after

[1] This is of course false, for carbon dioxide is much heavier than air or oxygen.

they have been in a certain manner prepared, by the influence of the same light, for beginning it; they are to be put in a very transparent glass vessel or jar, filled with fresh pump water (which seems the most adapted to promote this operation of the leaves, or at least not to obstruct it); which, being inverted in a tub full of the same water, is to be immediately exposed to the open air, or rather to the sun-shine. Thus the leaves continuing to live, continue also to perform the office they performed out of the water, as far as the water does not obstruct it. The water prevents only new atmospheric air being absorbed by the leaves, but does not prevent that air, which already existed in the leaves, from oozing out. This air, prepared in the leaves by the influence of the light of the sun, appears soon upon the surface of the leaves in different forms, most generally in the form of round bubbles, which, increasing gradually in size, and detaching themselves from the leaves, rise up and settle at the inverted bottom of the jar: they are succeeded by new bubbles, till the leaves, not being in the way of supplying themselves with new atmospheric air, become exhausted. This air, gathered in this manner, is really dephlogisticated air, of a more or less good quality, according to the nature of the plant from which the leaves are taken, and the clearness of the day-light to which they were exposed.

It is not very rare to see these bubbles so quickly succeeding one another, that they rise from the same spot almost in a continual stream: I saw this more than once, principally in the *nymphaea alba*.

Section VI

The production of the dephlogisticated air [oxygen] from the leaves not owning to the warmth of the sun, but chiefly, if not only, to the light

If the sun caused this air to ooze out of the leaves by rarifying the air in heating the water, it would follow that if a leaf, warmed in the middle of the sun-shine upon the tree, was immediately placed in water drawn directly from the pump, and thus being very cold, the air bubbles would not appear till, at least, some degree of warmth was communicated to the water; but quite the contrary happens. The leaves taken from trees or plants in the midst of a warm day, and plunged immediately into cold water, are remarkably quick in forming air bubbles, and yielding the best dephlogisticated air.

If it was the warmth of the sun, and not its light, that produced this operation, it would follow, that, by warming the water near the fire about as much as it would have been in the sun, this very air would be produced; but this is far from being the case.

I placed some leaves in pump water, inverted the jar, and kept it as near the fire as was required to receive a moderate warmth, near as much as a similar jar, filled with leaves of the same plant and placed in the open air, at the same time received from the sun. The result was that the air obtained by the fire was very bad, and that obtained in the sun was dephlogisticated air.

A jar full of walnut tree leaves was placed under the shade of other plants and near a wall, so that no rays of the sun could reach it. It stood there the whole day, so that the water in the jar had received there about the same degree of warmth as the surrounding air (the thermometer being then at $76°$); the air obtained was worse than common air, whereas the air obtained from other jars kept in the sun-shine during such a little time that the water had by no means received a degree of warmth approaching that of the atmosphere, was fine dephlogisticated air.

No dephlogisticated air is obtained in a warm room, if the sun does not shine upon the jar containing the leaves.

Section VII

Reflections

It might, perhaps, be objected, that the leaves of the plants are never in a natural state when surrounded by pump water; and that thus there may, perhaps, remain some degree of doubt, whether the same operation of the leaves in their natural situation takes place.

I cannot consider the plants kept thus under water to be in a situation so contrary to their nature as to derange their usual operation. Water, even more than they want, is not hurtful to plants, if it is not applied too considerable a time. The water only cuts off the communication with the external air; and we know that plants may live a long while without this free communication. . . .

As plants yield in a few hours such a considerable quantity of dephlogisticated air, though their situation seems rather unfavourable for it when they are kept under water, may it not with some degree of probability be conjectured that they yield much more of it when remaining in their natural situation; for then, being continually supplied by new common air, their stock of dephlogisticated air cannot be exhausted. It is an unfavourable circumstance that air is not an object of our sight; if it was, we should perhaps see that plants have a kind of respiration as animals have; that leaves are the organs of it; that, perhaps, they have pores which absorb air, and others which throw it out by way of excretion, as are the excretory ducts of animals; that the air secreted, being dephlogisticated air, is thrown out as noxious to the plant (which article is clearly demonstrated by Dr. Priestley and Mr. Scheele); that in the most part of plants, principally trees, the greatest part of inhaling pores are placed upon the upper side of the leaf, and the excretory ducts principally on the under side.

If these conjectures were well grounded, it would throw a great deal of new light upon the arrangement of the different parts of the globe, and the harmony between all its parts would become more conspicuous. We might find that partial tempests and hurricanes, by shaking the air and the waters, produce some partial evils for the universal benefit of nature; that, by these powerful agitations, the septic and noxious particles of the air are blown away and rendered of no effect, by being thus diluted with the body of air and partly buried in the waters. We might conceive a little more of the deep designs of the Supreme Wisdom in the different arrangement of sublunary beings. The stubborn atheist would, perhaps, find reason to humiliate himself before that Almighty Being, whose existence he denies because his limited senses represent to him nothing but a confused chaos of miseries and disorders in this world.

Section IX

All plants possess a power of correcting, in a few hours, foul air unfit for respiration; but only in clear day-light, or in the sun-shine

This remarkable property of plants is indeed very great; for in a few hours, nay even sometimes in an hour and a half, they purify so much a body of air quite unfit for respiration, as to be equal in goodness to atmospheric air. They will even do it when they are inclosed in a glass vessel, without any water. One leaf of a vine, shut up in an ounce phial, full of air fouled by breathing so that a candle could not burn in it, restored this air to the goodness of common air in the space of an hour and a half. But plants enjoy this privilege only in the day-time, and when they grow in unshaded places. . . .

Section XVI

The power of plants in correcting bad air is greater than their faculty of improving good air

The experiments already known of Dr. Priestley, by which it appears that plants thrive wonderfully well in air fouled by breathing and burning of candles, gave me a great suspicion, that the power of plants in correcting bad air might surpass their faculty of improving good common air. In order to put my conjecture to the trial, I placed at eleven o'clock, in a warm sun-shine, two jars of an equal size, each containing an equal quantity of sprigs of pepper-mint, in pump water. In one of these jars was let up a certain quantity of common air, whose test was at that time such, that one measure of it with one of nitrous air occupied 1.06½. In the other jar was let up the same quantity of air fouled by respiration, of which one measure with one measure of nitrous air occupied 1.34.

The air of both jars was examined at two o'clock, when I found the common air so much improved, that one measure of it with one of nitrous air occupied 1.00. The foul air was so much mended, that it was near as good as the atmospheric air, for one measure of it with one of nitrous air occupied now 1.08½.

I examined both airs again at four o'clock, when the common air was still more improved; for one measure of it with one of nitrous air occupied 0.95. The foul air now was not only become as good as respirable air, or air of the atmosphere, but even surpassed it in goodness, for one measure of it with one of nitrous air occupied 1.05.

Now, as the same plant brought the foul air from 1.34 to 1.05, and the common air from 1.06½ to 0.95, it appears clear, that the plant had corrected the foul air far more than it had improved the common air. This experiment was repeated several times with nearly the same results.

As plants seem to delight in foul air, probably because this air impregnated with phlogiston affords more proper nourishment, viz, phlogiston to the plant; it must of course happen, that a plant draws to it so much the more phlogiston as the air, in which it grows, contains more of this principle. . . .

VII

The Structure of the Human Body

MEDICAL SCHOLARS of the Middle Ages, who preferred to lean on authority rather than to study natural phenomena, relied on the old Greeks for the anatomy and physiology, as the astronomers relied on Aristotle and Ptolemy. But the Greek knowledge of the structure of man's body and of how it operates had been to a large extent corrupted and lost during the Dark Ages in Western Europe. Improvement began when, in the eleventh and twelfth centuries, the writings of learned Arab physicians were translated into Latin in Italy and Spain. And a century later the biological works of Aristotle and the medical classics of Hippocrates (about 460-370 B.C.), the father of Greek medicine, and of Galen (130-201 A.D.), skilled physician to the Emperor Marcus Aurelius, were reintroduced to the West through Arabic translations from the Greek. These treatises, however, although they stimulated interest in anatomy, tended to become the medieval doctor's bible and final authority, instead of a guide to independent study of the body on the doctor's part.

In the sixteenth century, Andreas Vesalius started the development of modern medicine by writing his *De fabrica humani corpus* (*On the Structure of the Human Body*) in rebellion against this professional subservience to authority. He agreed with Galen on many points, but disagreed with him boldly on many others, and castigated the schools for looking to books rather than to the human body itself for the basis of their learning. His work helped to make anatomy the first of the biological sciences to be freed from the restrictions of a backward-looking tradition.

Progress in physiology was slower, for dissection and experimentation tend inevitably to upset or destroy the natural operations of the body which it is the purpose of the experiment to observe. Galen had taught that the arteries and the veins formed two separate systems, each of which conducted its own type of blood out from the heart and back, alternately, in a sort of tidal flow and ebb. The blood of the veins, he said, was made from the products of digestion in the liver. It ebbed and flowed, and eventually reached the right side of the heart, where its impurities were carried to the lungs by the pulmonary artery. A small part of this venous blood meanwhile seeped through the thick muscle separating the cavities of the heart, to the left ventricle. There it mixed with the air brought back from the lungs by the pulmonary vein, and formed a *vital spirit*, which was then distributed to the body through the ebb and flow in the arteries. Some of this *vital spirit* was transformed at the base of the brain into *animal spirit*, the fluid substance of the nerves. Discovery of the true course of the circulation of the blood was obviously a first essential for the new physiology of the sixteenth, seventeenth, and eighteenth centuries.

Servetus, who died in 1553, a victim of religious intolerance, first described the circulation of the blood through the lungs. Fabricius published the earliest account of the valves in the veins, which prevent venous blood from flowing away from the heart. Harvey described the true course of the whole blood stream through the arteries and veins, but had no microscope powerful enough to see the blood move through the capillaries that connect the arteries and veins; Malpighi and Leeuwenhoek were able to observe this final step. They had the microscope —as revolutionary an instrument in the development of botany and biology as the telescope in the development of astronomy. Leeuwenhoek noticed also the red corpuscles in the blood and the capillaries in the intestines, and made the shrewd guess that nourishment passes through the intestinal walls into the bloodstream. A hundred years later, Spallanzani experimented with the action of enzymes in the digestion of food.

ANDREAS VESALIUS

1 5 1 4 - 1 5 6 4

FOR THREE HUNDRED years before Copernicus and Vesalius, the urge
to depend on observation and experiment more than on ancient
authority had been felt by a few students of nature here and there
in Europe. In the sixteenth century the insurgent spirit of the Renaissance and the Reformation gave a fresh impetus to this feeling. The
year 1543 saw the publication of the two greatest books of the new
science—the science built on observation and experiment; these
were Copernicus' On the Revolution of the Heavenly Bodies [1] and
Vesalius' On the Structure of the Human Body.

Andreas Vesalius was born and received his early education in
Brussels. He attended the universities of Louvain, Paris, and Padua,
and taught at Padua, Bologna, and Pisa, all before he published his
great work on anatomy at the age of twenty-nine. The academic
controversy which followed its publication so annoyed him that he
left the university and entered the employ of the Emperor Charles V,
to whom his book had been dedicated.

Vesalius was a rarely keen and careful dissector and observer.
Nevertheless he, like Servetus and Fabricius, as we shall see, was too
bound up in the old ways to discover the true course of the circula
tion of the blood. He stated clearly that "the extreme ramifications
of these veins [veins and arteries] inosculate [touch at the ends] with
each other and in many places appear to unite and be continuous."
But he did not perceive the passage of the blood from one to the
other.

The seven volumes of his Structure of the Human Body appeared

[1] See p. 6 for first version of this work.

465

in edition after edition for more than two hundred years, and the beautiful illustrations, drawn by a pupil of Titian, were many times borrowed for incorporation in the texts of later writers. The influence of these illustrations on the development of pictorial art in printed books was immense. Lancelot Hogben says in connection with them, "Italian art made anatomy a live subject, as the cinema might be used to make mathematics a live subject, if every school were equipped with a projector."

Our first selection, taken from Vesalius' Introduction, gives an interesting picture of the state of medical schools at the time he wrote. The second shows how he spoke of his dissections of heart, lungs, and blood vessels. The former passage we quote in B. Farrington's translation, as published in the Proceedings of the Royal Society of Medicine, July 1942. The latter, translated by Dr. Samuel W. Lambert, is printed in the Proceedings of the Charaka Club (Columbia University Press, 1935).

PREFACE TO THE ANATOMY OF
THE HUMAN BODY

Addressed to

The Most Great and Invincible Emperor

THE DIVINE CHARLES V [1]

THOSE ENGAGED in the arts and sciences, Most Gracious Emperor Charles, find many serious obstacles to the exact study and successful application of them. In the first place, no slight inconvenience results from too great separation between branches of study which serve for the perfection of one art. But much worse is the mischievous distribution among different practitioners of the practical applications of the art. This has been carried so far that those who have set before themselves the attainment of an art embrace one part of it to the neglect of the rest, although they are intimately bound up with it and can by no means be separated from it. Such never achieve any notable result; they never attain their goal or succeed in basing their art upon a proper foundation.

I shall pass over all the other arts in silence and confine myself to a few remarks on that which presides over the health of mankind. This, of all the arts which the mind of man has discovered, is by far the most beneficial, necessary, abstruse, and laborious. But in bygone times, that is to say after the Gothic deluge [2] and after

[1] Charles V (1500-1558), ruler over Austria, the German Empire, the Low Countries, Spain, and the Spanish domains beyond the seas, was perhaps the most conscientious and serious, as well as the most powerful, monarch of his day.
[2] That is, after the barbarian invasions that accompanied the fall of the Roman Empire in the West.

the reign of Mansor at Bochara in Persia,[3] under whom, as we know, the Arabs still lived as was right on terms of familiarity with the Greeks, medicine began to be sore distempered. Its primary instrument, the employment of the hand in healing, was so neglected that it was relegated to vulgar fellows with no instruction whatsoever in the branches of knowledge that subserve the art of medicine.

In ancient times there were three medical sects, to wit, the Dogmatic, the Empirical, and the Methodical, but the exponents of each of these embraced the whole of the art as the means to preserve health and to war against disease. To this end they referred all that they individually thought necessary in their particular sects, and employed the service of a threefold aid to health: first, a theory of diet; secondly, the whole use of drugs; and thirdly, manual operation. This last, above the rest, nicely proves the saying that medicine is the addition of that which is defective and the removal of that which is in excess; as often as we resort to the art of medicine for the treatment of disease we have occasion to employ it; and time and experience have taught, by the benefits it has conferred, that it is the greatest aid to human health.

This triple manner of treatment was equally familiar to the doctors of each sect; and those who applied manual operation according to the nature of the affection expended no less care in training their hands than in establishing a theory of diet, or in learning to recognize and compound drugs. This, not to mention his other books, is clearly shown by those most perfect of the compositions of Hippocrates: "On the Function of the Doctor," "On Fractures of Bones," "On Dislocations of Joints and Similar Ailments." Nay, more, Galen, after Hippocrates the prince of medicine, in addition to the fact that he boasts from time to time that the care of the

---

[3] Mansor, or Al-Mansur (about 712-775), caliph of the victorious Moslem Empire, when its power was rapidly approaching its height. He founded the splendid new capital at Bagdad, increased commerce with the Greeks at Constantinople and urged the translation of Greek philosophy and science into Arabic. For several centuries thereafter Arab medicine was the best in the European world.

gladiators of Pergamum was entrusted to his sole charge, and that when age was now becoming a burden he was reluctant for the monkeys he had for dissection to be skinned by the help of slaves, frequently impresses on us his joy in manual dexterity and how zealously he, in common with the other doctors of Asia, employed it. Indeed, there is no one of the ancients who does not seem as solicitous to hand down to posterity the method of cure which is effected by the hand as those methods which depend on diet and drugs.

But it was especially after the ruin spread by the Goths, when all the sciences, which before had flourished gloriously and were practiced as was fitting, went to ruin, that more fashionable doctors, first in Italy, in imitation of the old Romans, despising the work of the hand, began to delegate to slaves the manual attentions which they judged needful for their patients, and themselves merely to stand over them like master builders. Then, when all the rest also who practiced the true art of healing gradually declined the unpleasant duties of their profession, without, however, abating any of their claim to money or honor, they quickly fell away from the standard of the doctors of old. Methods of cooking, and all the preparation of food for the sick, they left to nurses; compounding of drugs they left to the apothecaries; manual operation to barbers. Thus in course of time the art of healing has been so wretchedly rent asunder that certain doctors, advertising themselves under the name of physicians, have arrogated to themselves alone the prescription of drugs and diet for obscure diseases, and have relegated the rest of medicine to those whom they call surgeons and scarcely regard as slaves, disgracefully banishing from themselves the chief and most ancient branch of the medical art, and that which principally (if indeed there be any other) bases itself upon the investigation of nature. . . .

But it was not at all my purpose to set one instrument of medicine above the rest, since the triple art of healing, as it is called, cannot at all be disunited and wrenched asunder, but belongs in its entirety to the same practitioner; and for the due attainment of this triple art, all the parts of medicine have been established and prepared on an equal footing, so that the individual parts are brought into use with a success proportioned to the degree in which one combines the cumulative force of all. How rarely indeed a disease occurs which does not at once require the triple manner of treatment; that is to say, a proper diet must be prescribed, some service must be rendered by medicine, and some by the hand.[4] Therefore the tyros in this art must by every means be exhorted to follow the Greeks in despising the whisperings of those physicians (save the mark!), and, as the fundamental nature and rational basis of the art prescribes, to apply their hands also to the treatment, lest they should rend the body of medicine and make of it a force destructive of the common life of man.

And they must be urged to this with all the greater earnestness because men today who have had an irreproachable training in the art are seen to abstain from the use of the hand as from the plague, and for this very reason, lest they should be slandered by the masters of the profession as barbers before the ignorant mob, and should henceforth lack equal gain and honor with those less than half doctors, losing their standing both with the uneducated commonalty and with princes. For it is indeed above all other things the wide prevalence of this hateful error that prevents us even in our age from taking up the healing art as a whole, makes us confine ourselves merely to the treatment of internal complaints, and, if I may utter the blunt truth once for all, causes us, to the great detriment of mankind, to study to be healers only in a very limited degree.

For when, in the first place, the whole compounding of drugs was handed over to the apothecaries, then the doctors promptly lost the knowledge of simple medicines which is absolutely essential to them; and they became responsible for the fact that the druggists' shops were filled with barbarous terms and false reme-

---

[4] That is, by surgery.

dies, and also that so many elegant compositions of the ancients were lost to us, several of which have not yet come to light; and, finally, they prepared an endless task for the learned men, not only of our own age, but for those who preceded it by some years, who devoted themselves with indefatigable zeal to research in simple medicines; so much so that they may be regarded as having gone far to restore the knowledge of them to its former brilliance.

But this perverse distribution of the instruments of healing among a variety of craftsmen inflicted a much more odious shipwreck and a far more cruel blow upon the chief branch of natural philosophy [anatomy], to which, since it comprises the natural history of man and should rightly be regarded as the firm foundation of the whole art of medicine and its essential preliminary, Hippocrates and Plato attached so much importance that they did not hesitate to put it first among the parts of medicine. For though originally it was the prime object of the doctors' care, and though they strained every nerve to acquire it, it finally began to perish miserably when the doctors themselves, by resigning manual operations to others, ruined anatomy. For when the doctors supposed that only the care of internal complaints concerned them, considering a mere knowledge of the viscera as more than enough for them, they neglected the structure of the bones and muscles, as well as of the nerves, veins, and arteries which run through bones and muscles, as of no importance for them. And further, when the whole conduct of manual operations was entrusted to barbers, not only did doctors lose the true knowledge of the viscera, but the practice of dissection soon died out, doubtless for the reason that the doctors did not attempt to operate, while those to whom the manual skill was resigned were too ignorant to read the writings of the teachers of anatomy.

It is thus utterly impossible for this class of men to preserve for us a difficult art which they have acquired only mechanically. And equally inevitably this deplorable dismemberment of the art of healing has introduced into our schools the detestable procedure now in vogue, that one man should carry out the dissection of the human body, and another give the description of the parts. These latter are perched up aloft in a pulpit like jackdaws, and with a notable air of disdain they drone out information about facts they have never approached at first hand, but which they merely commit to memory from the books of others, or of which they have descriptions before their eyes; the former are so ignorant of languages that they are unable to explain their dissections to the onlookers and botch what ought to be exhibited in accordance with the instruction of the physician, who never applies his hand to the dissection, and contemptuously steers the ship out of the manual, as the saying goes. Thus everything is wrongly taught, days are wasted in absurd questions, and in the confusion less is offered to the onlooker than a butcher in his stall could teach a doctor. I omit all mention of those schools in which there is scarcely even a thought of opening a human body to exhibit its structure. So far had ancient medicine fallen some years ago from its pristine glory. . . .

But this effort [to restore anatomy] could by no manner of means have succeeded if, when I was studying medicine at Paris, I had not myself applied my hand to this business, but had acquiesced in the casual and superficial display to me and my fellow students by certain barbers of a few organs at one or two public dissections. For in such a perfunctory manner was anatomy then treated in the place where we have lived to see medicine happily reborn that I myself, having trained myself without guidance in the dissection of brute creatures, at the third dissection at which it was my fortune ever to be present (this, as was the custom there, was concerned exclusively or principally with the viscera), led on by the encouragement of my fellow students and teachers, performed in public a more thorough dissection than was wont to be done. Later I attempted a second dissection, my purpose being to exhibit the muscles of the hand together with a more accurate dissection of the viscera. For except for eight muscles of the abdomen, disgracefully mangled and in the wrong order, no one (I speak the simple truth) ever demonstrated to me any single muscle, or any single bone, much less the network of nerves, veins, and arteries.

Subsequently at Louvain, where I had to return on account of the disturbance of war, because during eighteen years the doctors there had not even dreamed of anatomy, and in order that I might help the students of that academy, and that I myself might acquire greater skill in a matter both obscure and in my judgment of prime importance for the whole of medicine, I did somewhat more accurately than at Paris expound the whole structure of the human body in the course of dissecting, with the result that the younger teachers of that academy now appear to spend great and very serious study in acquiring a knowledge of the parts of man, clearly understanding what invaluable material for philosophizing is presented to them from this knowledge. Furthermore at Padua, in the most famous gymnasium of the whole world,[5] I was charged with the teaching of surgical medicine five years by the illustrious Senate of Venice, which is far the most liberal in the endowment of the higher branches of learning. And since the carrying out of anatomical inquiry is of importance for surgical medicine, I devoted much effort to the investigation of the structure of man, and so directed my inquiries, and, exploding the ridiculous fashion of the schools, so taught the subject that we could not find in my procedure anything that fell short of the tradition of the ancients.

However, the supineness of the medical profession has seen to it only too well that the writings of Eudemus, Herophilus, Marinus, Andreas, Lycus, and other princes of anatomy should not be preserved to us, since not even a fragment of any page has survived of all those famous writers whom Galen mentions, to the number of more than twenty, in his second commentary to the book of Hippocrates on "The Nature of Man." Nay, even of his own anatomical writings scarcely the half has been saved from destruction. But those

[5] It is interesting to note how many of the great original scientists of the sixteenth and seventeenth centuries studied or taught at Padua, then the university city for Venice.

who followed Galen, among whom I place Oribasius, Theophilus, the Arabs, and all our own writers whom I have read to date, all of them (and they must pardon me for saying this), if they handed on anything worth reading, borrowed it from him. And, believe me, the careful reader will discover that there is nothing they were further from attempting than the dissection of bodies. They placed an absolute trust in I know not what quality of the writing of their chief, and in the neglect of dissection by the rest, and shamefully reduced Galen to convenient summaries, never departing from him by so much as the breadth of a nail, that is, supposing they succeed in arriving at his meaning. Nay, they place it in the forefront of their books that their own writings are pieced together from the teachings of Galen, and that all that is theirs is his. And so completely have all surrendered to his authority that no doctor has been found to declare that in the anatomical books of Galen even the slightest error has ever been found, much less could now be found; though all the time (apart from the fact that Galen frequently corrects himself, and in later books, after acquiring more experience, removes oversights that he had committed in earlier books, and sometimes teaches contradictory views) it is quite clear to us, from the revival of the art of dissection, from a painstaking perusal of the works of Galen, and from a restoration of them in several places, of which we have no reason to be ashamed, that Galen himself never dissected a human body lately dead. Nay, more, deceived by his monkeys (although it is admitted that human bodies dried, and prepared as it were for an inspection of the bones, did come under his observation), he frequently wrongly controverts the ancient doctors who had trained themselves by dissecting human corpses.

And again, how many false observations you will find him to have made even on his monkeys. I shall say nothing about the astonishing fact that in the manifold and infinite divergences of the organs of the human body from those of the monkey Galen hardly noticed anything except in the fingers and the bend of the knee—which he would certainly have passed over with the rest, if they had not been obvious to him without dissection. But at the moment I do not propose to criticize the false statements of Galen, easily the foremost among the teachers of anatomy; and much less would I wish to be regarded now in the beginning as disloyal to the author of all good things and lacking in respect for his authority. For I am not unaware how the medical profession (in this so different from the followers of Aristotle) are wont to be upset when in more than two hundred instances, in the conduct of the single course of anatomy I now exhibit in the schools, they see that Galen has failed to give a true description of the interrelation, use, and function of the parts of man—how they scowl at times, and examine every inch of the dissection in their determination to defend him. Yet they too, drawn by the love of truth, gradually abandon that attitude and, growing less emphatic, begin to put faith in their own not ineffectual sight and powers of reason rather than in the writings of Galen. These true paradoxes, won not by slavish reliance on the efforts of others, nor supported merely by masses of authorities, they eagerly communicate in their correspondence to their friends; they exhort them so earnestly and so friendly-wise to examine for themselves, and to come at last to a true knowledge of anatomy, that there is ground for hope that anatomy will ere long be cultivated in all our academies as it was of old in Alexandria.

And that the muses might the more smile upon this hope, I have, so far as in me lay, and in addition to my other publications on this subject—which certain plagiarists, thinking me far away from Germany, have put out there as their own—made a completely fresh arrangement in seven books of my information about the parts of the human body in the order in which I am wont to lay the same before that learned assembly in this city, as well as at Bologna and at Pisa. Thus those present at the dissections will have a record of what was there demonstrated, and will be able to expound anatomy to others with less trouble. And also the books will be by no means useless to those who have no opportunity for personal examination, for they relate with sufficient fullness the number, position, shape, substance, connection with other parts, use and function of each part of the human body, together with many similar facts which we are wont to unravel during dissection concerning the nature of the parts, and also the method of dissection applicable to dead and living animals. Moreover, the books contain representations of all the parts inserted in the text of the discourse, in such a way that they place before the eyes of the student of nature's works, as it were, a dissected corpse.

Thus in the first book I have described the nature of all bones and cartilages, which, since the other parts are supported by them, and must be described in accordance with them, are the first to be known by students of anatomy. The second book treats of the ligaments by which bones and cartilages are linked one with another, and then the muscles that affect the movements that depend upon our will. The third comprises the close network of veins which carry to the muscles and bones and the other parts the ordinary blood by which they are nourished, and of arteries which control the mixture of innate heat and vital spirit. The fourth treats of the branches not only of the nerves which convey the animal spirit to the muscles, but of all the other nerves as well. The fifth explains the structure of the organs that subserve nutrition effected through food and drink; and furthermore, on account of the proximity of their position, it contains also the instruments designed by the Most High Creator for the propagation of the species. The sixth is devoted to the heart, the *fomes* of the vital faculty, and the parts that subserve it. The seventh describes the harmony between the structure of the brain and the organs of sense, without, however, repeating from the fourth book the description of the network of nerves arising from the brain. . . .

But here there comes into my mind the judgment of certain men who vehemently condemn the practice of setting before the eyes of students, as we do with the parts of plants, delineations, be they never so accurate, of the parts of the human body. These, they say, ought to be learned not by pictures but by careful dissection and examination of the things themselves. As if, forsooth, my object in adding to the text of my discourse images of the parts, which are most faithful, and which I wish could be free from the risk of being spoiled by the printers, was that students should rely upon them and refrain from dissecting bodies; whereas my practice has rather been to encourage students of medicine in every way I could to perform dissections with their own hands. Assuredly, if the practice of the ancients had lasted down to our day, namely, to train boys at home in carrying out dissections, just as in making their letters and in reading, I would gladly consent to our dispensing not only with pictures but with all commentaries. For the ancients only began to write about dissection when they decided that honor demanded that they should communicate the art not only to their children but to strangers whom they respected for their virtue. For, as soon as boys were no longer trained in dissection, the inevitable consequence at once followed that they learned anatomy less well, since the training had been abolished with which they had been wont to begin in youth. So much so that when the art had deserted the family of the Asclepiads,[6] and had been now for many centuries on the decline, books were needed to preserve a complete view of it. Yet how greatly pictures aid the understanding of these things, and how much more accurately they put the things before the eyes than even the clearest language, nobody can have failed to experience in geometry and the other mathematical disciplines.

But, however that may be, I have done my best to this single end, namely, in an equally recondite and laborious matter, to aid as many as possible, and truly and completely to describe the structure of the human body—which is built up not of some ten or twelve parts (as seems to those who give it a passing glance) but of some thousands of different parts—and to bring to students of medicine a substantial contribution toward the understanding of those books of Galen

[6] An association of the alleged descendants of Asclepius, the Greek god of medicine and healing; later, a school for the training of physicians.

treating of this branch of learning, which of all his writings most require the assistance of a teacher.

Moreover, I am aware how little authority my efforts will carry by reason of my youth (I am still in my twenty-eighth year); and how little, on account of the frequency with which I draw attention to the falsity of Galen's pronouncements, I shall be sheltered from the attacks of those who have not—as I have done in the schools of Italy—applied themselves earnestly to anatomy, and who, being now old men devoured by envy at the true discoveries of youths, will be ashamed, together with all the other sectaries of Galen, that they have been hitherto so purblind, failing to notice what I now set forth, yet arrogating to themselves a mighty reputation in the art— [I know, I say, how little authority my efforts will carry] unless they come forth auspiciously into the light, commended by the great patronage of some divine power. And, inasmuch as it cannot be more safely sheltered or more splendidly adorned than by the imperishable name of the Divine Charles, the Most Great and Invincible Emperor, I beseech Your Majesty to allow this useful work of mine, which on many accounts and for many reasons is dangerous to itself, to circulate for a short time under Your Majesty's auspices, glory, and patronage, until through experience of the facts, through judgment which matures with time, and through learning, I may make the fruit of my toil worthy of the Most High and Best Prince, or may offer another gift worthy of acceptance on another subject chosen from our art.

PADUA, *August 1, A.D. 1542.*

WHAT MAY BE LEARNED BY
DISSECTION OF THE DEAD
AND WHAT OF THE LIVING

§

JUST AS THE dissection of the dead teaches well the number, position and shape of each part, and most accurately the nature and composition of its material substance, thus also the dissection of a living animal clearly demonstrates at once the function itself, at another time it shows very clearly the reasons for the existence of the parts. Therefore, even though students deservedly first come to be skilled in the study of dead animals, afterward when about to investigate the action and use of the parts of the body they must become acquainted with the living animal. . . .

Examination of the Uses of the Veins and Arteries

Also when inquiring into the use of the veins the work is scarcely one for the dissection of the living, since we shall become sufficiently acquainted in the case of the dead with the fact that these veins carry the blood through the whole body and that any part is not nourished in which a prominent vein has been severed in wounds.

Likewise concerning the arteries we scarcely require a dissection of the living although it will be allowable for anyone to lay bare the artery running into the groin and to obstruct it with a band and to observe that the part of the artery cut off by the band pulsates no longer.

And thus it is observed by the easy experiment of opening an artery at any time in living animals that blood is contained in the arteries naturally.

In order that on the other hand we may be more certain that the material contained in the arteries is not the producer of the pulsation, for in truth this force depends for its strength upon the heart. Besides, because we see that an artery bound by a cord no longer beats under the cord, it will be permitted to undertake an extensive dissection of the artery of the groin or of the thigh, and to take a small tube made of a reed of such a thickness as is the capacity of the artery and to insert it by cutting in such a way that the upper part of the tube reaches higher into the cavity of the artery than the upper part of the dissection, and in the same manner also that the lower portion of the tube is introduced downward farther than the lower part of the dissection, and thus the ligature of the artery which constricts its caliber above the canulla is passed by a circuit.

To be sure, when this is done the blood and likewise the vital spirit run through the artery even as far as the foot; in fact the whole portion of the artery replaced by the canulla beats no longer. Moreover, when the ligature has been cut, that part of the artery which is beyond the canulla shows no less pulsation than the portion above.

We shall see next how much force is actually carried to the brain from the heart by the arteries. Now in this demonstration thou shalt wonder greatly at a vivisection of Galen in which he advises that all things be cut off which are common to the brain and heart, always excepting the arteries which seek the head through the transverse processes of the cervical vertebrae and carry also besides a substantial portion of the vital spirit into the primary sinuses of the dural mater and also in like manner into the brain. So much so that it is not surprising that the brain performs its functions under these conditions for a long time, which Galen observed could easily be done, for the animal breathes for a long time during this dissection, and sometimes moves about. If indeed it runs, and therefore requires much breath, it falls not long afterwards, although the brain will still afterwards receive the essense of the animal spirit from those arteries which I have closely observed seek the skull through the transverse processes of the cervical vertebrae. . . .

MICHAEL SERVETUS

1 5 0 9 · 1 5 5 3

IN THE MIDDLE of a religious tract, which ultimately brought death
to its author, Michael Servetus, there appeared the first description
of the circulation of the blood through the lungs. Servetus, a native
of Aragon, Spain, had studied law at Toulouse, and medicine at
Paris, where he followed Vesalius as assistant to the great teacher,
Johann Gunther, and won high praise for his skill at dissection and
his general culture. A man of remarkably diverse talents and inter-
ests, Servetus for a number of years edited scientific and philosophical works for a publisher at Lyons, and at intervals practiced medicine
in various parts of France.

But he was a theologian as well as a physician, and his Unitarian
ardor angered both Protestant and Catholic authorities. For fear of
the Inquisition, he eventually left Lyons. John Calvin had met Servetus in Paris in 1536, and some years later had begun a correspondence
with him on points of doctrine. Servetus had sent to Calvin some
copies of his theological writings, including The Restoration of
Christianity, the tract which contained his description of the pulmonary circulation of the blood. Hoping now for further discussion
with Calvin, Servetus stopped off in Geneva on his way to Italy,
though he had been warned of the dangers of such a step. He was
promptly arrested, tried for heresy, and burned at the stake. All but
three copies of his book were burned with him. The excerpt presented here was translated by R. Willis, and appeared in his book,
Servetus and Calvin (London, 1877).

. . . THERE IS commonly said to be a threefold spirit in the body of man, derived from the substance of the three superior elements—a natural, a vital, and an animal spirit; there are, however, not really three, but only two distinct spirits. One of these, the first, characterized as *natural*, is communicated from the arteries to the veins by their anastomoses [connecting branches], and is primarily associated with the blood, the proper seat or home of which is the liver and veins. The second is the *vital* spirit, whose seat or dwelling place is the heart and arteries. The third, the *animal* spirit, comparable to a ray of light, has its home in the brain and nerves. In each and all of these is the force—*energia*—of the one spirit and light of God comprised.

The heart is the first organ that lives, and, situated in the middle of the body, is the source of its heat. From the liver the heart receives the liquor, the material as it were of life, and in turn gives life to the source of the supply. The material of life is therefore derived from the liver; but, elaborated, as you shall hear, by a most admirable process, it comes to pass that the life itself is in the blood—yea that the blood is the life, as God himself declares (Gen. ix; Levit. xvii; Deut. xii).

Rightly to understand the question here, the first thing to be considered is the substantial generation of the vital spirit—a compound of the inspired air with the most subtle portion of the blood. The vital spirit has, therefore, its source in the left ventricle of the heart, the lungs aiding most essentially in its production. It is a fine attenuated spirit, elaborated by the power of heat, of a crimson colour and fiery potency—the lucid vapour, as it were, of the blood, substantially composed of water, air, and fire; for it is engendered, as said, by the mingling of the inspired air with the more subtle portion of the blood, which the right ventricle of the heart communicates to the left. This communication, however, does not take place through the septum, partition or midwall of the heart, as commonly believed, but by another admirable contrivance, the blood being transmitted from the pulmonary artery to the pulmonary vein, by a lengthened passage through the lungs, in the course of which it is elaborated and becomes of a crimson colour. Mingled with the inspired air in this passage, and freed from fuliginous vapours by the act of expiration, the mixture being now complete in every respect, and the blood become fit dwelling-place of the vital spirit, it is finally attracted by the diastole, and reaches the left ventricle of the heart.

Now that the communication and elaboration take place in the lungs in the manner described we are assured by the conjunctions and communications of the pulmonary artery with the pulmonary vein. The great size of the pulmonary artery seems of itself to declare how the matter stands; for this vessel would neither have been of such a size as it is, nor would such a force of the purest blood have been sent through it to the lungs for their nutrition only; neither would the heart have supplied the lungs in such fashion, seeing as we do that the lungs in the foetus are nourished from another source—those membranes or valves of the heart not coming into play until the hour of birth, as Galen teaches. The blood must consequently be poured in such large measure at the moment of birth from the heart to the lungs for another purpose than the nourishment of these organs. Moreover, it is not simply air, but air mingled with blood that is returned from the lungs to the heart by the pulmonary vein.

It is in the lungs, consequently, that the mixture [of the inspired air with the blood] takes place, and it is in the lungs also, not in the heart, that the crimson colour of the blood is acquired. There is not indeed capacity or room enough in the left ventricle of the heart for so great and important an elaboration, neither does it seem competent to produce the crimson colour. To conclude, the septum or middle partition of the heart, seeing that it is without vessels and special properties, is not fitted to permit and accomplish the communication and elaboration in question, although it may be that some transudation takes place through it. It is by a mechanism similar to that by which the transfusion from the *vena portae* to the *vena cava* takes place in the liver, in respect of the blood, that the transfusion from the pulmonary artery to the pulmonary vein takes place in the lungs, in respect of the spirit.

The vital spirit (elaborated in the manner described) is at length transfused from the left ventricle of the heart to the arteries of the body at large, and in such a way that the more attenuated portion tends upwards, and undergoes further elaboration in the retiform plexus of vessels situated at the base of the brain, in which the *vital* begins to be changed into the *animal* spirit, reaching as it now does the proper seat of the rational soul. Here, still further sublimated and elaborated by the igneous power of the soul, the blood is distributed to those extremely minute vessels or capillary arteries composing the choroid plexus, which contain or are the seat of the soul itself. The arterial plexus penetrates even the most intimate part of the brain, its constituent vessels, interwoven in highly complex fashion, being distributed over the ventricles, and sent to the origins of the nerves which subserve the faculties of sensation and motion. Most wonderfully and delicately interwoven, these vessels, although spoken of as arteries, are really the terminations of arteries proceeding to the origins of nerves in the meninges. They are in truth a new kind of vessels; for, as in the transfusion from arteries to veins within the lungs we find a new kind of vessels proceeding from the arteries and veins, so, in the transfusion from arteries to nerves, is there a new kind of vessels produced from the arterial coats and the cerebral meninges.

HIERONYMOUS FABRICIUS

1 5 3 7 · 1 6 1 9

THE NEXT STEP towards the discovery of the circulation of the blood
was made by Girolamo Fabrizio of Aquapendente in Tuscany,
known more often by the Latin form of his name as given above.
In 1574 he discovered the valves in the veins and showed them to
his students of anatomy at the University of Padua. Many years
earlier a distinguished Italian surgeon, Giambattista Canano, had
described these same valves to Vesalius. Vesalius, however, had
thought he was in error, and Canano left no written description of
his discovery.

But Fabricius failed to see how the valves served to ensure the
flow of all venous blood to the heart, for he held the prevailing view
that the veins both carried blood out to the tissues and brought it
back again.

Fabricius' book, On the Valves in the Veins, was published in
1603. Our translation was made by Dr. K. J. Franklin, of Oriel College, Oxford, for the Readings in the History of Physiology, edited
by Dr. John F. Fulton (Charles C. Thomas, Springfield, Ill., 1930)

485

DOORLETS IN THE VEINS

DOORLETS OF VEINS [hereafter translated as *valves*] is the name I give to some extremely delicate little membranes in the lumen [cavities] of veins. They occur at intervals, singly or in pairs, especially in the limb veins. They open upwards in the direction of the main venous trunk, and are closed below, while, viewed from the outside, they resemble the swellings in the stem and small branches of plants.

My theory is that Nature has formed them to delay the blood to some extent, and to prevent the whole mass of it flooding into the feet or hands and fingers, and collecting there. Two evils are thus avoided, namely, undernutrition of the upper parts of the limbs, and a permanently swollen condition of the hands and feet. Valves were made, therefore, to ensure a really fair all-round distribution of the blood for the nutrition of the various parts.

A discussion of these valves must be preceded by a feeling of wonder at the way in which they have hitherto escaped the notice of anatomists, both of our own and earlier generations; so much so that not only have they never been mentioned, but no one even set eye on them till 1574, when to my great delight I saw them in the course of my dissection. And this despite the fact that anatomy has claimed many distinguished men among its followers, men, moreover, whose research was conducted with great care and minuteness. But a certain amount of justification does exist for them in this case, for who would ever have thought that membranous valves could be found in the lumen of veins, especially as this lumen, designed for the passage of blood to the whole body, should be free for the free flow of the blood, just as in the case of the arteries, which are valveless, yet, inasmuch as they are channels for blood, are on the same footing as veins?

But a further justification can be advanced for the anatomists. All veins are not provided with valves. The *vena cava*, where it traverses the trunk of the body, the internal jugulars, and countless superficial veins in like manner are destitute of them. On the other hand, a reasonable charge may be made against the earlier workers. Either they neglected to investigate the function of the valves, a matter, one would think, of primary importance, or else they failed to see them in their actual demonstration of veins. Nay more, when assistants pass a ligature round the limbs preparatory to blood-letting, valves are quite obviously noticeable in the arms and legs of the living subject. And, indeed, at intervals along the course of the veins certain knotty swellings are visible from the outside; these are caused by the valves. In some people, in fact, such as porters and peasants, they appear to swell up like varices [varicose veins].

But here I must correct myself. It must be clearly stated that actual varices are due entirely to the dilatation of valves and veins by too long retention and thickening of the blood at the valves; since, in the absence of valves, the veins would be expected to swell up and dilate uniformly throughout their length, differing thus from varices. From which begins to be visible one function of valves, namely, a strengthening action on the veins *per se*. For as in cases of varix, with valvular incompetence or rupture as an expected finding, one always sees a greater or lesser degree of venous dilatation, one can doubtless say with safety that the Supreme Artificer made valves to prevent venous distention. Venous distention and dilatation would, moreover, have occurred readily had the veins been of a membranous texture, and that uniformly thin. And if they were to dilate, not only would the excessive accumulation of blood in them cause damage to themselves and the surrounding parts, and a swelling be caused, as has been known to occur in cases of limb varix. There would also be a more or less defective nutrition of the parts above, with the blood rushing in force, say, to a site of venous dilatation, and collected, as it were, in a pool. Arteries, on the other hand, had no need of valves, either to prevent distention—the thickness and strength of their coat suffices—or to delay the blood—an ebb and flow of blood goes on continuously within them.

But let us, if you will, consider the number, form, structure, site, distance, et cetera, of valves. It was certainly necessary to make valves in the limb veins either of large or medium calibre—not the small ones—in order, no doubt, to slow the blood flow everywhere to an extent compatible with sufficient time being given for each small part to make use of the nourishment provided. Otherwise the whole mass of blood, owing to the slope of the limbs, would flood into their extremities, and collect there, causing a swelling of these lower parts, and wasting of the parts above.

That the blood flow is slowed by the valves, evident even without this from their actual construction, can be tested by anyone either in the exposed veins of the cadaver, or in the living subject, if he passes a ligature round the limbs as in blood-letting. For if one tries to exert pressure on the blood, or to push it along by rubbing from above downwards, one will clearly see it held up and delayed by the valves. This indeed was the way in which I was led to an observation of such nature.

WILLIAM HARVEY

1 5 7 8 · 1 6 5 7

WILLIAM HARVEY, who finally discovered the true path of the circulation of the blood, was the son of a prosperous Kentish yeoman. After attending Cambridge University, he spent five years abroad, and in 1602 took the degree of Doctor of Physic at Padua. At Padua he came under the influence of Fabricius, which led him to study especially the movement of the blood in animal bodies, and also the embryology of chickens. In 1616 he announced his discovery of the circulation of the blood and the action of the heart as pump to the Royal College of Physicians in London, of which he was president.

Harvey left out the mystical and theological arguments of his predecessors, and discussed the circulation of the blood as a clear problem of physiological mechanics. He thus committed physiology wholly to the experimental method, as important a step in the development of modern medicine as his discovery itself. Both his method and his conclusion met at first with violent opposition from the English public. His book On the Movement of the Heart and Blood in Animals was written in Latin, the original title being Exercitatio anatomica de motu cordis et sanguinis in animalibus, and was first printed in 1628 by a small publisher in Frankfort, Germany. Our translation was made by R. Willis, and revised by Alexander Bouré (Charles C. Thomas, Springfield, Ill.).

ON THE CIRCULATION OF THE BLOOD

Chapter I

The Author's Motives for writing

WHEN I FIRST gave my mind to vivisections as a means of discovering the motions and uses of the heart, and sought to discover these from actual inspection and not from the writings of others, I found the task so truly arduous, so full of difficulties, that I was almost tempted to think, with Fracastorius, that the motion of the heart was only to be comprehended by God. For I could neither rightly perceive at first when the systole and when the diastole took place, nor when and where dilatation and contraction occurred, by reason of the rapidity of the motion, which in many animals is accomplished in the twinkling of an eye, coming and going like a flash of lightning; so that the systole presented itself to me now from this point, now from that; the diastole the same; and then everything was reversed, the motions occurring, as it seemed, variously and confusedly together. My mind was therefore greatly unsettled, nor did I know what I should myself conclude nor what believe from others. I was not surprised that Andreas Laurentius should have written that the motion of the heart was as perplexing as the flux and reflux of Euripus [1] had appeared to Aristotle.

At length, and by using greater and daily diligence and investigation, making frequent inspection of many and various animals, and collating numerous observations, I thought that I had attained to the truth, that I should extricate myself and escape from this labyrinth, and that I had discovered what I so much desired, both the

---

[1] A narrow strait off the coast of Attica, through which the tide rushes first in one direction and then in the other.

motion and the use of the heart and arteries. From that time I have not hesitated to expose my views upon these subjects, not only in private to my friends, but also in public, in my anatomical lectures, after the manner of the Academy of old.

These views, as usual, pleased some more, others less; some chid and calumniated me and laid it to me as a crime that I had dared to depart from the precepts and opinion of all anatomists; others desired further explanations of the novelties, which they said were both worthy of consideration and might perchance be found of signal use. At length, yielding to the requests of my friends, that all might be made participators in my labours, and partly moved by the envy of others, who, receiving my views with uncandid minds and understanding them indifferently, have essayed to traduce me publicly, I have been moved to commit these things to the press, in order that all may be enabled to form an opinion both of me and my labours. This step I take all the more willingly, seeing that Hieronymus Fabricius of Aquapendente, although he has accurately and learnedly delineated almost every one of the several parts of animals in a special work, has left the heart alone untouched. . . .

CHAPTER II

Of the Motions of the Heart, as seen in the Dissection of living Animals

In the first place, then, when the chest of a living animal is laid open and the capsule that immediately surrounds the heart is slit up or removed, the organ is seen now to move, now to be at rest; there is a time when it moves, and a time when it is motionless.

These things are more obvious in the colder animals, such as toads, frogs, serpents, small fishes, crabs, shrimps, snails, and shell-fish. They also become more distinct in warm-blooded animals, such as the dog and hog, if they be attentively noted when the heart begins to flag, to move more slowly, and, as it were, to die; the movements then become slower and rarer, the pauses longer, by which it is made much more easy to perceive and unravel what the motions really are, and how they are performed. In the pause, as in death, the heart is soft, flaccid, exhausted, lying, as it were, at rest.

In the motion and interval in which this is accomplished, three principal circumstances are to be noted:

1. That the heart is erected, and rises upwards to a point, so that at this time it strikes against the breast and the pulse is felt externally.

2. That it is everywhere contracted, but more especially towards the sides, so that it looks narrower, relatively longer, more drawn together. The heart of an eel taken out of the body of the animal and placed upon the table or the hand, shows these particulars; but the same things are manifest in the hearts of small fishes and of those colder animals where the organ is more conical or elongated.

3. The heart, being grasped in the hand, is felt to become harder during its action. Now this hardness proceeds from tension, precisely as, when the forearm is grasped, its tendons are perceived to become tense and resilient when the fingers are moved.

4. It may further be observed in fishes and the colder blooded animals, such as frogs, serpents, etc., that the heart, when it moves, becomes of a paler colour; when quiescent of a deeper blood-red colour.

From these particulars it appeared evident to me that the motion of the heart consists in a certain universal tension—both contraction in the line of its fibres, and constriction in every sense. It becomes erect, hard, and of diminished size during its action; the motion is plainly of the same nature as that of the muscles when they contract in the line of their sinews and fibres; for the muscles, when in action, acquire vigour and tenseness, and from soft become hard, prominent and thickened: in the same manner the heart.

We are therefore authorized to conclude that the heart, at the moment of its action, is at once constricted on all sides, rendered thicker in its parietes and smaller in its ventricles, and so made apt to project or expel its charge of blood. This, indeed, is made suffi-

ciently manifest by the preceding fourth observation in which we
have seen that the heart, by squeezing out the blood it contains,
becomes paler, and then when it sinks into repose and the ventricle
is filled anew with blood, that the deeper crimson colour returns.
But no one need remain in doubt of the fact, for if the ventricle
be pierced the blood will be seen to be forcibly projected outwards
upon each motion or pulsation when the heart is tense.

These things, therefore, happen together or at the same instant:
the tension of the heart, the pulse of its apex, which is felt externally
by its striking against the chest, the thickening of its parietes, and
the forcible expulsion of the blood it contains by the construction
of its ventricles. . . .

CHAPTER V

Of the Motion, Action, and Office of the Heart

From these and other observations of a similar nature, I am persuaded it will be found that the motion of the heart is as follows:

First of all, the auricle contracts, and in the course of its contraction forces the blood (which it contains in ample quantity as the
head of the veins, the store-house and cistern of the blood) into
the ventricle, which being filled, the heart raises itself straightway,
makes all its fibres tense, contracts the ventricles and performs a
beat, by which beat it immediately sends the blood supplied to it by
the auricle into the arteries. The right ventricle sends its charge
into the lungs by the vessel which is called *vena arteriosa*, but which,
in structure and function and all other respects, is an artery. The
left ventricle sends its charge into the aorta, and through this by
the arteries to the body at large.

These two motions, one of the ventricles, the other of the auricles,
take place consecutively, but in such a manner that there is a kind
of harmony or rhythm preserved between them, the two concurring
in such wise that but one motion is apparent, especially in the
warmer blooded animals, in which the movements in question are

rapid. Nor is this for any other reason than it is in a piece of machinery, in which, though one wheel gives motion to another, yet all the wheels seem to move simultaneously; or in that mechanical contrivance which is adapted to firearms, where the trigger being touched, down comes the flint, strikes against the steel, elicits a spark, which falling among the powder, ignites it, when the flame extends, enters the barrel, causes the explosion, propels the ball, and the mark is attained—all of which incidents, by reason of the celerity with which they happen, seem to take place in the twinkling of an eye. So also in deglutition: by the elevation of the root of the tongue and the compression of the mouth, the food or drink is pushed into the fauces, when the larynx is closed by its muscles and by the epiglottis. The pharynx is then raised and opened by its muscles in the same way as a sac that is to be filled is lifted up, and its mouth dilated. Upon the mouthful being received, it is forced downwards by the transverse muscles, and then carried farther by the longitudinal ones. Yet all these motions, though executed by different and distinct organs, are performed harmoniously, and in such order that they seem to constitute but a single motion and act, which we call deglutition.

Even so does it come to pass with the motions and action of the heart, which constitute a kind of deglutition, a transfusion of the blood from the veins to the arteries. And if anyone, bearing these things in mind, will carefully watch the motions of the heart in the body of a living animal, he will perceive not only all the particulars I have mentioned, viz, the heart becoming erect and making one continuous motion with its auricles; but farther, a certain obscure undulation and lateral inclination in the direction of the axis of the right ventricle, as if twisting itself slightly in performing its work. And indeed everyone may see, when a horse drinks, that the water is drawn in and transmitted to the stomach at each movement of the throat, which movement produces a sound and yields a pulse both to the ear and the touch; in the same way it is with each motion of the heart, when there is the delivery of a quantity of blood from the veins to the arteries, a pulse takes place, and can be heard within the chest.

The motion of the heart, then, is entirely of this description, and the one action of the heart is the transmission of the blood and its distribution, by means of the arteries, to the very extremities of the body; so that the pulse which we feel in the arteries is nothing more than the impulse of the blood derived from the heart.

Whether or not the heart, besides propelling the blood, giving it motion locally, and distributing it to the body, adds anything else to it—heat, spirit, perfection—must be inquired into by-and-by, and decided upon other grounds. So much may suffice of this time, when it is shown that by the action of the heart the blood is transfused through the ventricles, from the veins to the arteries, and distributed by them to all parts of the body. . . .

CHAPTER VIII

Of the Quantity of Blood passing through the Heart from the Veins to the Arteries, and of the Circular Motion of the Blood

Thus far I have spoken of the passage of the blood from the veins into the arteries, and of the manner in which it is transmitted and distributed by the action of the heart; points to which some, moved either by the authority of Galen or Columbus, or the reasonings of others, will give in their adhesion. But what remains to be said upon the quantity and source of the blood, which thus passes, is of a character so novel and unheard of that I not only fear injury to myself from the envy of a few, but I tremble lest I have mankind at large for my enemies, so much doth wont and custom become a second nature. Doctrine once sown strikes deep its root, and respect for antiquity influences all men. Still the die is cast, and my trust is in my love of truth and the candour of cultivated minds.

And sooth to say, when I surveyed my mass of evidence, whether derived from vivisections and my various reflections on them, or from the study of the ventricles of the heart and the vessels that enter into and issue from them, the symmetry and size of these conduits—for nature doing nothing in vain, would never have given them so large a relative size without a purpose—or from observing the arrangement and intimate structure of the valves in particular, and of the other parts of the heart in general, with many things besides, I frequently and seriously bethought me and long revolved in my mind what might be the quantity of blood which was transmitted, in how short a time its passage might be effected, and the like. But not finding it possible that this could be supplied by the juices of the ingested aliment without the veins on the one hand becoming drained, and the arteries on the other getting ruptured through the excessive charge of blood, unless the blood should somehow find its way from the arteries into the veins, and so return to the right side of the heart; I began to think whether there might not be *a motion, as it were, in a circle.*

Now this I afterwards found to be true; and I finally saw that the blood, forced by the action of the left ventricle into the arteries, was distributed to the body at large and its several parts in the same manner as it is sent through the lungs, impelled by the right ventricle into the pulmonary artery, and that it then passed through the veins and along the *vena cava,* and so round to the left ventricle in the manner already indicated.

This motion we may be allowed to call circular, in the same way as Aristotle says that the air and the rain emulate the circular motion of the superior bodies; for the moist earth, warmed by the sun, evaporates; the vapours drawn upwards are condensed, and descending in the form of rain, moisten the earth again. By this arrangement are generations of living things produced; and in like manner are tempests and meteors engendered by the circular motion, and by the approach and recession of the sun.

And similarly does it come to pass in the body, through the motion of the blood, that the various parts are nourished, cherished, quickened by the warmer, more perfect, vapourous, spiritous, and, as I may say, alimentive blood; which, on the other hand, owing to its contact with these parts, becomes cooled, coagulated, and, so to speak, effete. It then returns to its sovereign the heart, as if to its source, or to the inmost home of the body, there to recover its state of excellence or perfection. Here it renews its fluidity, natural heat, and becomes powerful, fervid, a kind of treasury of life, and impregnated with spirits—it might be said with balsam. Thence it is again dispersed. All this depends on the motion and action of the heart.

The heart, consequently, is the beginning of life; the sun of the microcosm, even as the sun in his turn might well be designated the heart of the world; for it is the heart by whose virtue and pulse the blood is moved, perfected, and made nutrient, and is preserved from corruption and coagulation; it is the household divinity which, discharging its function, nourishes, cherishes, quickens the whole body, and is indeed the foundation of life, the source of all action. But of these things we shall speak more opportunely when we come to speculate upon the final cause of this motion of the heart.

As the blood vessels, therefore, are the canals and agents that transport the blood, they are of two kinds, the cava and the aorta; and this not by reason of there being two sides of the body, as Aristotle has it, but because of the difference of office, not, as is commonly said, in consequence of any diversity of structure, for in many animals, as I have said, the vein does not differ from the artery in the thickness of its walls, but solely in virtue of their distinct functions and uses. A vein and an artery, both styled veins by the ancients, and that not without reason, as Galen has remarked; for the artery is the vessel which carries the blood from the heart to the body at large, the vein of the present day bringing it back from the general system to the heart; the former is the conduit from, the latter the channel to, the heart; the latter contains the cruder, effete blood, rendered unfit for nutrition; the former transmits the digested, perfect, peculiarly nutritive fluid.

Chapter IX

That there is a Circulation of the Blood is confirmed from the first proposition

But lest anyone should say that we give them words only, and make mere specious assertions without any foundation, and desire to innovate without sufficient cause, three points present themselves for confirmation, which being stated, I conceive that the truth I contend for will follow necessarily, and appear as a thing obvious to all.

First, the blood is incessantly transmitted by the action of the heart from the *vena cava* to the arteries in such quantity that it cannot be supplied from the ingesta, and in such a manner that the whole must very quickly pass through the organ.

Second, the blood under the influence of the arterial pulse enters and is impelled in a continuous, equable, and incessant stream through every part and member of the body, in much larger quantity than were sufficient for nutrition, or than the whole mass of fluids could supply.

Third, the veins in like manner return this blood incessantly to the heart from parts and members of the body.

These points proved, I conceive it will be manifest that the blood circulates, revolves, propelled and then returning, from the heart to the extremities, from the extremities to the heart, and thus that it performs a kind of circular motion.

Let us assume, either arbitrarily or from experiment, the quantity of blood which the left ventricle of the heart will contain, when distended, to be, say two ounces, three ounces, or one ounce and a half; in the dead body I have found it to hold upwards of two ounces. Let us assume, further, how much less the heart will hold in the contracted than in the dilated state; and how much blood will project into the aorta upon each contraction;—and all the world allows that with the systole something is always projected, a necessary consequence demonstrated in the third chapter, and obvious from the structure of the valves; and let us suppose, as approaching the truth, that the fourth, or fifth, or sixth, or even but the eighth part of its charge is thrown into the artery at each contraction; this would give either half an ounce, or three drachms, or one drachm of blood as propelled by the heart at each pulse into the aorta; which quantity, by reason of the valves at the root of the vessel, can by no means return into the ventricle.

Now in the course of half an hour, the heart will have made more than one thousand beats, in some as many as two, three, and even four thousand. Multiplying the number of drachms propelled by the number of pulses, we shall have either one thousand half ounces, or one thousand times three drachms, or a like proportional quantity of blood, according to the amount which we assume as propelled with each stroke of the heart, sent from this organ into the artery; a larger quantity in every case than is contained in the whole body! In the same way, in the sheep or dog, say that but a single scruple of blood passes with each stroke of the heart, in one half hour we should have one thousand scruples, or about three pounds and a half of blood injected into the aorta; but the body of neither animal contains above four pounds of blood, a fact which I have myself ascertained in the case of the sheep.

Upon this supposition, therefore, assumed merely as a ground for reasoning, we see the whole mass of blood passing through the heart, from the veins to the arteries, and in like manner through the lungs.

But let it be said that this does not take place in half an hour, but in an hour, or even in a day; any way it is still manifest that more blood passes through the heart in consequence of its action, than can either be supplied by the whole of the ingesta, or than can be contained in the veins at the same moment.

Nor can it be allowed that the heart in contracting sometimes propels and sometimes does not propel, or at most propels but very little. a mere nothing, or an imaginary something; all this, indeed, has already been refuted, and is, besides, contrary both to sense and reason. For if it be a necessary effect of the dilatation of the heart that its ventricles become filled with blood, it is equally so that, contracting, these cavities should expel their contents; and this not in any trifling measure. For neither are the conduits small, nor the contractions few in number, but frequent, and always in some certain proportion, whether it be a third or a sixth, or an eighth, to the total capacity of the ventricles, so that a like proportion of blood must be expelled and a like proportion received with each stroke of the heart, the capacity of the ventricle contracted always bearing a certain relation to the capacity of the ventricle when dilated. And since in dilating, the ventricles cannot be supposed to get filled with nothing, or with an imaginary something, so in contracting they never expel nothing or aught imaginary, but always a certain something, viz, blood, in proportion to the amount of the contraction.

Whence it is to be concluded that if one stroke of the heart in man, the ox or the sheep, ejects but a single drachm of blood, and there are one thousand strokes in half an hour, in this interval there will have been ten pounds, five ounces expelled; if with each stroke two drachms are expelled, the quantity would of course amount to twenty pounds and ten ounces; if half an ounce, the quantity would come to forty-one pounds and eight ounces; and were there one ounce it would be as much as eighty-three pounds and four ounces; the whole of which, in the course of one half hour, would have been transfused from the veins to the arteries. The actual quantity of blood expelled at each stroke of the heart, and the circumstances under which it is either greater or less than ordinary, I leave for particular determination afterwards, from numerous observations which I have made on the subject.

Meantime this much I know, and would here proclaim to all, that the blood is transfused, at one time in larger, at another in smaller quantity; and that the circuit of the blood is accomplished, now more rapidly, now more slowly, according to the temperament, age, etc., of the individual, to external and internal circumstances, to naturals and non-naturals—sleep, rest, food, exercise, affections of the mind, and the like. But, supposing even the smallest quantity of blood to be passed through the heart and the lungs with each pulsation, a vastly greater amount would still be thrown into the arteries and whole body than could by any possibility be supplied by the food consumed. It could be furnished in no other way than by making a circuit and returning.

This truth, indeed, presents itself obviously before us when we consider what happens in the dissection of living animals; the great artery need not be divided, but a very small branch only (as Galen even proves in regard to man), to have the whole of the blood in the body, as well that of the veins as of the arteries, drained away in the course of no long time, some half hour or less. Butchers are well aware of the fact and can bear witness to it; for, cutting the throat of an ox and so dividing the vessels of the neck, in less than a quarter of an hour they have all the vessels bloodless; the whole mass of blood has escaped. The same thing also occasionally occurs with great rapidity in performing amputations and removing tumours in the human subject.

Nor would this argument lose any of its force, did any one say that in killing animals in the shambles and performing amputations, the blood escaped in equal, if not perchance in larger quantity, by the veins than by the arteries. The contrary of this statement, indeed, is certainly the truth; the veins, in fact, collapsing and being without any propelling power, and, further, because of the impediment of the valves, as I shall show immediately, pour out but very little blood; whilst the arteries spout it forth with force abundantly, impetuously, and as if it were propelled by a syringe. And then the experiment is easily tried of leaving the vein untouched, and only dividing the artery in the neck of a sheep or dog, when it will be seen with what force, in what abundance, and how quickly, the whole blood in the body, of the veins as well as of the arteries, is emptied. But the arteries receive blood from the veins in no other way than by transmission through the heart, as we have already seen; so that if the aorta be tied at the base of the heart, and the carotid or any other artery be opened, no one will now be surprised to find it empty and the veins only replete with blood.

And now the cause is manifest why in our dissections we usually find so large a quantity of blood in the veins, so little in the arteries; why there is much in the right ventricle, little in the left, which probably led the ancients to believe that the arteries (as their name implies) contained nothing but spirits during the life of an animal. The true cause of the difference is perhaps this, that as there is no passage to the arteries, save through the lungs and heart, when an animal has ceased to breathe and the lungs to move, the blood in the pulmonary artery is prevented from passing into the pulmonary veins, and from thence into the left ventricle of the heart; just as we have already seen the same transit prevented in the embryo, by the want of movement in the lungs and the alternate opening and shutting of their hidden and invisible porosities and apertures. But the heart not ceasing to act at the same precise moment as the lungs, but surviving them and continuing to pulsate for a time, the left ventricle and arteries go on distributing their blood to the body at large and sending it into the veins; receiving none from the lungs, however, they are soon exhausted, and left, as it were, empty. But even this fact confirms our views in no trifling manner, seeing that it can be ascribed to no other than the cause we have just assumed.

Moreover it appears from this that the more frequently or forcibly the arteries pulsate, the more speedily will the body be exhausted of its blood during hemorrhage. Hence, also, it happens that in fainting fits and in states of alarm, when the heart beats more languidly and less forcibly, hemorrhages are diminished and arrested.

Still further, it is from this that after death, when the heart has ceased to beat, it is impossible by dividing either the jugular or femoral veins and arteries, by any effort, to force out more than one half of the whole mass of the blood. Neither could the butcher ever bleed the carcass effectually, did he neglect to cut the throat of the

ox which he has knocked on the head and stunned, before the heart
had ceased beating.

Finally, we are now in a condition to suspect wherefore it is that
no one has yet said anything to the purpose upon the anastomosis
[system of connecting branches] of the veins and arteries, either as
to where or how it is effected, or for what purpose. I now enter upon
the investigation of the subject.

CHAPTER X

*The first position: of the Quantity of Blood Passing from
the Veins to the Arteries. And that there is a Circuit of the
Blood, freed from Objections, and farther confirmed by
Experiment.*

. . . . Let us here conclude with a single example, confirming
all that has been said, and from which everyone may obtain conviction through the testimony of his own eyes.

If a live snake be laid open, the heart will be seen pulsating
quietly, distinctly, for more than an hour, moving like a worm, contracting in its longitudinal dimensions (for it is of an oblong shape),
and propelling its contents. It becomes of a paler colour in the
systole, of a deeper tint in the diastole; and almost all things else
are seen by which I have already said that the truth I contend for
is established, only that here, everything takes place more slowly
and is more distinct. This point in particular may be observed more
clearly than the noonday sun: the *vena cava* enters the heart at its
lower part, the artery quits it at the superior part; the vein being
now seized either with forceps or between the finger and thumb,
and the course of the blood for some space below the heart interrupted, you will perceive the part that intervenes between the
fingers and the heart almost immediately to become empty, the
blood being exhausted by the action of the heart; at the same time
the heart will become of a much paler colour, even in its state of

dilation, than it was before; it is also smaller than at first from wanting blood; and then it begins to beat more slowly, so that it seems at length as if it were about to die. But the impediment to the flow of blood being removed, instantly the colour and the size of the heart are restored.

If, on the contrary, the artery instead of the vein be compressed or tied, you will observe the part between the obstacle and the heart and the heart itself to become inordinately distended, to assume a deep purple or even livid colour, and at length to be so much oppressed with blood that you will believe it about to be choked; but the obstacle removed, all things immediately return to their natural state in colour, size, and impulse.

Here then we have evidence of two kinds of death: extinction from deficiency, and suffocation from excess. Examples of both have now been set before you, and you have had opportunity of viewing the truth contended for with your own eyes in the heart. . . .

Chapter XIII

The third Position is confirmed: and the Circulation of the Blood is demonstrated from it.

Thus far we have spoken of the quantity of blood passing through the heart and the lungs in the centre of the body, and in like manner from the arteries into the veins in the peripheral parts and the body at large. We have yet to explain, however, in what manner the blood finds its way back to the heart from the extremities by the veins, and how and in what way these are the only vessels that convey the blood from the external to the central parts; which done, I conceive that the three fundamental propositions laid down for the circulation of the blood will be so plain, so well established, so obviously true, that they may claim general credence. Now the remaining position will be made sufficiently clear from the valves which are found in the cavities of the veins themselves, from the uses of these, and from experiments cognizable by the senses.

The celebrated Hieronymus Fabricius of Aquapendente, a most skilful anatomist and venerable old man, or, as the learned Riolan will have it, Jacobus Silvius, first gave representations of the valves in the veins, which consist of raised or loose portions of the inner membranes of these vessels, of extreme delicacy, and a sigmoid or semilunar shape. They are situated at different distances from one another, and diversely in different individuals; they are connate at the sides of the veins; they are directed upwards or towards the trunks of the veins; the two—for there are for the most part two together—regard each other, mutually touch, and are so ready to come into contact by their edges, that if anything attempt to pass from the trunks into the branches of the veins, or from the greater vessels into the less, they completely prevent it; they are farther so arranged that the horns of those that succeed are opposite the middle of the convexity of those that precede, and so on alternately.

The discoverer of these valves did not rightly understand their use, nor have succeeding anatomists added anything to our knowledge; for their office is by no means explained when we are told that it is to hinder the blood, by its weight, from all flowing into inferior parts; for the edges of the valves in the jugular veins hang downwards, and are so contrived that they prevent the blood from rising upwards; the valves, in a word, do not invariably look upwards, but always towards the trunks of the veins, invariably towards the seat of the heart. I, and indeed others, have sometimes found valves in the emulgent veins, and in those of the mesentery, the edges of which were directed towards the *vena cava* and *vena portae*. Let it be added that there are no valves in the arteries, and that dogs, oxen, etc., have invariably valves at the divisions of their crural veins, in the veins that meet towards the top of the os sacrum, and in those branches which come from the haunches, in which no such effect of gravity from the erect position was to be apprehended. Neither are there valves in the jugular veins for the purpose of guarding against apoplexy, as some have said; because in sleep, the head is more apt to be influenced by the contents of the carotid arteries.

Neither are the valves present in order that the blood may be retained in the divarications or smaller trunks and minuter branches, and not be suffered to flow entirely into the more open and capacious channels; for they occur where there are no divarications; although it must be owned that they are most frequent at the points where branches join. Neither do they exist for the purpose of rendering the current of blood more slow from the centre of the body; for it seems likely that the blood would be disposed to flow with sufficient slowness of its own accord, as it would have to pass from larger into continually smaller vessels, being separated from the mass and fountain head, and attaining from warmer into colder places.

But the valves are solely made and instituted lest the blood should pass from the greater into the lesser veins, and either rupture them or cause them to become varicose; lest, instead of advancing from the extreme to the central parts of the body, the blood should rather proceed along the veins from the centre to the extremities; but the delicate valves, while they readily open in the right direction, entirely prevent all such contrary motion, being so situated and arranged that if anything escapes, or is less perfectly obstructed by the cornua of the one above, the fluid passing, as it were, by the chinks between the cornua, it is immediately received on the convexity of the one beneath, which is placed transversely with reference to the former, and so is effectually hindered from getting any farther.

And this I have frequently experienced in my dissections of veins; if I attempted to pass a probe from the trunk of the veins into one of the smaller branches, whatever care I took I found it impossible to introduce it far any way, by reason of the valves; whilst, on the contrary, it was most easy to push it along in the opposite direction, from without inwards, or from the branches towards the trunks and roots. In many places two valves are so placed and fitted, that, when raised, they come exactly together in the middle of the vein, and are there united by the contact of their margins; and so accurate is the adaptation that neither by the eye nor by any other means of examination can the slightest chink along the line of contact be perceived. But if the probe be now introduced from the extreme towards the more central parts, the valves, like the floodgates of a river, give way and are most readily pushed aside. The effect of this arrangement plainly is to prevent all motion of the blood from the heart and *vena cava*, whether it be upwards towards the head, or

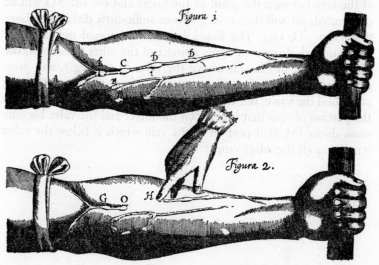

downwards towards the feet, or to either side towards the arms, not a drop can pass; all motion of the blood beginning in the larger and tending towards the smaller veins is opposed and resisted by them; whilst the motion that proceeds from the lesser to end in the larger branches is favoured, or, at all events, a free and open passage is left for it.

But that this truth may be made the more apparent, let an arm be tied up above the elbow as if for phlebotomy [the opening of a vein for letting blood] (A, A, Fig. 1). At intervals in the course of the veins, especially in labouring people and those whose veins are large, certain knots or elevations (B, C, D, E, F,) will be perceived, and this not only at the places where a branch is received (E, F,) but also where none enters (C, D,); these knots or risings are all formed by valves, which thus show themselves externally. And now if you press the blood from the space above one of the valves, from H to O (fig. 2), and keep the point of a finger upon the vein inferiorly, you will see no influx of blood from above; the portion of the vein between the point of the finger and the valve O will be obliterated; yet will the vessel continue sufficiently distended above that valve (O, G,). The blood being thus pressed out, and the vein emptied, if you now apply a finger of the other hand upon the distended part of the vein above the valve O (see fig.), and press downwards, you will find that you cannot force the blood through or beyond the valve; but the greater effort you use, you will only see the portion of vein that is between the finger and the valve become more distended, that portion of the vein which is below the valve remaining all the while empty.

ANTON VAN LEEUWENHOEK

1 6 3 2 · 1 7 2 3

HARVEY HAD PROVED that the blood circulated, but had not proved that it moved in a closed system. He had supposed that the arteries let the blood soak into the porous flesh, from which the veins then collected it. By the middle of the seventeenth century, improved microscopes were being developed and Robert Hooke (1635-1703),[1] in England, and Marcello Malpighi (1628-1694),[2] in Italy, set to using them for the study of anatomy. Malpighi, professor of medicine successively at Pisa, Messina, and Bologna, the so-called father of microscopic anatomy, saw in 1661 that the arteries in the lungs of a frog were connected by capillary tubes with the veins. "The blood flowed away along tortuous vessels," he wrote, "and was not poured into spaces but was always contained within tubules."

A fuller account of a similar discovery is contained in a letter sent in 1688 by the Dutch scientist Anton van Leeuwenhoek to the Royal Society of London. Perennially exuberant in the joy of his various discoveries, Leeuwenhoek was one of the most tireless microscopic observers of nature in the history of science. A highly skilled craftsman, he made two hundred and forty-nine microscopes with his own hands. He sent over three hundred letters describing his findings to the Royal Society of London, which translated and published many of them, and elected him to membership. On his death, it was found that he had willed twenty-six of his best microscopes to the Society

In the first selection here cited, from the Philosophical Transactions of the Royal Society for 1677, Leeuwenhoek relates his dis-

[1] On Hooke, see above, p. 87.
[2] On Malpighi, see above, p. 464.

covery of protozoa, the little one-celled aquatic animals which had never before been seen by human eye. The second selection, "On the Slime in the Gut," which appeared in the Transactions for 1684, reports his study of the inner surface of the intestine, in which he found capillaries connecting the arteries and the veins. It also describes the passage of food through the walls of the intestine into the blood stream. The third selection, from a letter of 1688, we take from an English translation of the Opuscula selecta Neerlandicarum de arte medica, vol. I, 1907. It refers to his previous discovery of red corpuscles in the blood and tells of his new observation of these same blood cells in the process of passing from arteries to veins through the capillaries in the tail of a tadpole. This evidence furnished the final confirmation needed to prove beyond question Harvey's theory of the circulation of the blood.

CONCERNING LITTLE ANIMALS
OBSERVED IN RAIN WATER

IN THE YEAR 1675, about halfway through September, being busy
with studying air, when I had much compressed it by means of
water, I discovered living creatures in rain, which had stood but a
few days in a new tub, that was painted blue within. This observation provoked me to investigate this water more narrowly; and
especially because these little animals were, to my eye, more than
ten thousand times smaller than the animalcule which Swammer-
dam has portrayed and called by the name of Water-flea, or Water-
louse, which you can see alive and moving in water with the bare eye.

Of the first sort that I discovered in the said water, I saw, after
divers observations, that the bodies consisted of 5, 6, 7, or 8 very clear
globules, but without being able to discern any membrane or skin
that held these globules together, or in which they were inclosed.
When these animalcules bestirred themselves, they sometimes
stuck out two little horns, which were continually moved after the
fashion of a horse's ears. The part between these little horns was
flat, their body else being roundish, save only that it ran somewhat
to a point at the hind end; at which pointed end it had a tail, near
four times as long as the whole body, and looking as thick, when
viewed through my microscope, as a spider's web. At the end of
this tail there was a pellet, of the bigness of one of the globules of
the body; and this tail I could not perceive to be used by them for
their movements in very clear water. These little animals were the
most wretched creatures that I have ever seen; for when with the
pellet they did but hit on any particles or little filaments (of which
there are many in water, especially if it hath but stood some days),

they stuck intangled in them; and then pulled their body out into an oval and did struggle, by stretching themselves, to get their tail loose; whereby their whole body then sprang back towards the pellet of the tail, and their tails then coiled up serpent-wise, after the fashion of a copper or iron wire that, having been wound close about a round stick, and then taken off, kept all its windings. This motion, of stretching out and pulling together the tail, continued; and I have seen several hundred animalcules, caught fast by one another in a few filaments, lying within the compass of a coarse grain of sand.

I also discovered a second sort of animalcules, whose figure was an oval; and I imagine that their head was placed at the pointed end. These were a little bit bigger than the animalcules first mentioned. Their belly is flat, provided with divers incredibly thin little feet or little legs, which were moved very nimbly, and which I was able to discover only after sundry great efforts, and wherewith they brought off incredibly quick motions. The upper part of their body was round and furnished inside with 8, 10, or 12 globules: otherwise these animalcules were very clear. These little animals would change their body into a perfect round, but mostly when they came to lie high and dry. Their body was also very yielding: for if they so much as brushed against a tiny filament, their body bent in, which bend also presently sprang out again; just as if you stuck your finger into a bladder full of water, and then, on removing the finger, the inpitting went away. Yet the greatest marvel was when I brought any of the animalcules on a dry place, for I then saw them change themselves at last into a round, and then the upper part of the body rose up pyramid-like, with a point jutting out in the middle; and after having thus lain moving with their feet for a little while, they burst asunder and the globules and a watery humour flowed away on all sides, without my being able to discern even the least sign of any skin wherein these globules and the liquid had, to all appearance, been inclosed; and at such times I could discern more globules than when they were alive. This bursting asunder I figure to myself to happen thus: imagine, for example, that you have a sheep's bladder filled with shot, peas, and water; then, if you were to dash it apieces on the ground, the shot, peas, and water would scatter themselves all over the place.

Furthermore, I discovered a third sort of little animals that were about twice as long as broad, and to my eye quite eight times smaller than the animalcules first mentioned: and I imagined, although they were so small, that I could yet make out their little legs or little fins. Their motion was very quick, both roundabout and in a straight line.

The fourth sort of animalcules, which I also saw a-moving, were so small, that for my part I can't assign any figure to them. These little animals were more than a thousand times less than the eye of a full-grown louse (for I judge the diameter of the louse's eye to be more than ten times as long as that of the said creature), and they surpassed in quickness the animalcules already spoken of. I have divers times seen them standing still, as 'twere, in one spot, and twirling themselves round with a swiftness such as you see in a whip-top a-spinning before your eyes; and then again they had a circular motion, the circumference whereof was no bigger than that of a small sand-grain; and anon they would go straight ahead, or their course would be crooked. . . .

On June 9th, collected rain-water betimes in a dish and put it in a clean wine-glass, in my closet; and on examining it, I descried no animalcules. (Note. My closet standeth towards the north-east, and is partitioned off from my antechamber with pine-wood, very close joined, having no other opening than a slit an inch and a half high and 8 inches long, through which the wooden spring of my lathe passeth. 'Tis furnished towards the street with four windows, whereof the two lowermost can be opened from within, and which by night are closed outside with two wooden shutters; so that little or no air comes in from without, unless it chance that in making my observations I use a candle, when I draw up one casement a little, lest the candle inconvenience me; and I also then pull a curtain almost right across the panes.)

The 10th of June, observing this foresaid rain-water, which had now stood about 24 hours in my closet, I perceived some few very little living creatures, to which, because of their littleness, no figure can be ascribed; and among others, I discovered a little animal that was a bit bigger, and that I could perceive to be oval. (Note. When I say that I have observed the water, I mean I have examined no more than 3, 4, or 5 drops thereof, which I also then throw away; and in narrowly scrutinizing 3 or 4 drops I may do such a deal of work that I put myself into a sweat.)

ANATOMY OF THE SLIME
WITHIN THE GUTS
AND THE USE THEREOF

I HAVE BEEN a long time desirous to examine the slimy matter which lines the inside of the Guts, and so much the rather because it is generally esteemed as a superfluous part and fit to be removed: whereas, on the contrary, it appears to me to be a part instrumental and necessary for the uses of the Bowels. I took then this woolly substance, and having cleared it from the Excrement as much as I could, I found a great number of very thin blood vessels branched out, and lying so thick together that the space of half the Diameter of a hair was not void between the branches. Besides the blood vessels, there were also other vessels that had no distinguishable colour, which I suspected to be Limphaticks or Lacteals; I could not discern any Membrane that encompassed them, but all about them lay a glutinous clear slime, beset with small Globules, which slime and Globules I took to be the Excrements lying upon the Guts; but when I went to scrape gently this slime away, I found that I not only wounded the blood vessels, but tore away many blood vessels and other vessels together.

These blood vessels do not spread their Branches on all sides, like the blood vessels in other parts of the body, but as they lye in a Bow, send all their Branches inward and none outward. They also lye so close by one another that I imagine ten thousand of them may be in the space of an inch square; I have described the circumference of one of these vessels in Fig. 3, which circumference is no greater then to be covered with a sand. The thickness or Diameter is about the 25th part of a hair of my head. From the inside many small vessels issuing out do as it were joyn together, but of these only 4 are specified as in Fig. 3.

Fig. 4 H.I.K. is a small vessel, and though I have placed it at some distance from the former, nevertheless it was partly covered by it, as is usual with the rest of them to cover one another. The Bows also

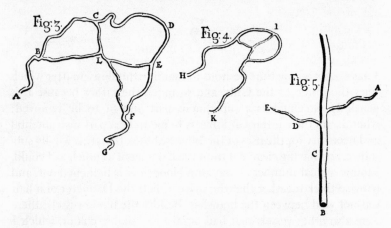

Leeuwenhoek's drawing of the capillary blood vessels found in the wall of the intestine.

lye all the same way, bending towards the passage of the Excrement out of the Guts.

I could not track H.G. and H.K. any further, by reason that they hid themselves among the other parts of the woolly substances.

From the foregoing Observation, I have been doubtful whether the Arteries and Veins were not in this place joined together, viz, whether A. were not an Artery and G. a Vein, for among all the Experience that I have had of the blood vessels I never perceived such a probability of an *Anastomosis*. For in other places, the Arteries, being variously disseminated for the nourishment of the parts, the veins are so likewise for the carrying the blood back again into the heart; but in this place the Arteries going no further than the hollow of the Guts, seem to have no other business then to empty themselves into the Veins.

These observations also make me more then ever reject the Opinion that the Extremities of the Lacteal and Limphatick Vessels have mouths or openings, whereby they receive and take in the Chyle [1] out of the Guts, for I am perswaded that the extremities of the Lactae in the Guts are as well covered with their Coat or Membrane in that place as in other parts of the body, which nevertheless will not hinder the food from passing out of the Guts. For let Fig. 5 A.B.C.D.E. be the root of a tree, the nourishment that this Root receives out of the Earth, shall pass no easier thro the Extremities A. and E. than thro any other place about D. or C. which is of the same bigness. For example, I have seen the small Roots of a Vine an hundred times thinner than an hair of my head, their farther ends A. and E. take up a place of the one thousandth part of the bigness of a sand. Now if a place be no bigger than this, the moisture or nourishment of the Tree will as well pass thro any part of the Bark or wood of the Root, as thro the places A.E. So that a thin capillary Root may as well receive the nourishment at any other place as at the end. And as the Arteries, whose Coats are made up of a threddy substance, can strain the blood thro them (as I have formerly said), so the nutritive Juice also may pass thro the threddy Coats of the Blood, water, and milk vessels. And in the same manner, the small Branches of the veins may take up substances out of the Bowels and carry them to the heart.

This will not seem strange when we consider that if a milk, water, or blood vessel be a thousand times less than a hair of ones head, the Coats of them must needs be very thin, and the threds whereof the Coats are made yet thinner. How easy must moisture pass thro the sides of such Vessels. . . .

---

[1] Chyle is the chief medium for the transfer of ingested fat to the blood.

CIRCULATION OF BLOOD

IN THE TADPOLE

ॐ

Most Honourable Gentlemen, etc.

My last, most respectful letter to you was of the 24th of last month, in which I treated of the sting of the gnat, namely, that this sting, taken out of its case, consists of four distinct stings.

Herewith I again send you some of my trifling observations.

In our country we have two species of frogs. The first, which we used to have in great abundance round about our town, is commonly called frog. Of late years, however, these frogs have been very rare. I suppose because our sluggish water-courses have lately been filled, as it were, with a kind of noxious little fish (hitherto unknown, so far as I am aware), called stickle-backs, which devoured the frogs when they were still tadpoles.

I was greatly pleased to see very distinctly the circulation of the blood [in the tadpole], which was driven on from the parts that were nearest to the body to those on the outside, thus causing an uninterrupted, very rapid circulation. This circulation was not regular in its movement, but at very short intervals it was continually brought about anew with sudden impulses, and before there was another sudden impulse we might (in case we had not observed a continual increase in the rapidity) have thought that a stoppage in the circulation would follow. But scarcely had the blood begun to move more slowly when there was again a sudden impulse of the blood, so that there was an uninterrupted current; and trying accurately to measure the very short time in which each impulse took place, I found that in the time wanted to count rapidly to a hundred, there were as many as a hundred sudden impulses. From this

I concluded that as often as these sudden impulses occurred, the blood was driven from the heart.

In another place I saw that three of the thinnest arteries, each running in a curve, all met together in one point and there formed a blood vessel or vein, and consequently this blood vessel was as wide as the three arteries mentioned. These three distinct vessels with their somewhat circular course, in which the circulation took place, were so small that a grain of sand could have covered them.

Such blood vessels running across each other I often noticed before when I tried to discover the junction of arteries and veins in other animals, but I was quite certain that the return circuit of the blood does not take place in the large vessels, but in the smallest or thinnest; for if it were otherwise, I conclude that all the parts of the body could not be fed. And as these discoveries seemed inscrutable to me, I gave up my investigations on this head for some years. If now we see clearly with our eyes that the passing of the blood from the arteries into the veins in the tadpoles only takes place in such blood vessels as are so thin that only one corpuscle can be driven through at one time, we may conclude that the same thing takes place in the same way in our bodies, as well as in that of all animals. And this being so, it is impossible for us to discover the passing of the blood from the arteries into the veins in our bodies or that of other animals, first, because a single globule of blood being in a vein, has no colour; secondly, because the blood does not move in the blood vessels when we make this investigation.

I have said before that the corpuscles or globules that make the blood red are so small that ten hundred thousand of them are not so big as a grain of coarse sand; and so we can easily imagine how very small the blood vessels are in which the circulation of the blood takes place.

The observations told here have not been made once, but they have been resumed repeatedly, giving me much pleasure, and every time on different tadpoles, and the result has almost always been the same. But it is remarkable that in the very small vessels mentioned above and placed furthest from the heart, as there at the end of the tail, the impulse was not by far so sudden and strong as in the vessels nearest to the heart. And though the uninterrupted current could be clearly observed, it could be distinctly seen that at each impulse from the heart the current was a little quicker.

When I looked along the length of the tail and at the thickest part of it, I could clearly see that on either side of the bone there was a large artery, through which the blood was carried to the extremity of the tail, and which on its way sent out several small branches.

When I looked at the part of the tail beside these arteries on the outside, I discovered there two large veins, which carried the blood back again to the heart, and, moreover, I saw that blood was driven into this large vein from several small veins. In short, I saw here the circulation of the blood to my perfect satisfaction, because there was nothing, though ever so slight, that caused me any doubt.

Also, I observed the young frogs when they had changed from tadpoles into frogs, and I also discovered in them a very large number of small blood vessels, which, continually running in curves, formed the vessels called "arteries and veins" [capillaries], from which it was perfectly clear to me that the arteries and veins are one and the same continuous blood vessels. But I saw them clearest of all and most of all at the end of the projecting parts of the legs, which we may call fingers, and of which the frog has four on each fore-leg and five on each hind-leg.

These blood vessels, called "arteries and veins" (being nevertheless identical), were exceedingly numerous at the ends of these fingers, and each ran in a curve, which made it impossible to follow the particular course of each vessel. All these vessels were so small or thin that no more than one corpuscle could pass through it at a time. But when I examined these fingers about the first or second joint, I found the blood vessels there, which we call arteries and veins, bigger, so big even that the blood in these vessels had a red colour.

LAZARO SPALLANZANI

1 7 2 9 - 1 7 9 9

ONE OF THE MOST original biological experimenters of the eighteenth century was the Abbé Spallanzani, professor in turn at Reggio, Modena, and Pavia. He entered into a vigorous argument with a Jesuit contemporary, John T. Needham (1713-1781), who upheld the Aristotelian theory of the spontaneous generation of maggots, worms, and other low forms of life in muck or slime. Spallanzani showed that boiling infusions of any substance for three quarters of an hour would kill all the germs, and that a carefully boiled infusion, sealed in a flask away from air, would not generate growth. He was the first to experiment extensively with artificial insemination. In addition to hundreds of experiments with eggs of frogs, toads, and silkworms, he inseminated a bitch artificially, and had "after the ordinary time of gestation, the satisfaction of seeing her bring forth several whelps."

In one of his less known experiments, he found that blinded bats could fly through a network of wires, while deafened bats were afraid to attempt the flight and unable to avoid the wires. Recent discovery has explained this phenomenon by showing that bats emit a whistle so high in pitch as to be inaudible to human ears and that the echo of this whistle warns them of obstructions in their path, like a primitive radar device.

In the field of animal digestion, Spallanzani showed that gastric juice was a powerful chemical solvent, whose action was neither that of fermentation nor of putrefaction, as had previously been supposed. The experiment related below was part of a series of experiments on gastric juice. The account was translated by Dr. John F

Fulton for his Selected Readings in the History of Physiology (Charles C. Thomas, Springfield, Ill.), from Spallanzani's essay "On the Digestion of Animals," contained in his book on Animal Physique, published at Modena in 1780.

ON DIGESTION

. . . I MUST NOW turn to man, to conclude my investigations upon digestion in different animals with membranous stomachs. It is true that the studies designed for this purpose on numerous animals of this class—especially birds of prey, cats and dogs, whose stomachs are very like ours—lead us to conclude that their digestive functions are the same as our own: this, however, is proof by analogy and is, therefore, only a probability; besides, after having reached certain positive conclusions with regard to animals, I had at least to try and do the same with regard to man. Glancing over the works of doctors, both ancient and modern, I find the commonest object of their study is human digestion, but, if I may be allowed to say so, they have sought to guess the way in which digestion works rather than to discover it. Direct experiments on man are altogether lacking, and all that has been done is limited to more or less doubtful conjectures and hypotheses. If, therefore, I had to have recourse to my own experiments when dealing with animal digestion, how much more necessary was it to do so with regard to human digestion.

Thinking over the most important experiments which it would be possible to make on man, it seemed to me that they could be brought under two principal groups, i.e., those in which human gastric juice is obtained in order to repeat the experiments made with the same juice in animals, and those in which tubes containing various animal and vegetable substances are swallowed, in order to study the changes which they will have undergone when they emerge from the body.

I intended to make these experiments on myself, but I admit that those involving the use of tubes seemed to me rather dangerous, for I knew that bodies held up in the stomach without being digested had led to dire consequences and, after a considerable time, had been vomited up. I remembered, too, cases where similar bodies had been held up in the intestines. However, the various contradictory facts which are current encouraged me to try these experiments. I knew that very hard stones, like those of cherries, morellas, medlars, and plums were swallowed with impunity by children and country people and that they passed through the anus very easily without causing the slightest discomfort. In the midst of this struggle, the previous events which I have recorded induced me to overcome my reluctance. . . .

<h2 style="text-align:center">LX</h2>

It was a question of swallowing a little linen bag, containing 52 grains of masticated bread. I began this experiment one morning on rising and while fasting, and the circumstances which I am about to relate apply to all my experiments of this kind. I retained this bag for 23 hours, without experiencing any ill effects; on emerging it contained no bread, the thread with which the two sides of the bag had been sewn was neither broken nor damaged; the same applied to the thread at the mouth of the bag. The linen was not torn in any way, so that, evidently, it had not undergone any alteration either in the stomach or intestine. The success of this experiment encouraged me to try others; I repeated it with two similar bags, containing an equal amount of masticated bread, but with this difference, one of the bags was made of two thicknesses of linen, the other of three. You may guess, from what I have said elsewhere, that I wanted to find out whether the thickness of the bag would make digestion more difficult. I observed as follows: the two small bags emerged from my body after twenty-seven hours; the bread in the bag made of two thicknesses had been entirely digested, but there was a little left in the one made of three thicknesses. . . .

<h2 style="text-align:center">LXII</h2>

Having discovered that I could digest meat which had been cooked and masticated, I wanted to find out whether I could digest the same meat unmasticated; I swallowed, therefore, 80 grains of gristly meat from a chicken's breast in a small bag: I ejected it only after 37 hours. It had lost 56 grains and what was left, far from being gelatinous or tender, was dry and the inmost fleshy fibres seemed less dry than those outside. Otherwise, digestion appeared to have taken place equally, as the piece of meat kept the shape into which I had cut it.

VIII

The Science of Healing

THE PRACTICE of medicine, alone among the learned professions, has continued in an unbroken line from the Greek physicians of three and four hundred years before Christ, who began the separation of medicine from magic, to the highly equipped specialists of the present day. For some centuries after the fall of Rome, the shadow of the ignorance of the Dark Ages blighted all science, and medicine stagnated. But during the later Middle Ages, new techniques and new drugs were acquired from Arab and Jewish doctors. By a system of quarantine the age-old plague of leprosy was stamped out of Europe. With the sixteenth and seventeenth centuries came bold experiment and discovery along every line, and progress in medicine was rapid and spectacular.

Medicine was at all times linked with other sciences. In the fourteenth century medical interest in curing poor eyesight stimulated the spectacle trade, which meant lens grinding. In the seventeenth century interest in optics among lens grinders created the microscope, which for the first time made possible a study of the hidden life processes of men and plants, and of minute organisms. As healers, doctors were in general more prone to naturalistic inquiry than other men, and hence were constantly open to charges of impiety, heresy, and the desecration of corpses. Some doctors of the time, in fact, seem to have spent far more time on scientific research than on medical practice. In the eighteenth century the study of current electricity started as a piece of medical research on the nervous system.

Even in the sixteenth century, physicians still prescribed what would seem strange remedies to a modern. As Wolf [1] says: "Since people rarely distinguish between recovery *after* a certain treatment, recovery because of it, and recovery *in spite of it*, a very extensive unofficial collection of alleged remedies accumulated in the course of the ages. It was an amazing collection. Even the official London *Pharmacopoeia* of 1618 included such delectable medicaments as bile, blood, claws, cock's comb, feathers, fur, hair, perspiration, saliva, scorpions, snake skin, spider web, and wood-lice!"

Anyone at that time could practice medicine. Only the wealthy could afford university-trained doctors; but apothecaries, barbers, indeed anyone who could gain confidence of the ailing, ministered to them. Even learned medical men frequently purged or bled their patients to death, being still misled by the Greek doctrine of the four "humours" or fluids (blood, phlegm, black bile, yellow bile) that together were supposed to make up the liquids of the body. Health, by this doctrine, depended on a proper balance of the four "humours." Accordingly, purging, bloodletting, and special diets were freely prescribed for the sick man, in order to restore the upset balance.

Astrology also played a conspicuous part in medical practice. Some practitioners, for example, let blood only in months in which the stars were considered favorable. A trace of the association of medicine with astrology survives today in the name "influenza," which was given to the common ailment by the seventeenth-century Italian doctors in the belief that influenza was caused by an adverse *influence* of the stars.

Against this complicated background of mingled superstition, faulty tradition, and limited knowledge, the simplicity of the approach of Fracastorius, of Paré, of Sydenham, as shown in the following selections, stands out in clear relief. These men belonged to their age; they still bled and purged and compounded odd remedies. But in a spirit of fresh independence, they observed, noted, and reasoned from their results, and were not afraid to challenge the common views of their day.

Fracastorius' essay *On Contagion* is remarkably modern in its ap-

[1] Wolf, A., A *History of Science, Technology, and Philosophy in the Sixteenth and Seventeenth Centuries*, London, George Allen and Unwin, 1935.

proach, although the reader of today may smile at his suggestion that ophthalmia might be transmitted by a glance from a sufferer from that ailment. Our own present ignorance of the mode of transmission of a disease as common as infantile paralysis should prevent us from being too scornful of Fracastorius' theory.

The selection from Paré tells of his drastic reforms in surgery, especially in the treatment of battle wounds caused by the newly invented firearms. Sydenham was also a famous and popular practitioner. The extract from his work, *On Peruvian Bark,* is one of the first accounts of the use of quinine for malaria.

The passages from the letters of Lady Mary Wortley Montagu and from Jenner's book on vaccination describe the beginnings of control of the dread plague, smallpox, "a disease," according to Jenner, "which is every hour devouring its victims; a disease that has ever been considered as the severest scourge of the human race!"—a disease which might still be common among us today, if the eighteenth century had not started the preventive measures which led in time to the form of vaccination now required of every American school child. There was a time lag, we may note, of almost eighty years between the writing of Lady Montagu's letter on vaccination as practiced in Turkey and the publication of Jenner's English experiments with cowpox inoculation at the very end of the century.

The essay by Captain Cook on scurvy deals, of course, with a vitamin deficiency and the first successful use of practical measures to prevent it. Auenbrugger reports his discovery of chest-tapping as a method of detecting trouble in the lungs, a procedure now familiar to everyone who has ever consulted a physician.

The writers of the selections in this section were naturally more concerned with their branch of applied science, the practice of medicine, than they were with the underlying theories, but the excerpts taken together give a picture of remarkable intellectual development during three centuries. They show how medicine came up to its period of most rapid progress.

HIERONYMOUS FRACASTORIUS

1 4 8 3 · 1 5 5 3

HIERONYMOUS FRACASTORIUS, or, to use the Italian form, Girolamo Fracastoro, came from Verona to be a fellow student with Copernicus at the University of Padua, and received there a typical humanist education in literature, law, science, philosophy, and medicine. He did pioneer work in geology as well as in medicine, but he is chiefly remembered today for his theory of contagious diseases, and for a medical tract, written in Latin verse, on syphilis.

Fracastorius' most important work, On Contagions, 1546, contains a suggestion of a germ theory of infectious disease. Such infections, he believed, were transmitted by minute bodies, capable of self-multiplication, which passed from the infector to the infected. Pulmonary tuberculosis (phthisis), he said, was one of the diseases so transmitted. From this work we quote his discussion of three kinds of infection. His speculations on the possibility of infection by a poisonous glance shows how persistent was the superstition of the "evil eye." Our passage was translated from a French version by Logan Clendening for his Source Book of Medical History (Paul B. Hoeber, New York, 1942).

THE DIFFERENT TYPES OF INFECTION

THE ESSENTIAL types of contagion are three in number: 1. Infection by contact only. 2. Infection by contact and by *fomites*, as scabies, phthisis [tuberculosis], leprosy, and their kind. I call *fomites* such things as clothes, linen, etc., which, although not themselves corrupt, can nevertheless foster the *essential seeds* of the contagion and thus cause infection. 3. Finally, there is another class of infection which acts not only by contact and by fomites, but can also be transmitted to a distance. Such are the pestilential fevers, phthisis, certain ophthalmias, the exanthem [eruptive disease] that is called variola [smallpox], and the like.

Infection by Contact Alone

The infection which passes between fruits is markedly of this kind, e.g., as from one cluster of grapes to another, and from one apple to another apple. . . . The putrefaction that thus passes from one fruit to another is really a dissolution of the combination of innate heat and moisture by the process of evaporation.

The humidity [thus set free] softens and relaxes the parts and makes them separable, and the heat affects the separation. . . . I regard the particles of heat and of moisture separately, or, in the case of moisture, perhaps in *combination*, as the essential *germs* of the resulting putrefaction. I speak here of the particles of humidity in combination because in the evaporative process of putrefaction, it often happens that the very minute particles mingle themselves and thus generate new corruptions. This mingling is indeed especially favorable for the propagation of putrefactions and infections.

Infection by means of Fomites

It may be questioned whether the infection by a fomes is of the same nature as infection that acts only by actual contact. The nature of infection by a fomes appears, indeed, to be different, since having left its original focus and passed into a fomes it may there last for long unchanged. It is, indeed, wonderful how the infection of phthisis or pestilential fevers may cling to bedding, clothes, wooden articles, and objects of that kind for two or three years, as we have ourselves observed.

On the other hand, those minute particles given off by a body affected with putrefaction do not appear to preserve their virulence for long, and on that account are not to be regarded as of identical essential nature either with those of fomites or with those that act by contact alone. . . . Not all substances are liable to become fomites, but only those that are porous and more or less calorific [warm]; for in their recesses, the seeds of contagion can lurk hidden and unaltered either by the medium itself or by external causes, unless these are excessive; e.g., they cannot withstand fire. Thus, iron, stone, and cold and impervious substances of this kind are hardly likely to act as fomites; on the other hand linen, cloth, and wood are more apt to do so.

Infection at a Distance

It is well known that the pestilential fevers, phthisis, and many other diseases are liable to seize on those who live with the infected, although they have come into no direct contact with them. It is no small mystery by what force the disease thus propagates itself. . . . For this type of contagion appears to be of quite a different nature and to act on quite a separate method from the others. . . . Thus a patient with ophthalmia may give his disease to another by merely looking at him. . . .

The Affinities of Infection

The affinities of infection are numerous and interesting. Thus there are plagues of trees which do not affect beasts, and others of beasts which leave trees exempt. Again among animals, there are diseases peculiar to men, oxen, horses, and so forth. Or, if separate kinds of living creatures are considered, there are diseases affecting children and young people, from which the aged are exempt and vice versa. Some again attack only men, others women, and others again both sexes. There are some men that walk unharmed amid the pestilence, while others fall. Again there are infections which have affinities for special organs. Thus ophthalmia affects only the eye. Phthisis has no effect upon that most delicate organ but acts especially upon the lungs. *Alopeciae* [baldness] and *areae* [bald spots] confine themselves to the head.

Is Infection a sort of Putrefaction?

We here consider whether all infection is a sort of putrefaction and also whether putrefaction is not itself infection. . . . Now with rabies have we not infection without putrefaction? Again, when wine becomes vinegar have we not infection without putrefaction? For, if left to putrefy, it is later that it becomes fetid and undrinkable—the sure signs of putrefaction—and thus differs from vinegar which is pleasant to take and is indeed resistant to putrefaction.

But it must be remembered as regards putrefaction, that sometimes there is but a simple dissolution of the combination of humidity and innate heat without any new *generation*—we then speak of it as *simple* putrefaction. Sometimes on the other hand, in the process of this dissolution, there is a true animal generation or generation of some substance definitely organized and arranged.[1] . . .

It is an observed fact, however, that dogs which are becoming

[1] An allusion to the ancient belief, which Fracastorius still held, that maggots and worms were spontaneously generated in muck and other substances, a belief not disproved until the eighteenth century. See above, under Spallanzani, p. 521.

rabid are usually seized with febrile symptoms. If, therefore, we regard the matter inductively, we shall consider that all infections may be reduced ultimately to putrefaction. . . . Furthermore, all putrefactions are liable to produce putrefactions like themselves, and, if all infection is putrefaction, infection in the ordinary sense of the word is nothing else than the passage of a putrefaction from one body to another either continuous with it or separated from it.

AMBROISE PARÉ

1 5 1 7 · 1 5 9 0

IT WAS ONCE THE practice of military surgeons to treat battle wounds by pouring boiling oil into them. Doubtless this procedure disinfected the parts, and it certainly stopped the bleeding, but it was exceedingly painful. The humane Doctor Paré showed that such drastic treatment was also highly dangerous, and that many patients who might have been saved died under it.

Ambroise Paré was born in a small French village in the province of Maine. His brother-in-law, a master barber-surgeon of Paris,[1] gave him a start in medicine. From the age of twenty-two or three to twenty-six, he worked in the Hôtel-Dieu, the sole public hospital in Paris. He then joined the French army as a military surgeon. The use of gunpowder in warfare was still comparatively new, and only the crudest methods of dealing with powder burns and gunshot wounds had yet been tried. On his first campaign, Paré found that a mild ointment was a better remedy for powder burns than boiling oil.

Ligature of arteries (tying them to stop their bleeding) was not itself a new technique, but Paré involved himself in a bitter controversy with other doctors when he ventured to advocate ligature as a method to be used in the amputation of limbs in place of cauterizing the severed blood vessels with hot oil. His Apology and Treatise, from which we quote below, was written on his return to civilian practice, to answer the heated objections of one of his critics, Stephen Gourmelen. After quoting a passage from Gourmelen's

[1] For a description of the work of these barber-surgeons, see pp. 469-470.

book against him, Paré goes on to prove "by authority, reason, and experience that the said veins and arteries should be tied."

His experiences during a long and eventful career included many hair-raising adventures. Once, for example, he was captured by the Spaniards but was released without ransom as a reward for medical services performed for one of his captors. He died in Paris at the age of eighty, surgeon to King Henry III, prosperous and highly respected.

The translation here used is from The Life and Times of Ambroise Paré, by Francis R. Packard, M.D. (Paul B. Hoeber, New York, 1921).

THE TREATMENT OF GUNSHOT WOUNDS

§

. . . TRULY I HAVE not put my hand to the pen to write in such a manner, had it not been that some have impudently taxed and insulted me and disgraced me, more by particular hate than by any good zeal they should have to the public, concerning my manner of tying the veins and arteries, writing that which follows:

"Badly then and too arrogantly, indiscreetly, and temerariously, a certain personage has wished to condemn and blame the cauterization of the vessels after the amputation of a corrupt and rotten member, much praised and recommended by the ancients and always approved, wishing and desiring to show and teach us, without reason, judgment or experience, a new way of tying the vessels, against the opinion of all the ancient physicians, giving no caution nor advice that there frequently happen many more great perils and accidents from this new fashion of tying the vessels (which he wishes to be done by a needle piercing profoundly the healthy part) than by burning and combustion of the said vessel. Because, if with the needle one should prick some nervous part, to wit, even the nerve itself, when he wishes by this new and untried means grossly to constrain the vein in tying it, necessarily there will follow a new inflammation, from the inflammation a convulsion, from the convulsion death. For fear of which accidents Galen never dared to stitch a transverse wound (that which is always less dangerous) before uncovering the aponeuroses [membranous sheaths] of the muscles.

"Moreover, this forceps, with which, after the section he once more tears the flesh, while he thinks it possible to draw forth the vessels which are drawn back towards their origin, causes no less pain than the hot iron. And if anyone, having experienced this new

537

fashion of cruelty, has recovered from it, he should render thanks to God forever, by the goodness of whom he has escaped such cruelty, feeling it was rather his executioner than his methodical chirurgeon [surgeon]."

Oh, what beautiful words! for an aged man, who calls himself a wise doctor. He does not remember that his white beard admonisheth him not to say anything unworthy of his years, and that he should put off and drive out from him all envy and rancor conceived against his neighbor. But, now I wish to prove to him by authority, reason, and experience that the said veins and arteries should be tied.

As to authorities I will come to that of that grand man Hippocrates,[1] who wills and commands the recovery of fistulas [ulcers] of the fundament [rectum] by ligature, as much to absorb the callosity as to avoid haemorrhage.

Galen, in his Method, speaking of a flow of blood made by an external cause, of whom see here the words. "It is," saith he, "most sure to tie the root of the vessel, which I understand to be that [part] which is most near to the liver or to the heart."

Avicenna commands to tie the vein and the artery, after having uncovered it towards its origin.

Gui de Chauliac, speaking of wounds of the veins and arteries, enjoins the surgeon to make the ligature on the vessel.

Monsieur Hollier, in Book III, chapter 5, of his Matiére du Chirurgie, speaking of the flow of blood, commands expressly to tie the vessels.

Calmetheus, in his chapter on the Wounds of Veins and Arteries, treats of a very sure means of arresting the flow of blood by ligature of the vessels.

Celsus, from whom the said physician hath taken the greater part

1 Paré cites here a number of medical authorities, beginning with Hippocrates and Galen, the classical Greek physicians, taking in Celsus and Avicenna, the most famous Roman and Arabic writers on medicine, and coming down to men of his own time, including Vesalius, on whom see above, p. 465.

of his book, recommends expressly to tie the vessels in the flow of blood following wounds as a very easy and very sure remedy.

Vesalius, in his *Surgery*, directs that the vessels be tied in a flow of blood.

Jean de Vigo, treating of haemorrhage from recent wounds, commands to tie the vein and artery.

Tagault, treating of the means of arresting a flow of blood, commands to pinch the vein or artery with a crow beak, or a parrot beak, then to tie it with a strong enough thread. . . .

The Journey to Turin in 1536

Moreover, I will here show to my readers the towns and places where I have been enabled to learn the art of surgery, always the better to instruct the young surgeon.

And first, in the year 1536, the great King François [Francis I] sent a great army to Turin to recover the cities and castles which had been taken by the Marquis de Guast, lieutenant-general of the Emperor [Charles V]; when Monsieur the Constable, then grand-master, was lieutenant-general of the army, and Monsieur de Montejan was colonel general of the infantry, to whom I was then surgeon. A great part of the army having arrived at the Pass of Suze, we found the enemy holding the passage and having made certain forts and trenches, insomuch that to make them dislodge and quit the place it was necessary to fight. There were many killed and wounded, as many on one side as on the other, but the enemy were constrained to retire and gain the castle, which was taken in part by Captain Le Rat, who climbed with many soldiers from his company on a little hill, from whence they fired directly on the enemy. He received a shot from an arquebus in the ankle of his right foot, wherewith he suddenly fell to the ground and then said: "Now the Rat is taken." I dressed him, and God healed him.

We thronged into the city and passed over the dead bodies and some that were not yet dead, hearing them cry under the feet of our horses, which made a great pity in my heart, and truly I re-

pented that I had gone forth from Paris to see so pitiful a spectacle.
Being in the city, I entered a stable, thinking to lodge my horse and
that of my man, where I found four dead soldiers and three who
were propped against the wall, their faces wholly disfigured; and
they neither saw, nor heard, nor spake, and their clothes yet flaming
from the gunpowder which had burnt them. Beholding them with
pity, there came an old soldier who asked me if there was any means
of curing them. I told him no. At once he approached them and
cut their throats gently and without anger. Seeing this great cruelty,
I said to him that he was a bad man. He answered me that he
prayed God that when he should be in such a case, he might find
someone who would do the same for him, to the end that he might
not languish miserably.

And, to return to our discourse, the enemy was summoned to
surrender, which they did, and went forth, their lives only saved, and
a white staff in their hands; but the greater part went on to gain the
Chateau de Villaine, where there were about two hundred Spaniards. Monsieur le Connestable would not leave them in his rear,
in order to render the road free. The Chateau is seated upon a little
mountain, which gave great assurance to those within that we could
not place the artillery so as to bear upon them. They were summoned to surrender themselves or they should be cut in pieces,
which they flatly refused, making answer that they were as good
and faithful servants of the Emperor as Monsieur le Connestable
could be of the King his master. Their answer heard, we mounted
two great cannon by night with ropes drawn with the strength of
arms by the Swiss and the Lansquenets [mercenary troops], when,
as ill-luck would have it, the two cannon being placed, a gunner by
inadvertence set fire to a sack full of gunpowder, by which he was
burned together with ten or twelve soldiers; and further, the flame
of the powder was the cause of discovering our artillery, which
caused those in the Chateau to fire all the night many arquebus
shots at the place where they had been able to discover the two
cannon, which killed and wounded a number of our men.

The next day, early in the morning, we fired with the battery, which in a few hours made a breach; which being done, they demanded a parley; but it was too late, for in the meantime our French infantry, seeing them surprised, had mounted in the breach and cut them all in pieces, except a very pretty, young, lusty girl of Piedmont, whom a great seigneur wished to have to keep him company in the night for fear of the greedy wolf (loupgarou). The captain and the ensign were taken alive, but soon after hung and strangled on the battlements of the gate of the city, to the end that they might give example and fear to the imperial soldiers not to be so rash and foolish as to wish to hold such places against so great an army.

Now all the said soldiers at the Chateau, seeing our men coming with a great fury, did all they could to defend themselves, and killed and wounded a great number of our soldiers with pikes, arquebuses, and stones, wherefore the surgeons had much work cut out for them. Now I was at that time a freshwater soldier; I had not yet seen wounds made by gunshot at the first dressing. It is true that I had read in Jean de Vigo, first book, *Of wounds in General*, chapter eight, that wounds made by firearms partake of venenosity [poison] because of the powder, and for their cure he commands to cauterize them with oil of elder, scalding hot, in which should be mixed a little theriac [healing ointment]. In order not to err before using the said oil, knowing that such a thing would bring great pain to the patient, I wished to know first how the other surgeons did for the first dressing; which was to apply the said oil as hot as possible into the wound, with tents [drains] and setons [wicks]; of whom I took courage to do as they did.

At last my oil lacked and I was constrained to apply in its place a digestive [substance to promote suppuration] made of the yolks of eggs, oil of roses and turpentine. That night I could not sleep at my ease, fearing by lack of cauterization that I should find the wounded on whom I had failed to put the said oil dead or empoisoned; which made me rise very early to visit them, where, beyond

my hope, I found those upon whom I had put the digestive medicament feeling little pain and their wounds without inflammation or
swelling, having rested fairly well throughout the night; the others,
to whom I had applied the said boiling oil, I found feverish, with
great pain and swelling about their wounds. Then I resolved with
myself never more to burn thus cruelly poor men wounded with
gunshot.

Being at Turin, I found a surgeon who was famous above all for
good treatment of gunshot wounds, into whose grace I found means
to insinuate myself, to have the recipe which he called his balm,
with which he treated gunshot wounds, and he made me court him
for years before I could draw his recipe from him. At last by gifts
and presents he gave it to me, which was to boil in oil of lilies little
puppies just born, with earthworms prepared with Venetian turpentine. Then I was joyful and my heart made glad to have understood
his remedy, which was like to that which I had obtained by chance.

See how I learned to treat wounds made by gunshot, not from
books. . . .

The Journey to Flanders

Monsieur Le Duc D'Ascot did not fail to send a gentleman to
the King with a letter to pray him humbly that he would do him so
much good and honor as to permit and command his premier surgeon to come to see Monsieur le Marquis d'Auret, his brother, who
had received an arquebus shot near the knee, with fracture of the
bone, about seven months ago, and that the physicians and surgeons
of those parts were much troubled to cure. The King sent for me
and commanded me to go to see the said Seigneur d'Auret, and to
help him by all that which I could for the cure of his wound. I told
him that I would use all the little knowledge which it had pleased
God to give me.

I went away, accompanied by two gentlemen, to the Chateau
d'Auret where the Marquis was. As soon as I arrived, I visited him
and told him that the King had commanded me to come to see him

and dress his wound. He said to me that he was very glad of my coming, and was greatly beholden to the King for having done him so much honor in sending me to him.

I found him with great fever, his eyes very much sunken, with a moribund and yellowish face, his tongue dry and parched, and all his body very emaciated and thin, his voice low as of a man very near to death; then I found his thigh much swollen, abscessed and ulcerated, discharging a greenish and fetid sanies [pus]. I probed it with a silver probe. By it I found a cavity near the groin, ending in the middle of the thigh, and others around the knee, sanious and caniculate [pussy and unwholesome]; also certain splinters of bone, some separated and others not. The leg was very swollen and imbued with a pituitous humor [watery mucus], cold and humid and flatu-lent, in such sort that the natural heat was by way of being suffo-cated and extinguished, and bent and drawn towards the buttocks; the buttocks ulcerated of the size of the palm of the hand. And he said he felt there extreme heat and pain and likewise in his loins, in such sort that he could not rest day or night, and had not appetite to eat, but to drink enough. It was told me that he often fell with weakness of the heart, and sometimes as in epilepsy, and often desired to vomit, with a trembling such that he could not carry his hands to his mouth.

Seeing and considering all these great complications, and his strength much abated, truly I had a very great regret to have gone to him, because it seemed to me there was little appearance that he could escape from death. Notwithstanding, to give him courage and good hope, I told him I would soon set him right, by the grace of God and the help of his physicians and surgeons.

Having seen him I went away to walk in a garden, and there I prayed God that he would do me this grace that he should recover; and that he would bless our hands and the medicaments to fight against so many complicated maladies. I discussed in my mind the means it would be necessary for me to hold to do this. They called me to dinner; I entered by the kitchen, where I saw taken out of a great pot half a sheep, a quarter of veal, three great pieces of beef, and two fowls and a very great piece of bacon, with abundance of good herbs; then I said to myself, that this broth of the pot was succulent and of good nourishment.

After dinner, all the physicians and surgeons assembled; we entered into consultation in the presence of Monsieur le Duc d' Ascot and some gentlemen who accompanied him. I began by saying to the surgeons that I was greatly astonished that they had not made openings in the thigh of Monsieur le Marquis, which was all abscessed, and the pus which went forth from it very fetid and stinking, which showed it had been stagnant there a long time; and that I had found with the probe caries of the bone and splinters of bone which had already separated. They answered me that he never would consent to it and, indeed, that it was near two months that they had not been able to get leave to put clean sheets on his bed; and they scarcely dared to touch the coverlet, so great was his pain.

Then I said that to cure him it was necessary to touch other things than the coverlet of the bed. Each said what he thought of the sickness of the said seigneur, and for conclusion held it altogether hopeless. I said to them there was yet some hope because of his youth, and that God and Nature sometimes do things which seem to physicians and surgeons to be impossible.

My advice was that the cause of all these accidents came (reason of) the bullet hitting near the joint of the knee, which had broken the ligaments, tendons, and aponeuroses of the muscles, which bound the said joint together with the femoral bone, as well as the nerves, veins, and arteries; from which had followed pain, inflammation, abscess formation, and ulceration; and that we must commence the cure by that of the disease that was the cause of all the aforesaid accidents, to wit, to make openings to give issue to the sanious matter retained in the spaces between the muscles and in their substance; likewise to the bone [splinters], which caused a great corruption in the whole thigh, from which the vapors arose and were carried to the heart, which caused syncope [collapse] and fever, and from the fever a universal heat in all the body, and by consequence depravation [degeneration] of the economy.

Likewise the said vapors were communicated to the brain, which caused the epilepsy and tremors and nausea of the stomach and prevented it from performing its functions, which are chiefly to digest and concoct the viands and convert them into chyle, which if they are not well concocted, ingender crudities and obstructions, which makes that the parts are not nourished, and in consequence the body dries and becomes emaciated, and likewise because it gets no exercise.

And as to the edema [swelling caused by accumulation of serous fluid in the tissue] of his leg, that had come because of lack of aliment and of the arrest of the natural heat through all the thigh, and also because it had no power of movement, because every part which is incapable of movement remains languid and atrophied, because the heat and [vital] spirits are not sent nor drawn hither, from which ensues mortification. "And to nourish and fatten the body it is necessary to make universal frictions with warm linen cloths, above, below, on the right and on the left and round about, for the purpose of drawing the blood and [vital] spirits from within outwards; and for dispersing any fuliginous vapors retained between the skin and the flesh. Thus the parts shall thereafter be nourished and restored (as I have said before in Book Nine, treating of arquebus wounds). But it is necessary to stop when we see heat and redness in the skin, for fear of dispersing that which has been drawn out and in consequence make it more emaciated.

"Now the bedsore on his buttock has come from having been too long a time lying on it without moving himself, which has been the cause that the [vital] spirits have not been able to shine in it. From this cause there has been inflammation, from the inflammation abscess, then ulceration, even with loss of substance of the flesh subjected, with very great pain, because of the nerves which spread through this part. It is necessary, likewise, that we should put him in another bed, very soft, and give him a clean shirt and sheets.

Otherwise all the things which one could do for him would be of no service, because the excrements and vapors of the discharges, retained for so long a time in his bed, are drawn in by the systole and diastole of the arteries, which are carried through the skin, and cause the [vital] spirits to change and acquire a bad diathesia, or quality, and corruption, which is seen in those who lie in a bed whereon a smallpox patient has lain and sweat, who get the smallpox by the putrid vapors which are imbued and remain in the sheets and coverlets.

"Now the reason that he cannot sleep and is almost in a consumption is because he eats little and takes no exercise and is vexed with great pains; because there is nothing which lowers and prostrates the [body] forces more than pain. The cause of his parched, dry tongue comes from the vehemence and heat of the fever, through the vapors which ascend from all the body to the mouth, for, as is said in a common proverb, 'When an oven is well heated, the mouth feels it.' "

Having discoursed of the causes and complications, I said that it was necessary to cure them by their contraries; and first, to ease the pains, make incisions in the thigh to evacuate the retained pus, not letting it out all at a time, for fear that a sudden great evacuation would cause a resolution of the [vital] spirits, which would greatly debilitate the patient and shorten his days. Secondly, having regard to the great swelling and coldness of the leg, fearing lest it should fall into a gangrene, and that it would be necessary to apply actual heat (the actual cautery); . . . for this reason we should apply about it hot bricks, on which should be sprinkled a decoction made of nerval herbs [herbs soothing to the nerves], boiled in wine and vinegar and then wrapped in napkins; and to his feet an earthenware bottle filled with the said decoction, corked and wrapped in linen. Also it is necessary to make fomentations on the thigh and the whole of the leg of a decoction made of sage, rosemary, thyme, lavender, flowers of camomile, and melilot, red roses boiled in white wine, and a desiccant [dryer] made of oak ashes, and a little vinegar, and half a handful of salt. This decoction has the property to sub-tilize, attenuate, incise, resolve, wither and dry up the thick, vis-cous humor. The said fomentations should be kept up a long time to the end that the resolution should be greater, because being thus made for a long time, more is resolved than is attracted, because as one liquefies the humor contained in the part, the skin and the flesh of the muscles are rarefied [dried up].

Thirdly, there must be applied on the buttock a large plaster made of desiccative red ointment, and *unguentum comitissae*, equal parts mixed together for the purpose of easing his pain and drying the ulcer; also we should make him a little pillow of down to keep his buttock in the air without his being supported on it. Fourthly, to refresh the heat of his loins, we should apply over them the refrig-erant ointment of Galen, freshly made, and over it fresh leaves of the water-lily, and then a napkin soaked in oxycrate, frequently sprinkled and renewed. And to support the heart, we must apply over it a refrigerant medicament, made of oil of water-lilies, oint-ment of roses and a little saffron, dissolved in rose-vinegar and theriac, spread on a piece of scarlet cloth.

For the syncope, which proceeded from the exhaustion of the natural forces troubling also the brain, it was necessary to use good succulent food, such as soft-boiled eggs, plums stewed in wine and sugar, also broth of the juice of the great pot, of which I have spoken before; with the white meat of capons, wings of partridges minced small, and other roasted meats easy to digest, as veal, kid, pigeons, partridges, thrushes, and the like. The sauce should be oranges, verjuice, sorrel, bitter pomegranates; and he should likewise eat them boiled with good herbs, as sorrel, lettuce, parsley, chicory, bugloss, marigolds, and the like. At night he can take barley-water, with the juice of sorrel and water-lilies, of each two ounces, with four or five grains of opium, and of the four cold seeds bruised, of each a half an ounce, which is a nourishing and medicinal remedy and will make him sleep. His bread should be that of the farm, neither too stale nor too fresh.

And for the great pain in his head, it would be necessary to cut his hair and to rub it with oxyrrhodinum, a little warm, and to leave on it a double cloth soaked in it; also, on his forehead, one with oil of roses and water-lilies and poppies, with a little opium and rose-vinegar and a little camphor, renewed at times. Moreover, he should smell flowers of henbane and water-lilies, bruised with vinegar and rose-water, with a little camphor, wrapped together in a handkerchief, which should be held for a long time against the nose, so that the odor can communicate itself to the brain; and these things should be continued only until the great inflammation and pain shall be passed, for fear of refrigerating too much the brain. Furthermore, one should make artificial rain, by making water run from some high place into a cauldron, that it may make such a noise that the patient can hear it; by these means sleep will be provoked in him.

And as to the retraction of his leg, there was hope of correcting it when one should have made evacuation of the pus and other humors contained in the thigh, which by their extension, made by repletion, have drawn back the leg. It would remedy itself after first rubbing all the knee joint with ointment of althea and oil of lilies and a little brandy, and putting above it black wool with the grease in it, likewise by putting under the knee a feather pillow, folded double; and little by little we shall extend his leg.

This my discourse was well approved by the physicians and surgeons.

The consultation ended, we went to the patient, and I made three openings in his thigh, from which went forth a great quantity of pus and sanies, and at the same time I took from him some little splinters of bone, but did not wish to let go forth too great a quantity of the said sanies for fear of too much exhaustion of his forces. Two or three hours afterwards, I had a bed made for him near his own, on which were clean white sheets; then a strong man placed him in it, and he was glad to be taken out of his dirty, stinking bed. Soon after, he asked to sleep, which he did for near four hours;

whereat everybody in the house commenced to rejoice, and especially Monsieur le Duc d'Ascot, his brother.

The following days I made injections into the depth and cavities of the ulcers, composed of aegyptiacum dissolved sometimes in brandy, other times in wine. I applied compresses to the bottom of the sinuses, to cleanse and dry the spongy soft flesh, with tents [drains] of lead cannulas [tubes] for the purpose of always giving issue to the sanies; and over them a large plaster of diacalcitheos, dissolved in wine. Likewise I bandaged him so dexterously that he had no pain, which ceasing, the fever began to diminish very much. Then I made him drink wine moderately tempered with water, knowing that it restores and quickens the forces. And all the things that we had ordered in the consultation were accomplished according to their time and order; his pains and the fever ceased and he began always to grow better. He discharged two of his surgeons and one of his physicians so that we were but three with him.

. . . In one month we had so wrought that he could sit up in a chair; and he had himself carried to and fro in his garden and to the gate of his chateau to see the people pass. . . . And the citizens of Mons in Hainault and other gentlemen, his neighbors, came to see him in wonder, as a man coming forth from the grave; and from then that he was so well, he was never without company; and as one went forth, another would enter to visit him. . . .

THOMAS SYDENHAM

1 6 2 4 - 1 6 8 9

THOMAS SYDENHAM was born of Puritan stock, in Dorset. After a
term of military service and two years at Oxford, he was granted the
degree of Bachelor of Medicine in 1648. His friendship with Robert
Boyle,[1] who sometimes went with him on his medical rounds, may
have encouraged him in his experimental approach to medicine.

Like Paré, Sydenham placed much more value on facts of observation than on traditional theories. "It is my nature," he said, "to
think where others read; to ask less whether the world agrees with
me than whether I agree with the truth." He made careful, accurate
descriptions of many diseases and his method of cure, though enlightened for his time, was still cautious and conservative. Again like
Paré, he made the patient as comfortable as possible, with a simple
diet and proper exercise to help nature complete the cure. "A disease," he once remarked, "is the effort of nature to restore the health
of the patient by elimination of morbific matter." Sydenham was
greatly respected and admired by his own generation, and by succeeding generations of English physicians.

Our extract is from his book on Epidemic Diseases, Epistle I, in
a translation from the Latin by R. G. Latham for the Sydenham
Society, in 1848. It shows his independent and experimental approach to the problem of working out a mode of curing intermittent
fever, now called malaria, by well-calculated doses of Peruvian bark
(the bark of the cinchona tree), which is the source of our modern
quinine.

[1] On Robert Boyle see above, p. 242.

THE USE OF PERUVIAN BARK

FOR MALARIA

'THE PERUVIAN BARK, commonly called Jesuit's bark, has, if I rightly remember, been famous in London for the cure of intermittent fevers for upwards of five and twenty years, and that rightly. The disease in question was seldom or never cured by any remedy before it. Hence agues were justly called the *opprobria medicorum* [the doctors' disgrace]. A short time back, however, the bark went out of use, being condemned on two grounds, and those not light ones. Firstly, when given a few hours before the fit, as was the usual practice, it would sometimes kill the patient at once. This happened to an alderman of London, named Underwood, and also to a Captain Potter. Now this terrible effect of the powder, although rare, frightened the more prudent physicians, and that rightly. Secondly, the patient who by the help of the bark had been freed from an impending fit, would, at the end of a fortnight, generally have a relapse, as if the disease was still fresh and had not abated in violence by running its course. All this shook the generality in their good opinion of the bark, since they considered it no great gain to put off the fit by endangering the life of the patient.

Now for many years I have been reflecting on the remarkable powers of this bark, considering that, with care and diligence, it was really the great remedy for intermittents. Hence I looked at two things, the danger to life, and the chance of a relapse. Guard against these, and I could cure the patient perfectly.

With respect to the danger to life, I laid it less to the bark than to its unseasonable administration. During the days when there is no fit, a vast mass of febrile matter accumulates in the body. Now

551

if in this case we give the powder just before the fit, we check the method by which Nature would get rid of it, so that, being kept in, it endangers life. Now this I thought I could remedy by checking the generation of any new febrile matter. Hence I gave the powder immediately after the fit. This allayed the succeeding one. Then on the days of intermission I repeated it at regular intervals, until a fresh fit impended. Thus, by degrees, I brought the blood under the healing influence of the bark.

The relapse, which generally happens at the end of a fortnight, seemed to me to arise from the blood not being sufficiently saturated with the febrifuge, which, efficient as it was, could not exterminate the disease at once. Whence I concluded that to guard against this I must repeat the powder—even where the disease was overcome for the present—at regular intervals, and before the effects of the preceding dose had gone off.

On these principles my method was and is as follows. If I visit a patient on (say) a Monday, and the ague be a quartan [with a paroxysm every fourth day] and it be expected that day, I do nothing; I only hope that he will escape the fit next after. Then on the two days of intermission, the Tuesday and Wednesday, I prescribe the bark thus:

> Rx. Peruvian bark, very finely powdered, ounces one;
>   Syrup of cloves, or
>   Syrup of dried rose-leaves, q.s.
> Make into an electuary [paste of powder and syrup]; to be
>   divided into twelve parts, of which one is to be taken
>   every fourth hour, beginning immediately after the
>   paroxysm, and washing down with a draught of wine.

If form of pill be preferred:

> Rx. Bark, finely powdered, ounces one;
>   Syrup of cloves, q.s.
> Make into moderately-sized pills. Take six every four hours.

With less trouble and equal success, you may mix an ounce of bark with two pints of claret and give it as before, in doses of eight or nine spoonsful. On Thursday the fit is expected. I do nothing; generally the fit keeps off. The remnants of the febrile matter have been cleared away and thrown off from the blood by the sweats of Monday's fit, and new accumulations have been checked by the use of the bark in the interval.

To prevent the disease from returning on the eighth day exactly, after the last dose, I give another exactly as before. Now though this often puts an end to the ague, the patient is all the safer for repeating the process three or even four times, especially if the blood be weakened by the previous evacuation, or the patient have exposed himself to the cold air.

LADY MARY WORTLEY MONTAGU

1 6 8 9 · 1 7 6 2

A CASE OF SMALLPOX is seldom seen today except in remote and backward countries. The very name of the disease is known to us chiefly for its connection with vaccination, the modern means of immunizing a population against its ravages. Before the development of this means of control, Macaulay wrote: "The smallpox was always present, filling the churchyards with corpses, tormenting with constant fears all whom it had not yet stricken, leaving on those whose lives it spared the hideous traces of its power, turning the babe into a changeling at which the mother shuddered, and making the eyes and cheeks of the betrothed maiden objects of horror to her lover."

An Eastern method of controlling smallpox by inoculation with the germs of the disease was reported in England in 1718, by the observant Lady Mary Wortley Montagu, who wrote home about it from Turkey, where her husband was the English ambassador. The efficacy of such inoculation results from the fact that smallpox does not strike the same person twice. It is a way of infecting the subject with a mild case of smallpox, so that he will not afterward suffer a severe attack.

Lady Mary's letter is reprinted from her Letters from the Levant, 1716-1718, as edited by J. A. St. John, Esq., London, 1838.

INOCULATION AGAINST SMALLPOX

I AM GOING to tell you a thing that I am sure will make you wish yourself here. The smallpox, so fatal and so general among us, is here rendered entirely harmless by the invention of *ingrafting*, which is the term they give it. There is a set of old women who make it their business to perform the operation every autumn, in the month of September, when the great heat is abated. People send to one another to know if any of their family has a mind to have the small-pox: they make parties for this purpose, and when they are met (commonly fifteen or sixteen together), the old woman comes with a nutshell full of the matter of the best sort of smallpox and asks what vein you please to have opened. She immediately rips open that you offer to her with a large needle (which gives you no more pain than a common scratch), and puts into the vein as much mat-ter as can lie upon the head of her needle, and after that binds up the little wound with a hollow bit of shell; and in this manner opens four or five veins. The Grecians have commonly the superstition of opening one in the middle of the forehead, in each arm, and on the breast to mark the sign of the cross; but this has a very ill effect, all these wounds leaving little scars, and is not done by those that are not superstitious, who choose to have them in the legs, or that part of the arm that is concealed. The children or young patients play together all the rest of the day and are in perfect health to the eighth. Then the fever begins to seize them, and they keep their beds two days, very seldom three. They have very rarely above twenty or thirty in their faces, which never mark; and in eight days' time, they are as well as before their illness. Where they are wounded, there remain running sores during the distemper, which I do not doubt is a great relief to it. Every year thousands undergo this operation; and the

French ambassador says pleasantly that they take the smallpox here by way of diversion, as they take the waters in other countries. There is no example of anyone that has died in it; and you may believe I am very well satisfied of the safety of this experiment, since I intend to try it on my dear little son.

LEOPOLD AUENBRUGGER

1 7 2 2 · 1 8 0 9

GALILEO HAD constructed a pendulum machine to measure the rapidity of the heart beat, and Sanctorius (1561-1636) had devised a form of air-thermometer which he used in a crude effort to measure body heat. Early in the eighteenth century Sir John Floyer invented a pocket watch with a second hand, and made an intensive study of pulse-rates. But other instrumental aids to diagnosis did not come until much later in medical history. Accurate clinical thermometry was not firmly established until about 1860.

Before 1760 it was almost impossible to diagnose chest diseases, such as tuberculosis and pneumonia, until the patient was already in a hopeless state. But in that year, Leopold Auenbrugger, a Viennese physician attached to the Spanish Military Hospital in Vienna, wrote a little essay on "Percussion of the Chest," in which he explained how chest conditions could be explored by listening to the resonance of the sound the chest gave out when tapped. The method is, of course, in universal use today, but few doctors then took it up until after Jean Nicolas Corvisart (1755-1821), later physician to Napoleon, had translated Auenbrugger's book from Latin into French. The extract below is from an English translation by Dr. John Forbes, published in 1824.

ON PERCUSSION OF THE CHEST

The Author's Preface

I HERE PRESENT the reader with a new sign which I have discovered for detecting diseases of the chest. This consists in the percussion of the human thorax, whereby, according to the character of the particular sounds thence elicited, an opinion is formed of the internal state of that cavity. In making public my discoveries respecting this matter I have been actuated neither by an itch for writing nor a fondness for speculation, but by the desire of submitting to my brethren the fruits of seven years' observation and reflexion. In doing so I have not been unconscious of the dangers I must encounter; since it has always been the fate of those who have illustrated or improved the arts and sciences by their discoveries to be beset by envy, malice, hatred, detraction, and calumny. This, the common lot, I have chosen to undergo; but with the determination to refuse to everyone who is actuated by such motives as these all explanation of my doctrines. What I have written I have proved again and again, by the testimony of my own senses and amid laborious and tedious exertions; still guarding, on all occasions, against the seductive influence of self-love.

And then, lest any one should imagine that this new sign [method] has been thoroughly investigated, even as far as regards the diseases noticed in my Treatise, I think it necessary candidly to confess that there still remain many defects to be remedied—and which I expect will be remedied—by careful observation and experience. Perhaps, also, the same observation and experience may lead to the discovery of other truths, in these or other diseases, of like value in the diagnosis, prognosis, and cure of thoracic affections. Owing to this acknowledged imperfection it will be seen that, in my difficulties, I have had recourse to the *Commentaries* of the most illustrious Baron Van Swieten, as containing everything which can be desired by the faithful observer of nature; by which means I have not only avoided the vice of tedious and prolix writing, but have, at the same time, possessed myself of the firmest basis whereon to raise most securely and creditably the rudiments of my discovery. In submitting this to the public I doubt not that I shall be considered, by all those who can justly appreciate medical science, as having thereby rendered a grateful service to our art, inasmuch as it must be allowed to throw no small degree of light upon the obscurer diseases of the chest, of which a more perfect knowledge has hitherto been much wanted.

In drawing up my little work I have omitted many things that were doubtful and not sufficiently digested; to the due perfection of which it will be my endeavour henceforth to apply myself. To conclude, I have not been ambitious of ornament in my mode or style of writing, being content if I shall be understood.

December 31, 1760.

First Observation

Of the Natural Sound of the Chest and Its Character in Different Parts

I. The thorax of a healthy person makes a sound when struck. I deem it unnecessary to give in this place any description of the thorax. I think it sufficient to say that, by this term, I mean that cavity bounded above by the neck and clavicles, and below by the diaphragm: in the sound state, the viscera it contains are fitted for their respective uses.

II. The sound thus elicited (I) from the healthy chest resembles the stifled sound of a drum covered with a thick woolen cloth or other envelope.

III. This sound is perceptible on different parts of the chest in the following manner:

1. On the right side anteriorly it is observed from the clavicle to the sixth true rib; laterally, from the axilla to the seventh rib; and posteriorly, from the scapula to the second and third false ribs.

2. The left side yields this sound from the clavicle to the fourth true rib anteriorly; and on the back and laterally to the same extent as the other side; over the space occupied by the heart, the sound loses part of its usual clearness and becomes dull.

3. The whole sternum yields as distinct a sound as the sides of the chest, except in the cardiac region, where it is somewhat duller.

4. The same sound is perceptible over that part of the spinal column which contributes to form the chest.

The sound is more distinct in the lean, and proportionably duller in the robust; in very fat persons it is almost lost. The most sonorous region is from the clavicle to the fourth rib anteriorly; lower down, the mammae and pectoral muscles deaden the sound. Sometimes, owing to the presence of muscle, the sound is dull beneath the axilla. In the scapular regions on the back, owing to the obstacle afforded by the bones and thick muscles there, it is also less distinct. Sometimes, but rarely, it exists over the third false rib—owing, I conceive, to a very unwonted length of the thoracic cavity.

Second Observation

Of the Method of Percussion

IV. The thorax ought to be struck slowly and gently, with the points of the fingers brought close together and at the same time extended.

Robust and fat subjects require a stronger percussion; such, indeed, as to elicit a degree of sound equal to that produced by a slight percussion in a lean subject.

V. During percussion, the shirt is to be drawn tight over the chest, or the hand of the operator covered with a glove made of unpolished leather.

If the naked chest is struck by the naked hand, the contact of the polished surfaces produces a kind of noise which alters or obscures the natural character of the sound.

VI. During the application of percussion, the patient is, first, to go on breathing in the natural manner, and then, is to hold his breath after a full inspiration. The difference of sound during inspiration, expiration, and the retention of the breath is important in fixing our diagnosis.

VII. While undergoing percussion on the fore parts of the chest, the patient is to hold his head erect and the shoulders are to be thrown back, in order that the chest may protrude and the skin and muscles be drawn tight over it; a clear sound is thus obtained.

VIII. While we are striking the lateral parts of the chest, the patient is to hold his arms across his head; as, thereby, the thoracic parietes [walls] are made more tense and a clearer sound obtained.

IX. When operating on the back, you are to cause the patient to bend forwards and draw his shoulders towards the anterior parts of the chest, so as to render the dorsal region rounded; and for the same reason as stated in VIII.

Any healthy person may make experience of percussion on his own person or that of other sound subjects; and will thus be convinced from the variety of the sounds obtained that this sign is not to be despised in forming a diagnosis.

Third Observation

Of the Preternatural or Morbid Sound of the Chest and Its General Import

X. To be able justly to appreciate the value of the various sounds elicited from the chest in cases of disease, it is necessary to have learned by experience on many subjects the modifications of sound, general or partial, produced by the habit of the body—natural conformation as to the scapulae, the mammae, the heart, the capacity of the thorax, the degree of fleshiness, fatness, etc., etc.; inasmuch as these various circumstances modify the sound very considerably.

XI. If, then, a distinct sound, equal on both sides and commensurate to the degree of percussion, is not obtained from the sonorous regions above mentioned, a morbid condition of some of the parts within the chest is indicated.

On this truth a general rule is to be founded, and from this certain predictions can be deduced, as will be shown in order. For 1 have learned from much experience that diseases of the worst description may exist within the chest, unmarked by any symptoms and undiscoverable by any other means than percussion alone.

A clear and equal sound, elicited from both sides of the chest, indicates that the air cells of the lungs are free and uncompressed either by a solid or a liquid body. (Exceptions to this rule will be mentioned in their place.)

XII and XIII. If a sonorous part of the chest, struck with the same intensity, yields a sound duller than natural, disease exists in that part.

XIV. If a sonorous region of the chest appears, on percussion, entirely destitute of the natural sound—that is, if it yields only a sound like that of a fleshy limb when struck, disease exists in that region.

The nature of the indications above pointed out will be understood by anyone who attends to the difference of sound elicited by percussion of the chest and of the thigh in his own person.

XV. The superficial extent of this unnatural sound (XIV) in a sonorous region is commensurate with the extent of the morbid affection.

XVI. If a place, naturally sonorous and now sounding only as a piece of flesh when struck, still retains the same sound (on percussion) when the breath is held after a deep inspiration, we are to conclude that the disease extends deep into the cavity of the chest.

XVII. If the same results (XVI) are obtained both before and behind, on points precisely opposite, we are to conclude that the disease occupies the whole diameter of the chest.

These varying results depend on the greater or less diminution of the volume of air usually contained in the thorax [lungs]; and the cause which occasions this diminution, whether solid or liquid, produces analogous results to those obtained by striking a cask, for example, in different degrees of emptiness or fulness: the diminution of sound being proportioned to the diminution of the volume of air contained in it.

JAMES COOK

1 7 2 8 · 1 7 7 9

SCURVY is a disease formerly much dreaded by navigators. Vasco da Gama lost by it a hundred out of a hundred and sixty men when he rounded the Cape of Good Hope in 1498. Ships were actually found derelict, with every man on board dead of scurvy.

In 1753 James Lind (1716-1794) published a Treatise on Scurvy, which outlined the methods that had hitherto been used in vain to ward off the disease. He properly diagnosed its cause as "want of fresh vegetables and greens," and recommended extract of lemons for its prevention and cure. Captain James Cook, during his second long voyage of three years and eighteen days, employed the means suggested by Lind, together with some discoveries of his own, to keep his crew in health. For his report of his success he was awarded, in 1776, the Copley Medal of the Royal Society, a prize designed "to crown that paper of the year which should contain the most useful and most successful experimental inquiry." We give here his letter on "The Method Taken for preserving the Health of the Crew of His Majesty's Ship, the Resolution," as printed in the Philosophical Transactions for 1776. The diet recommended by Cook came eventually into such wide use in the British Navy that man-of-war sailors were called "limeys." The regulated administration of lime juice was begun in 1795. The knowledge, however, did not spread at once. As late as 1832, Dana, in his Two Years Before the Mast, reports American sailors as helpless victims of scurvy.

Captain Cook had started his career as explorer with a voyage to the Society Islands, for the purpose of observing from there the 1769 Transit of Venus, after which achievement he circumnavigated Australia and New Zealand. The aim of his second trip was to find a great southern continent which he believed existed, but which he finally concluded lay too far to the south for him to reach. On his third trip, he tried in vain to discover a northwest passage between the Atlantic and the Pacific oceans from the west. He did discover the Hawaiian Islands, and was killed in a skirmish with the natives there.

THE PREVENTION

AND TREATMENT OF SCURVY

The Method taken for preserving the Health of the Crew of His Majesty's Ship the Resolution during her late Voyage round the World. By Captain James Cook, F.R.S. Addressed to Sir John Pringle, Bart. F.R.S.

Mile-end, March 5, 1776.
(read Mar. 7, 1776.)

SIR,

As many gentlemen have expressed some surprize at the uncommon good state of health which the crew of the *Resolution*, under my command, experienced during her late voyage, I take the liberty to communicate to you the methods that were taken to obtain that end. Much was owing to the extraordinary attention given by the Admiralty, in causing such articles to be put on board as either by experience or conjecture were judged to tend most to preserve the health of seamen. I shall not trespass upon your time in mentioning all those articles, but confine myself to such as were found the most useful.

We had on board a large quantity of Malt, of which was made sweet-wort [infusion of malt], and given (not only to those men who had manifest symptoms of the scurvy, but to such also as were, from circumstances, judged to be most liable to that disorder) from one to two or three pints in the day to each man, or in such proportion as the surgeon thought necessary; which sometimes amounted to three quarts in the twenty-four hours. This is without doubt one of the best antiscorbutic sea-medicines yet found out; and if given

566

in time, will, with proper attention to other things, I am persuaded, prevent the scurvy from making any great progress for a considerable time: but I am not altogether of opinion that it will cure it in an advanced state at sea.

Sour Kraut, of which we had also a large provision, is not only a wholesome vegetable food, but, in my judgment, highly antiscorbu-tic and spoils not by keeping. A pound of it was served to each man, when at sea, twice a week or oftener, when it was thought necessary.

Portable Soup or Broth was another essential article, of which we had likewise a liberal supply. An ounce of this to each man, or such other proportion as was thought necessary, was boiled with their pease three days in the week; and when we were in places where fresh vegetables could be procured, it was boiled with them and with wheat or oatmeal every morning for breakfast, and also with dried pease and fresh vegetables for dinner. It enabled us to make several nourishing and wholesome messes, and was the means of making the people eat a greater quantity of greens than they would have done otherwise.

Further, we were provided with Rob [conserve] of lemons and oranges; which the surgeon found useful in several cases.

Amongst other articles of victualling we were furnished with sugar in the room of oil, and with wheat instead of much oatmeal, and were certainly gainers by the exchange. Sugar, I imagine, is a very good antiscorbutic;[1] whereas oil, such at least as is usually given to the navy, I apprehend has the contrary effect. But the introduction of the most salutary articles, either as provision or medicines, will generally prove unsuccessful, unless supported by certain rules of living.

On this principle, many years' experience, together with some hints I had from Sir Hugh Palliser, the Captains Campbell, Wallis, and other intelligent officers, enabled me to lay down a plan whereby all was to be conducted. The crew were at three watches, except

[1] This was long before modern refining methods eliminated most of the "impurities" from sugar.

upon some extraordinary occasions. By this means they were not so much exposed to the weather as if they had been at watch and watch: and they had generally dry cloaths to shift themselves when they happened to get wet. Care was also taken to expose them as little as possible. Proper methods were employed to keep their persons, hammocks, bedding, cloaths, &c. constantly clean and dry. Equal pains were taken to keep the ship clean and dry between decks. Once or twice a week she was smoaked with gunpowder moistened with vinegar or water. I had also frequently a fire made in an iron pot at the bottom of the well, which greatly purified the air in the lower parts of the ship. To this and cleanliness, as well in the ship as amongst the people, too great attention cannot be paid; the least neglect occasions a putrid, offensive smell below, which nothing but fires will remove: and if these be not used in time, those smells will be attended with bad consequences.

Proper care was taken of the ship's coppers, so that they were kept constantly clean. The fat which boiled out of the salt beef and pork I never suffered to be given to the people, as is customary; being of opinion that it promotes the scurvy. I never failed to take in water wherever it was to be procured, even when we did not seem to want it; because I look upon fresh water from the shore to be much more wholesome than that which has been kept some time on board. Of this essential article we were never at an allowance, but had always abundance for every necessary purpose.

I am convinced that with plenty of fresh water and a close attention to cleanliness, a ship's company will seldom be much afflicted with the scurvy, though they should not be provided with any of the antiscorbutics before mentioned. We came to few places where either the art of man or nature did not afford some sort of refreshment or other, either of the animal or vegetable kind. It was my first care to procure what could be met with of either by every means in my power, and to oblige our people to make use thereof, both by my example and authority; but the benefits arising from such refreshments soon became so obvious that I had little occasion to employ either the one or the other.

These, Sir, were the methods, under the care of Providence, by which the *Resolution* performed a voyage of three years and eighteen days, through all the climates from 52° North to 71° South, with the loss of one man only by disease, who died of a complicated and lingering illness, without any mixture of scurvy. Two others were unfortunately drowned, and one killed by a fall; so that of the whole number with which I set out from England, I lost only four.

I have the honour to be, Sir, &c.,

JAMES COOK

EDWARD JENNER

1 7 4 9 · 1 8 2 3

INOCULATING PEOPLE with smallpox virus, in the hope that they would have a light case of the disease rather than a heavy one, and so be immunized against the worst effects of that dreaded plague, was like fighting fire with fire. Sometimes the method of protection got out of hand, for inoculation occasionally produced a very serious case of smallpox.

Vaccination, the present method of immunization, was invented by Edward Jenner, about the year 1795. Jenner, a native of rural Gloucestershire, had returned there to a country practice after having studied for some years in London with John Hunter (1728-1793), one of England's leading surgeons and pathologists.

Country folk knew that dairy maids who had contracted cowpox when milking seemed afterward to be immune to smallpox. Jenner himself noticed that certain people who had been inoculated with smallpox virus did not develop the expected symptoms, and found that these were all persons known to have had cowpox at some time before their inoculation. He finally was able to demonstrate that vaccination with the virus of the mild disease of cowpox established an immunity to smallpox.

He published his findings in a beautifully printed book, with many plates showing cowpox sores, An Inquiry into the Causes and Effects of the Variolae Vaccinae, London, 1798. For this great step in preventive medicine, Parliament awarded Jenner two prizes, totaling £30,000.

THE INVENTION OF VACCINATION

§

The deviation of man from the state in which he was originally placed by nature seems to have proved to him a prolific source of diseases. From the love of splendour, from the indulgences of luxury, and from his fondness for amusement, he has familiarised himself with a great number of animals which may not originally have been intended for his associates.

The Wolf, disarmed of ferocity, is now pillowed in the lady's lap. The Cat, the little Tyger of our island, whose natural home is the forest, is equally domesticated and caressed. The Cow, the Hog, the Sheep, and the Horse are all, for a variety of purposes, brought under his care and dominion.

There is a disease to which the Horse, from his state of domestication, is frequently subject. The Farriers have termed it *the Grease*. It is an inflammation and swelling in the heel, from which issues matter possessing properties of a very peculiar kind, which seems capable of generating a disease in the Human Body (after it has undergone the modification which I shall presently speak of) which bears so strong a resemblance to the Small-pox, that I think it highly probable it may be the source of that disease.

In this Dairy Country a great number of Cows are kept, and the office of milking is performed indiscriminately by Men and Maid Servants. One of the former, having been appointed to apply dressings to the heels of a Horse affected with *the Grease*, and not paying due attention to cleanliness, incautiously bears his part in milking the Cows, with some particles of the infectious matter adhering to his fingers. When this is the case, it commonly happens that a disease is communicated to the Cows, and from Cows to the Dairymaids, which spreads through the farm until most of the cattle and domestics feel its unpleasant consequences.

This disease has obtained the name of the Cow Pox. It appears on the nipples of the Cows in the form of irregular pustules. At their first appearance, they are commonly of a palish blue, or rather of a colour somewhat approaching to livid, and are surrounded by an erysipelatous inflammation. These pustules, unless a timely remedy be applied, frequently degenerate into phagedenic [eating] ulcers, which prove extremely troublesome. The animals become indisposed, and the secretion of milk is much lessened.

Inflamed spots now begin to appear on different parts of the hands of the domestics employed in milking, and sometimes on the wrists, which quickly run on to suppuration, first assuming the appearance of the small vesications [blisters] produced by a burn. Most commonly they appear about the joints of the fingers and at their extremities; but whatever parts are affected, if the situation will admit, these superficial suppurations put on a circular form, with their edges more elevated than their centre, and of a colour distantly approaching to blue. Absorption takes place and tumours appear in each axilla. The system becomes affected—the pulse is quickened; and shiverings, with general lassitude and pains about the loins and limbs, with vomiting, come on. The head is painful, and the patient is now and then even affected with delirium.

These symptoms, varying in their degrees of violence, generally continue from one day to three or four, leaving ulcerated sores about the hands, which, from the sensibility of the parts, are very troublesome, and commonly heal slowly, frequently becoming phagedenic, like those from whence they sprung. The lips, nostrils, eyelids and other parts of the body are sometimes affected with sores; but these evidently arise from their being needlessly rubbed or scratched with the patient's infected fingers. No eruptions on the skin have followed the decline of the feverish symptoms in any instance that has come under my inspection, one only excepted, and in this case a very few appeared on the arms; they were very minute, of a vivid red colour, and soon died away without advancing to maturation; so that I cannot determine whether they had any connection with the preceding symptoms.

Thus the disease makes its progress from the Horse to the nipple of the Cow, and from the Cow to the Human Subject. Morbid matter of various kinds, when absorbed into the system, may produce effects in some degree similar; but what renders the Cow-pox virus so extremely singular is, that the person who has been thus affected is for ever after secure from the infection of the Small Pox; neither exposure to the variolous [small pox] effluvia, nor the insertion of the matter into the skin producing this distemper.

In support of so extraordinary a fact, I shall lay before my Reader a number of instances. . . .

Case IV Mary Barge, of Woodford in this parish, was inoculated with variolous matter in the year 1791. An efflorescence of a palish red colour soon appeared about the parts where the matter was inserted and spread itself rather extensively, but died away in a few days without producing any variolous symptoms.[1] She has since been repeatedly employed as a nurse to Small-pox patients, without experiencing any ill consequences. This woman had the Cow-Pox when she lived in the service of a Farmer in this parish thirty-one years before. . . .

After the many fruitless attempts to give the Small-pox to those who had had the Cow-pox, it did not appear necessary, nor was it convenient to me, to inoculate the whole of those who had been the subjects of these late trials; yet I thought it right to see the effects

[1] It is remarkable that variolous matter, when the system is disposed to reject it, should excite inflammation on the part to which it is applied more speedily than when it produces the Small-Pox. Indeed it becomes almost a criterion by which we can determine whether the infection will be received or not. It seems as if a change, which endures through life, had been produced in the action or disposition to action in the vessels of the skin; and it is remarkable, too, that whether this change has been effected by the Small-Pox or the Cow-Pox, that the disposition to sudden cuticular [skin] inflammation is the same on the application of variolous matter. [Original note by Jenner.]

of variolous matter on some of them, particularly William Summers, the first of these patients who had been infected with matter taken from the cow. He was therefore inoculated with variolous matter from a fresh pustule; but, as in the preceding Cases, the system did not feel the effects of it in the smallest degree. I had an opportunity also of having this boy and William Pead inoculated by my Nephew, Mr. Henry Jenner, whose report to me is as follows:

"I have inoculated Pead and Barge, two of the boys whom you lately infected with the Cow-pox. On the 2d day, the incisions were inflamed and there was a pale inflammatory stain around them. On the 3d day, these appearances were still increasing and their arms itched considerably. On the 4th day, the inflammation was evidently subsiding, and on the 6th, it was scarcely perceptible. No symptom of indisposition followed.

"To convince myself that the variolous matter made use of was in a perfect state, I at the same time inoculated a patient with some of it, who never had gone through the Cow-pox, and it produced the Small-pox in the usual regular manner."

These experiments afforded me much satisfaction; they proved that the matter in passing from one human subject to another, through five gradations, lost none of its original properties, J. Barge being the fifth who received the infection successively from William Summers, the boy to whom it was communicated from the cow.

I shall now conclude this Inquiry with some general observations on the subject and on some others which are interwoven with it. Although I presume it may be unnecessary to produce further testimony in support of my assertion "that the Cow-pox protects the human constitution from the infection of the Small-pox," yet it affords me considerable satisfaction to say that Lord Somerville, the President of the Board of Agriculture, to whom this paper was shewn by Sir Joseph Banks, has found upon inquiry that the statements were confirmed by the concurring testimony of Mr. Dolland, a surgeon, who resides in a dairy country remote from this in which these observations were made. With respect to the opinion adduced "that the source of the infection is a peculiar morbid matter arising in the horse," although I have not been able to prove it from actual experiments conducted immediately under my own eye, yet the evidence I have adduced appears sufficient to establish it.

They who are not in the habit of conducting experiments may not be aware of the coincidence of circumstances necessary for their being managed so as to prove perfectly decisive; nor how often men engaged in professional pursuits are liable to interruptions, which disappoint them almost at the instant of their being accomplished; however, I feel no room for hesitation respecting the common origin of the disease, being well convinced that it never appears among the cows (except it can be traced to a cow introduced among the general herd which has been previously infected, or to an infected servant) unless they have been milked by someone who, at the same time, has the care of a horse affected with diseased heels. . . .

It is curious also to observe that the virus, which with respect to its effects is undetermined and uncertain, previously to its passing from the horse through the medium of the cow, should then not only become more active, but should invariably and completely possess those specific properties which induce in the human constitution symptoms similar to those of the variolous fever, and effect in it that peculiar change which for ever renders it unsusceptible of the variolous contagion.

May it not, then, be reasonably conjectured, that the source of the Small-pox is morbid matter of a peculiar kind, generated by a disease in the horse, and that accidental circumstances may have again and again arisen, still working new changes upon it, until it has acquired the contagious and malignant form under which we now commonly see it making its devastations amongst us? And, from a consideration of the change which the infectious matter undergoes from producing a disease on the cow, may we not conceive that many contagious diseases, now prevalent among us, may owe their present appearance not to a simple, but to a compound origin? For example, is it difficult to imagine that the measles, the scarlet fever, and the ulcerous sore throat with a spotted skin, have all sprung from the same source, assuming some variety in their forms according to the nature of their new combinations? The same question will apply respecting the origin of many other contagious diseases, which bear a strong analogy to each other.

There are certainly more forms than one, without considering the common variation between the confluent and distinct, in which the Small-pox appears in what is called the natural way. About seven years ago a species of Small-pox spread through many of the towns and villages of this part of Gloucestershire. It was of so mild a nature that a fatal instance was scarcely ever heard of, and consequently so little dreaded by the lower orders of the community, that they scrupled not to hold the same intercourse with each other as if no infectious disease had been present among them. I never saw nor heard of an instance of its being confluent. The most accurate manner, perhaps, in which I can convey an idea of it is by saying that had fifty individuals been taken promiscuously and infected by exposure to this contagion, they would have had as mild and light a disease as if they had been inoculated with variolous matter in the usual way. The harmless manner in which it shewed itself could not arise from any peculiarity either in the season or the weather, for I watched its progress upwards of a year without perceiving any variation in its general appearance. I consider it then as a *variety* of Small-pox. . . .

Whether it be yet ascertained by experiment that the quantity of variolous matter inserted into the skin makes any difference with respect to the subsequent mildness or violence of the disease, I know not; but I have the strongest reason for supposing that if either the punctures or incisions be made so deep as to go *through* it and wound the adipose membrane, that the risk of bringing on a violent disease is greatly increased. I have known an inoculator whose practice was "to cut deep enough (to use his own expression) to see a bit of fat," and there to lodge the matter. The great number of bad Cases, independent of inflammations and abscesses on the arms, and the fatality which attended this practice was almost inconceivable; and I cannot account for it on any other principle than that of the matter being placed in this situation instead of the skin. . . .

A very respectable friend of mine, Dr. Hardwicke, of Sodbury in this county, inoculated great numbers of patients previous to the introduction of the more modern method by Sutton, and with such success that a fatal instance occurred rarely since that method has been adopted. It was the doctor's practice to make as slight an incision as possible *upon* the skin, and there to lodge a thread saturated with the variolous matter. When his patients became indisposed, agreeably to the custom then prevailing, they were directed to go to bed and were kept moderately warm. Is it not probable then, that the success of the modern practice may depend more upon the method of invariably depositing the virus in or upon the skin, than on the subsequent treatment of the disease? . . .

Should it be asked whether this investigation is a matter of mere curiosity, or whether it tends to any beneficial purpose? I should answer that, notwithstanding the happy effects of Inoculation, with all the improvements which the practice has received since its first introduction into this country, it not very unfrequently produces deformity of the skin, and sometimes, under the best management, proves fatal.

These circumstances must naturally create in every instance some degree of painful solicitude for its consequences. But as I have never known fatal effects arise from the Cow-pox, even when impressed in the most unfavourable manner, producing extensive inflammations and suppurations on the hands; and as it clearly appears that this disease leaves the constitution in a state of perfect security from the infection of the Small-pox, may we not infer that a mode of Inoculation may be introduced preferable to that at present adopted, especially among those families which, from previous circumstances, we may judge to be predisposed to have the disease unfavourably? It is an excess in the number of pustules which we chiefly dread in the Small-pox; but in the Cow-pox, no pustules appear, nor does it seem possible for the contagious matter to produce the disease from effluvia, or by any other means than contact, and that probably not simply between the virus and the cuticle; so that a single individual in a family might at any time receive it without the risk of infecting the rest, or of spreading a distemper that fills a country with terror. . . .

Scientists Think About Science

A MISLEADING modern myth, endlessly repeated in our newspapers and magazines, is about scientists who "accidentally" make a new discovery, or who succeed after trying every improbable combination of elements. The myth is misleading because very little scientific progress is made in this way. It makes us forget that most scientific work is so carefully planned and organized that even a failure to get the expected results may be almost as important to the worker as success.

At the beginning of the modern era, the philosopher-scientists had first to solve a problem more important than finding new facts about the world. They had to learn how to test and support their reasoning and their intuition by accurate and convincing experiment. They had to create a method organizing both their thinking and experimentation in such a way that an undiscovered truth would become incontestably apparent.

Scientists of this period inherited the laws and habits of clear thinking from the early Greeks, but they also inherited a scornful attitude toward experimentation. The Greek philosopher Aristotle, sometimes called the first modern thinker, had formulated certain definite laws of logic, and begun the division of knowledge into the separate sciences. Since his philosophy was the basis of medieval thought about the world, he prepared Europe for the Renaissance, in which modern science was born. Aristotelian logic and Euclidean geometry, taught in every school at that time, were the roots from which the tree of modern thought has grown. But although Aristotle himself, the great Archimedes after him, and other ancients had performed experiments as a basis for their teachings, they had left no clear account of the experimental method as such. Their results alone had seemed worth recording.

Education in the sixteenth century of our era was for the most part the privilege of the upper classes, and experimentation, being a form of manual labor, was widely considered menial and degrading. The first modern experimentalists were derisively called "sooty empirics"; they had not only to find a way of performing experiments effectively, but they had also to endure considerable personal abuse. Without men brave enough to withstand the hardships of pioneering in a new method, science would have remained in the stagnant state which was the result of confining learning to what could be logically deduced from ideas and facts that for centuries past had been uncritically accepted as true.

At best it is difficult to tell what is true from what is false. What is considered reasonable and obvious in one era may later be looked on as the most foolish sort of superstition and ignorance. In his extreme youth, for example, Newton, one of the most gifted and productive scientists of all time, studied astrology. If this statement seems incredible, we must remember that up to Newton's time astrology was considered a highly respectable branch of learning. Newton later atoned for his youthful error by creating such an understanding of the order of the heavens that astrology was in time relegated to the background to become the interest of charlatans and quacks, who even today, as when Marlowe satirized them in *Dr. Faustus*, make a good thing out of public ignorance and credulity.

For reaching out into new fields of knowledge, even the best of deductive thinking, which is logical reasoning from principles already acknowledged to be true, has its serious limitations. Deductive thinking alone can only build up theories as to facts and possibilities on a basis of accepted ideas. New truths may be discovered either by intuition, the sudden subjective perception of a new fact which is not included in existing knowledge, or by experimentation and inductive thinking, the drawing of new conclusions from a fresh study of actual phenomena. The ancients depended more on the intuitive method. Modern science leans more on the experimental and requires that every intuition be verified by experiment before it gains acceptance as truth.

Science, then, is more than a branch of human knowledge; it is a system of investigation and thought, a method of procedure and reasoning, by means of which we have discovered and are still discovering novel truths about the physical order of the universe, and by which we have verified and are still verifying its laws until some day they are established beyond the shadow of a doubt.

This final section presents, in the words of the innovators themselves, some of the high lights in the history of modes of scientific thought. Bacon, Descartes, and Newton were engaged in a battle against traditional authority. By the time of Lavoisier, the fight to make the new experimental method respectable was won. He and Laplace accordingly could devote themselves to the development of improvements in that great method on which modern scientific progress is based.

GEORGIUS AGRICOLA

1 4 9 4 · 1 5 5 5

MINERS ARE practical men. For thousands of years they have been delving into the bowels of the earth, assaying, smelting, casting, and forging. Few of them did much theorizing until about the year 1500, when several books on the subject were written. The chief of these were the work of Georg Bauer, who Latinized his name to Agricola.

Agricola was born in Saxony in 1494, and studied at the Universities of Leipzig, Bologna, and Venice. In 1527, he began medical practice at Joachimsthal in Bohemia, then the greatest mining district in Central Europe.

The twelve books of De re metallica, his last and greatest work, cover every phase of mining and metallurgy from prospecting with the divining rod (which he rejected as less useful than careful observation of natural indications) to smelting and refining. For two centuries it was the standard treatise on metals.

Our excerpt, "Arts and Sciences a Miner Must Know," shows his view of the dependence of the progressive technical man on every branch of science. De re metallica was published in 1556; the translation here used was made by ex-President Herbert Hoover and his wife, Lou Henry Hoover, in 1912; it originally appeared in the Mining Journal of London.

ARTS AND SCIENCES
A MINER MUST KNOW

MANY PERSONS hold the opinion that the metal industries are fortuitous and that the occupation is one of sordid toil, and altogether a
kind of business requiring not so much skill as labor. But as for myself, when I reflect carefully upon its special points one by one, it
appears to be far otherwise. For a miner must have the greatest skill
in his work, that he may know first of all what mountain or hill,
what valley or plain, can be prospected most profitably, or what he
should leave alone; moreover, he must understand the veins, stringers, and seams in the rocks. Then he must be thoroughly familiar
with the many and varied species of earths, juices, gems, stones,
marbles, rocks, metals, and compounds. He must also have a complete knowledge of the method of making all underground works.
Lastly, there are the various systems of assaying substances and of
preparing them for smelting; and here again there are many altogether diverse methods. For there is one method for gold and silver,
another for copper, another for quicksilver, another for iron, another
for lead, and even tin and bismuth are treated differently from lead.
Although the evaporation of juices is an art apparently quite distinct
from metallurgy, yet they ought not to be considered separately, inasmuch as these juices are also often dug out of the ground solidified, or they are produced from certain kinds of earth, and stones
which the miners dig up, and some of the juices are not themselves
devoid of metals. Again, their treatment is not simple, since there
is one method for common salt, another for soda, another for alum,
another for vitriol, another for sulphur, and another for bitumen.

Furthermore, there are many arts and sciences of which a miner should not be ignorant. First there is philosophy, that he may discern the origin, cause, and nature of subterranean things; for then he will be able to dig out the veins easily and advantageously, and to obtain more abundant results from his mining. Secondly, there is medicine, that he may be able to look after his diggers and other workmen, that they do not meet with those diseases to which they are more liable than workmen in other occupations, or if they do meet with them, that he himself may be able to heal them or may see that the doctors do so. Thirdly follows astronomy, that he may know the divisions of the heavens and from them judge the direction of the veins. Fourthly, there is the science of surveying, that he may be able to estimate how deep a shaft should be sunk to reach the tunnel which is being driven to it and to determine the limits and boundaries in these workings, especially in depth. Fifthly, his knowledge of arithmetical science should be such that he may calculate the cost to be incurred in the machinery and the working of the mine. Sixthly, his learning must comprise architecture, that he himself may construct the various machines and timberwork required underground, or that he may be able to explain the method of the construction to others. Next, he must have knowledge of drawing, that he can draw plans of his machinery. Lastly, there is the law, especially that dealing with metals, that he may claim his own rights, that he may undertake the duty of giving others his opinion on legal matters, that he may not take another man's property and so make trouble for himself, and that he may fulfill his obligations to others according to the law.

It is therefore necessary that those who take an interest in the methods and precepts of mining and metallurgy should read these and others of our books studiously and diligently; or on every point they should consult expert mining people, though they will discover few who are skilled in the whole art. As a rule one man understands only the methods of mining, another possesses the knowledge of washing, another is experienced in the art of smelting, another has the knowledge of measuring the hidden parts of the earth, another is skillful in the art of making machines, and finally, another is learned in mining law. But as for us, though we may not have perfected the whole art of discovery and preparation of metals, at least we can be of great assistance to persons studious in its acquisition.

FRANCIS BACON

1 5 6 1 - 1 6 2 6

Two RULING passions governed Francis Bacon's life—ambition for personal glory and contempt for the thought patterns of the mediaeval schools. He was the son of one of Queen Elizabeth's wisest counsellors, and in his youth one of her favorites. Under the learned King James I, he was created successively Knight, Solicitor General, Keeper of the Great Seal, Lord Chancellor, Baron Verulam and Viscount of St. Albans. Being charged, however, in his old age, with irregularities in the administration of his high office, he confessed himself guilty of bribery, was sentenced to imprisonment in the Tower, and disqualified for any further post of honor. But if a desire for glory brought about Bacon's downfall and disgrace, his battles against intellectual sterility won him an important place in the history of science.

Two steps were necessary, Bacon held, in the path to fruitful knowledge. The first was the renunciation of various deep-seated and common prejudices—idols, he called them. The second was the adoption of sound scientific procedure. Our selection is taken from a long passage in which he is beginning to formulate what later came to be known as the "scientific method."

If Bacon cared little for what seemed to him the empty arguments of the scholastics, neither did he like the planless experimenter. Such experimenters "are like the ant," he said; "they collect and use; the reasoners resemble spiders who make cobwebs out of their own substance. But the bee takes a middle course; it gathers its material from the flowers of the garden and of the field, but transforms and digests it by a power of its own." (Novum Organum, Book I, Aphorism XCV.)

As a part of his revolt against old methods, Bacon wrote some of his works in English instead of in Latin. He was himself, however, always more of a theorist than a practitioner and made no important discoveries of his own. But the influence of his criticism of past scholarship and of his enthusiastic belief in the science of the future and in the riches it would confer on human life was immense.

The selection presented here, "Conduct of the Investigation of Nature," is from the Novum Organum of 1620, as reprinted in an edition of 1844, edited by Basil Montague, and published by Carey and Hunt, Philadelphia.

CONDUCT OF THE
INVESTIGATION OF NATURE

A SEPARATION AND solution of bodies, therefore, is to be effected, not by fire indeed, but rather by reasoning and true induction, with the assistance of experiment, and by a comparison with other bodies . . . and a reduction to those simple natures and their forms which meet and are combined in the compound; and we must assuredly pass from Vulcan to Minerva,[1] if we wish to bring to light the real texture and conformation of bodies, upon which every occult and (as it is sometimes called) specific property and virtue of things depends, and whence, also, every rule of powerful change and transformation is deduced.

For instance, we must examine what spirit is in every body, what tangible essence; whether that spirit is copious and exuberant, or meagre and scarce, fine or course, aeriform or igniform, active or sluggish, weak or robust, progressive or retrograde, abrupt or continuous, agreeing with external and surrounding objects, or differing from them, etc. In like manner must we treat tangible essence (which admits of as many distinctions as the spirit), and its hairs, fibres, and varied texture. Again, the situation of the spirit in the corporeal mass, its pores, passages, veins, and cells, and the rudiments or first essays of the organic body are subject to the same examination. In these, however, as in our former inquiries, and therefore in the whole investigation of latent conformation, the only genuine and clear light which completely dispels all darkness and subtile difficulties, is admitted by means of the primary axioms. . . .

8. This method will not bring us to atoms, which takes for

[1] That is, from mere furnace work to reasoning about our findings.

granted the vacuum, and the immutability of matter (neither of which hypotheses is correct); but to the real particles, such as we discover them to be. Nor is there any ground for alarm at this refinement, as if it were inexplicable, for, on the contrary, the more inquiry is directed to simple natures, the more will everything be placed in a plain and perspicuous light; since we transfer our attention from the complicated to the simple, from the incommensurable to the commensurable, from surds to rational quantities, from the indefinite and vague to the definite and certain: as when we arrive at the elements of letters, and the simple tones of concords. The investigation of nature is best conducted when mathematics are applied to physics. Again, let none be alarmed at vast numbers and fractions; for, in calculation, it is as easy to set down or to reflect upon a thousand as a unit, or the thousandth part of an integer as an integer itself.

9. From the two kinds of axioms above specified arise the two divisions of philosophy and the sciences, and we will use the commonly adopted terms, which approach the nearest to our meaning, in our own sense. Let the investigation of forms, which (in reasoning, at least, and after their own laws) are eternal and immutable, constitute *metaphysics*, and let the investigation of the efficient cause of matter, latent process, and latent conformation (which all relate merely to the ordinary course of nature, and not to her fundamental and eternal laws) constitute *physics*. Parallel to these let there be two practical divisions; to *physics* that of *mechanics*; to *metaphysics* that of *magic*, in the purest sense of the term, as applied to its ample means and its command over nature.

10. The object of our philosophy being thus laid down, we proceed to precepts, in the most clear and regular order. The signs for the interpretation of nature comprehend two divisions: the first regards the eliciting or creating the axioms from experiment, the second the deducing or deriving of new experiments from axioms. The first admits of three subdivisions into *ministrations*. 1. To the senses. 2. To the memory. 3. To the mind or reason. For we must first pre-

pare as a foundation for the whole a complete and accurate natural and experimental history. We must not imagine or invent, but discover the acts and properties of nature.

But natural and experimental history is so varied and diffuse that it confounds and distracts the understanding unless it be fixed and exhibited in due order. We must, therefore, form tables and coordinations of instances, upon such a plan, and in such order, that the understanding may be enabled to act upon them.

Even when this is done, the understanding, left to itself and its own operation, is incompetent and unfit to construct its axioms without direction and support. Our third ministration, therefore, must be true and legitimate induction, the very key of interpretation. We must begin, however, at the end, and go back again to the others.

11. The investigation of Forms proceeds thus: A nature being given, we must first present to the understanding all the known instances which agree in the same nature, although the subject matter be considerably diversified. And this collection must be made as a mere history, and without any premature reflection, or too great degree of refinement. For instance: take the investigation of the form of heat.

Instances agreeing in the form of heat

1. The rays of the sun, particularly in summer, and at noon.
2. The same reflected and condensed, as between mountains, or along walls, and particularly in burning mirrors.
3. Ignited meteors.
4. Burning lightning.
5. Eruptions of flames from the cavities of mountains, etc.
6. Flame of every kind.
7. Ignited solids.
8. Natural warm baths.
9. Warm or heated liquids.
10. Warm vapours and smoke: and the air itself, which admits a

most powerful and violent heat if confined, as in reverberating furnaces.

11. Damp hot weather, arising from the constitution of the air, without any reference to the time of the year.

12. Confined and subterraneous air in some caverns, particularly in winter.

13. All shaggy substances, as wool, the skins of animals, and the plumage of birds, contain some heat.

14. All bodies, both solid and liquid, dense and rare (as the air itself), placed near fire for any time.

15. Sparks arising from the violent percussion of flint and steel.

16. All bodies rubbed violently, as stone, wood, cloth, etc., so that rudders and axles of wheels, sometimes catch fire, and the West Indians obtain fire by attrition.

17. Green and moist vegetable matter confined and rubbed together; as roses, peas in baskets; so hay, if it be damp when stacked, often catches fire.

18. Quicklime sprinkled with water.

19. Iron, when first dissolved by acids in a glass, and without any application to fire; the same of tin, but not so intensely.

20. Animals, particularly internally; although the heat is not perceivable by the touch in insects, on account of their small size.

21. Horse dung, and the like excrement from other animals, when fresh.

22. Strong oil of sulphur and of vitriol exhibit the operation of heat in burning linen.

23. As does the oil of marjoram, and like substances, in burning the bony substance of the teeth.

24. Strong and well rectified spirits of wine exhibit the same effects; so that white of eggs, when thrown into it, grows hard and white, almost in the same manner as when boiled, and bread becomes burnt and brown as if toasted.

25. Aromatic substances and warm plants, as the dracunculus [arum], old nasturtium, etc.; which, though they be not warm to the

touch (whether whole or pulverized), yet are discovered by the tongue and palate to be warm and almost burning when slightly masticated.

26. Strong vinegar and all acids, or any part of the body not clothed with the epidermis, as the eye, tongue, or any wounded part, or where the skin is removed, excite a pain differing but little from that produced by heat.

27. Even a severe and intense cold produces a sensation of burning.

"Nam Boreae penetrabile adurit."

28. Other instances.

We are wont to call this a table of existence and presence.

12. We must next present to the understanding instances which do not admit of the given nature; for form (as we have observed) ought no less to be absent where the given nature is absent, than to be present where it is present. If, however, we were to examine every instance, our labour would be infinite. . . .

RENÉ DESCARTES[1]

1 5 9 6 · 1 6 5 0

A MATHEMATICIAN first of all, the Frenchman, René Descartes, was a student also of optics, chemistry, physics, anatomy, embryology, medicine, astronomy, meteorology, magnetism, philosophy, and theology. The day of specialization had not yet arrived, and it was still possible for one man to master all that was known in science.

Descartes also looked behind all these fields of knowledge in an effort to grasp the methods and assumptions that were common to them all. Like Bacon, he did not himself perform experiments, but he had a deeper intuitive insight into the theoretical background than had Bacon. Like his English predecessor, he emphasized the importance of abandoning false traditional ideas and prejudices and of constructing sound new methods. He went so far indeed in his rejection of possibly false ideas that he left nothing at all to build on but the self-evident principle, "I think; therefore I am." He rejected all the older types of argumentation, particularly the theological and metaphysical reasoning of the scholastic philosophers. He preferred, as the essay here quoted will show, to find within himself a secure, common-sense basis for knowledge, from which further knowledge might be rationally developed by strict logic. Deductive reasoning, he believed, was sound, provided it rested on principles that were themselves unshakable.

Descartes had read and praised Bacon's Novum Organum and was therefore familiar with his view that knowledge of external nature should be derived by induction from actual experience. True discoveries of the reason, he also said, may be better made by perceiving

[1] For another example of Descartes' scientific speculations, see p. 214.

universal principles in many individual instances than by deducing particular conclusions from universal principles that themselves can never be proved true. And like Bacon he condemned the prevalent habit of relying on past authority. His Jesuit teachers had not relied on authority in the field of mathematics. He would apply their rigid mathematical reasoning to the results of experiment.

Descartes published his works in Holland, where he found greater liberty of thought than then obtained in France. His Principles of Philosophy, printed in both Latin and French at Amsterdam in 1644, is the source of the extract below. The English translation used is based on that made by John Veitch in 1854, and included in the Everyman's edition of the Discourse on Method (E. P. Dutton, New York).

OF THE PRINCIPLES

OF HUMAN KNOWLEDGE

I. THAT IN order to see truth, it is necessary once in the course of our life to doubt, as far as possible, of all things.

As we were at one time children, and as we formed various judgments regarding the objects presented to our senses, when as yet we had not the entire use of our reason, so numerous prejudices stand in the way of our arriving at the knowledge of truth; and of these it seems impossible for us to rid ourselves, unless we undertake, once in our lifetime, to doubt of all those things in which we may discover even the smallest suspicion of uncertainty.

II. That we ought also to consider as false all that is doubtful.

Moreover, it will be useful likewise to esteem as false the things of which we shall be able to doubt, that we may with greater clearness discover what possesses most certainty and is the easiest to know.

III. That we ought not meanwhile to make use of doubt in the conduct of life.

In the meantime, it is to be observed that we are to avail ourselves of this general doubt only while engaged in the contemplation of truth. For, as far as concerns the conduct of life, we are very frequently obliged to follow opinions merely probable, or even sometimes, when of two courses of action we may not perceive more probability in the one than in the other, to choose one or other, seeing the opportunity of acting would not unfrequently pass away before we could free ourselves from our doubts.

IV. Why we may doubt of sensible things.

Accordingly, since we now design only to apply ourselves to the

investigation of truth, we will doubt, first, whether of all the things
that have ever fallen under our senses or which we have ever imagined, any one really exists; in the first place, because we know by
experience that the senses sometimes err, and it would be imprudent
to trust too much to what has even once deceived us; secondly,
because in dreams we perpetually seem to perceive or imagine innumerable objects which have no existence. And to one who has
thus resolved upon a general doubt, there appear no marks by which
he can with certainty distinguish sleep from the waking state.

V. Why we may also doubt of mathematical demonstrations.

We will also doubt of the other things we have before held as
most certain, even of the demonstrations of mathematics, and of
their principles which we have hitherto deemed self-evident; in the
first place, because we have sometimes seen men fall into error in
such matters, and admit as absolutely certain and self-evident what
to us appeared false; but chiefly because we have learnt that God
who created us is all-powerful, for we do not yet know whether
perhaps it was his will to create us so that we are always deceived,
even in the things we think we know best; since this does not appear
more impossible than our being occasionally deceived, which, however, as observation teaches us, is the case. And if we suppose that
an all-powerful God is not the author of our being, and that we
exist of ourselves or by some other means, still, the less powerful
we suppose our author to be, the greater reason will we have for
believing that we are not so perfect as that we may not be continually deceived.

VI. That we possess a free-will, by which we can withhold our
assent from what is doubtful, and thus avoid error.

But meanwhile, whoever in the end may be the author of our
being, and however powerful and deceitful he may be, we are nevertheless conscious of a freedom, by which we can refrain from admitting to a place in our belief aught that is not manifestly certain and
undoubted, and thus guard against ever being deceived.

VII. That we cannot doubt of our existence while we doubt, and that this is the first knowledge we acquire when we philosophize in order.

While we thus reject all of which we can entertain the smallest doubt, and even imagine that it is false, we can easily suppose that there is neither God, nor sky, nor bodies, and that we ourselves even have neither hands nor feet, nor, finally, a body. But we cannot in the same way suppose that *we* are not, while we doubt of the truth of these things; for there is a repugnance in conceiving that what thinks does not exist at the very time when it thinks. Accordingly, the knowledge, *I think, therefore I am,* is the first and most certain that occurs to one who philosophizes in an orderly way.

VIII. That we hence discover the distinction between the mind and the body, or between a thinking and a corporeal thing.

And this is the best mode of discovering the nature of the mind, and its distinctness from the body. For examining what we are, while supposing, as we now do, that there is nothing really existing apart from our thought, we clearly perceive that neither extension, nor figure, nor local motion, nor anything similar, that can be attributed to body, pertains to our nature, nothing save thought alone; and, consequently, that the notion we have of our mind precedes that of any corporeal thing, and is more certain, seeing we still doubt whether there is anybody in existence, while we already perceive that we think. . . .

X. That the notions which are simplest and self-evident, are obscured by logical definitions, and are not to be reckoned among the cognitions acquired by study [but as born with us].

I do not here explain several other terms which I have used, or design to use in the sequel, because their meaning seems to me sufficiently self-evident. And I have frequently remarked that philosophers erred in attempting to explain, by logical definitions, such truths as are most simple and self-evident; for they thus only rendered them more obscure. And when I said that the proposition, *I think, therefore I am,* is of all others the first and most certain which occurs to one philosophizing in an orderly way, I did not therefore deny that it was necessary to know what thought, existence, and certitude are, and the truth that in order to think it is necessary to be, and the like. But, because these are the most simple notions, and such as of themselves afford knowledge of nothing existing, I did not judge it proper there to enumerate them. . . .

XXXIII. That we never err unless when we judge of something which we do not sufficiently apprehend.

When we observe anything we are in no danger of error, if we refrain from judging of it in any way. And even when we have formed a judgment regarding it, we would never fall into error, provided we gave our assent only to what we clearly and distinctly perceived. But the reason why we are usually deceived, is that we judge without possessing an exact knowledge of that of which we judge. . . .

XXXVI. That our errors cannot be imputed to God.

But although God has not given us an omniscient understanding, he is not on this account to be considered in any wise the author of our errors; for it is of the nature of created intellect to be finite, and of finite intellect not to embrace all things. . . .

LXXI. That the chief cause of our errors is to be found in the prejudices of our childhood.

And here we may notice the first and chief cause of our errors. In early life, the mind was so closely bound to the body that it attended to nothing beyond the thoughts by which it perceived the objects that made impression on the body. Nor as yet did it refer these thoughts to anything existing beyond itself, but simply felt pain when the body was hurt, or pleasure when anything beneficial to the body occurred, or if the body was so slightly affected that it was neither greatly benefited nor hurt, the mind experienced the sensations we call tastes, smells, sounds, heat, cold, light, colors, and the like, which in truth are representative of nothing existing out of our mind, and which vary according to the diversities of the parts and modes in which the body is affected.

The mind at the same time also perceived magnitudes, figures, motions, and the like, which were not presented to it as sensations but as parts of the modes of things existing, or at least capable of existing outside of thought; although it did not yet observe this difference between these two kinds of perceptions. But afterwards, when the machine of the body, which has been so fabricated by nature that it can of its own inherent power move itself in various ways, by turning at random to every side, followed after what was useful and avoided what was detrimental; then the mind, which was closely connected with it, reflecting on the objects it pursued or avoided, remarked, for the first time, that they existed outside itself, and not only attributed to them magnitudes, figures, motions, and the like, which it perceived either as things or as modes of things, but, in addition, attributed to them tastes, odors, and other ideas of that sort, the sensations of which were caused by the mind itself.

And as it only considered other objects in so far as they were useful to the body in which it was immersed, it judged that there was greater or less reality in each object, according as the impressions it caused on the body were more or less powerful. Hence arose the belief that there was more substance or body in rocks and metals than in air or water, because the mind perceived in them more hardness and weight. Moreover, the air was thought to be merely nothing so long as we experienced no agitation of it by the wind, or did not feel it hot or cold. And because the stars gave hardly more light than the slender flames of candles, we supposed that each star was but of this size. Again, since the mind did not observe that the earth moved on its axis, or that its surface was curved like that of a globe, it was on that account more ready to judge the earth immovable and its surface flat.

And our mind has been imbued from our infancy with a thousand other prejudices of the same sort, which afterwards in our youth we forgot we had accepted without sufficient examination, and admitted as possessed of the highest truth and clearness, as if they had been known to us through our senses, or implanted in us by nature.

LXXII. That the second cause of our errors is that we cannot forget these prejudices.

And although now in our mature years, when the mind, being no longer wholly subject to the body, is not in the habit of referring all things to it, but also seeks to discover the truth of things considered in themselves, we observe the falsehood of a great many of the judgments we had before formed; yet we experience a difficulty in expunging them from our memory, and, so long as they remain there, they give rise to various errors. Thus, for example, since from our earliest years we imagined the stars to be of very small size, we find it highly difficult to rid ourselves of this imagination, although assured by plain astronomical reasons that they are of the greatest— so prevailing is the power of preconceived opinion.

LXXIII. The third cause is that we become fatigued by attending to those objects which are not present to the senses; and that we are thus accustomed to judge of them not from present perception but from preconceived opinion.

Besides, our mind cannot attend to any object without at length experiencing some pain and fatigue; and of all objects it has the greatest difficulty in attending to those which are present neither to the senses nor to the imagination, whether for the reason that this is natural to it from its union with the body, or because in our early years, being occupied merely with perceptions and imaginations, it has become more familiar with and acquired greater facility in thinking in those modes than in any other. Hence it also happens that many are unable to conceive any substance except what is imaginable and corporeal, and even sensible. For they are ignorant of the circumstance that those objects alone are imaginable which consist of extension, motion, and figure, though there are many others besides these that are intelligible; and they persuade themselves that nothing can subsist but body, and, finally, that there is no body which is not sensible. And since in truth we perceive no object such as it is by sense alone (but only by our reason exercised upon sensible objects), as will hereafter be clearly shown, it thus happens that the majority during life perceive nothing except in a confused way.

LXXIV. The fourth source of our errors is that we attach our thoughts to words which do not express them with accuracy.

Finally, since for the use of speech we attach all our conceptions to words by which to express them, and commit to memory our thoughts in connection with these terms, and as we afterwards find it more easy to recall the words than the things signified by them, we can scarcely conceive anything with such distinctness as to separate entirely what we conceive from the words that were selected to express it. On this account the majority attend to words rather than to things; and thus very frequently assent to terms without attaching to them any meaning, either because they think they once understood them, or imagine they learned them from others by whom they were correctly understood. This, however, is not the place to treat of this matter in detail, seeing the nature of the human body has not yet been expounded, nor the existence even of body established. Enough, nevertheless, appears to have been said to enable one to distinguish such of our conceptions as are clear and distinct from those that are obscure and confused.

LXXV. Summary of what must be observed in order to philosophize correctly.

Wherefore, if we would philosophize in earnest, and give ourselves to the search for all the truths we are capable of knowing, we must, in the first place, lay aside our prejudices; in other words, we must take care scrupulously to withhold our assent from the opinions we have formerly admitted, until upon new examination we discover that they are true. We must, in the next place, make an orderly review of the notions we have in our minds, and hold as true all and only those which we clearly and distinctly apprehend. In this way we will observe, first of all, that we exist in so far as it is our nature to think; and, at the same time, that there is a God upon whom we depend; and that after considering his attributes, we shall be able to investigate the truth of all other things, since God is the cause of them. Besides the notions we have of God and of our own mind, we will likewise find that we possess the knowledge of many propositions which are eternally true, as, for example, that nothing cannot be the cause of anything, etc. We will further discover in our minds the knowledge of a corporeal or extended nature, that can be moved, divided, etc., and also of certain sensations that affect us, as of pain, colors, tastes, etc., although we do not yet know the cause of our being so affected. And, comparing what we have now learned by examining those things in their order with our former confused knowledge of them, we shall acquire the habit of forming clear and distinct conceptions of all the objects we are capable of knowing. In these few precepts seem to me to be comprised the most general and important principles of human knowledge.

LXXVI. That we ought to prefer the Divine authority to our perception, but that, apart from things revealed, we ought to assent to nothing that we do not clearly apprehend.

Above all, we must impress on our memory the infallible rule, that what God has revealed is incomparably more certain than anything else; and that we ought to submit our belief to the Divine authority rather than to our own judgment, even although perhaps the light of reason may, with the greatest clearness and evidence, appear to suggest to us something contrary to what is revealed. But in things regarding which there is no revelation, it is by no means consistent with the character of a philosopher to accept as true what he has not ascertained to be such, or to trust more to the senses, in other words, to the inconsiderate judgments of childhood, than to the dictates of mature reason.

ISAAC NEWTON[1]

1 6 4 2 · 1 7 2 7

"I DO NOT know what I appear to the world; but to myself I seem to have been only like a boy playing on the seashore and diverting myself in now and then finding a smoother pebble or a prettier shell than ordinary, whilst the great ocean of truth lay all undiscovered before me," wrote the Cambridge scholar, Isaac Newton, late in a long life devoted to study and teaching. Others have held that his achievements in science were equal to all that had been discovered in previous history.

Although Newton owed a debt to Descartes for analytic geometry; to Copernicus, Kepler, and Galileo for astronomy and mechanics; to Francis Bacon for scientific method, his own brilliant experimentation and masterful synthesis of scientific knowledge place his contribution far ahead of any of these. His "Rules of Reasoning in Philosophy," quoted here in entirety, show to what degree he had simplified and clarified the thinking about science in general, as compared with Descartes and Bacon. Later sections in this book will present his laws of mechanics, his law of universal gravitation, and a demonstration, in optics, of his experimental method.

The last paragraph given here, on the use of hypothesis in scientific method, is from a letter to Gaston Pardies, professor of mathematics in the College of Clermont, Paris. Hypotheses are useful, he says, when they explain existing facts, but as pure conjectures, unrelated to experimental evidence, they are detrimental to progress and to be shunned. Both passages are taken from Florian Cajori's edition of the Principia Mathematica, originally translated by Andrew Motte in 1729 (University of California Press, 1934).

[1] For more of the work of Newton, see p. 63 and p. 148.

RULES OF REASONING IN PHILOSOPHY

RULE I

We are to admit no more causes of natural things than such as are both true and sufficient to explain their appearances.

To this purpose the philosophers say that Nature does nothing in vain, and more is in vain when less will serve; for Nature is pleased with simplicity, and affects not the pomp of superfluous causes.

RULE II

Therefore to the same natural effects we must, as far as possible, assign the same causes.

As to respiration in a man and in a beast; the descent of stones in Europe and in America; the light of our culinary fire and of the sun; the reflection of light in the earth, and in the planets.

RULE III

The qualities of bodies which admit neither intensification nor remission of degrees, and which are found to belong to all bodies within the reach of our experiments, are to be esteemed the universal qualities of all bodies whatsoever.

For since the qualities of bodies are only known to us by experiments, we are to hold for universal all such as universally agree with experiments; and such as are not liable to diminution can never be quite taken away. We are certainly not to relinquish the evidence of experiments for the sake of dreams and vain fictions of our own devising; nor are we to recede from the analogy of Nature, which is wont to be simple, and always consonant to itself.

We no other way know the extension of bodies than by our senses, nor do these reach it in all bodies; but because we perceive extension in all that are sensible, therefore we ascribe it universally to all others also. That abundance of bodies are hard, we learn by experience; and because the hardness of the whole arises from the hardness of the parts, we therefore justly infer the hardness of the undivided particles not only of the bodies we feel but of all others. That all bodies are impenetrable, we gather not from reason, but from sensation. The bodies which we handle we find impenetrable, and thence conclude impenetrability to be an universal property of all bodies whatsoever. That all bodies are movable, and endowed with certain powers (which we call the inertia) of persevering in their motion, or in their rest, we only infer from the like properties observed in the bodies which we have seen. The extension, hardness, impenetrability, mobility, and inertia of the whole, result from the extension, hardness, impenetrability, mobility, and inertia of the parts; and hence we conclude the least particles of all bodies to be also all extended, and hard and impenetrable, and movable, and endowed with their proper inertia. And this is the foundation of all philosophy.

Moreover, that the divided but contiguous particles of bodies may be separated from one another is matter of observation; and, in the particles that remain undivided, our minds are able to distinguish yet lesser parts, as is mathematically demonstrated. But whether the parts so distinguished, and not yet divided, may, by the powers of Nature, be actually divided and separated from one another, we cannot certainly determine. Yet, had we the proof of but one experiment that any undivided particle, in breaking a hard and solid body, suffered a division, we might by virtue of this rule conclude that the undivided as well as the divided particles may be divided and actually separated to infinity.

Lastly, if it universally appears, by experiments and astronomical observations, that all bodies about the earth gravitate towards the earth, and that in proportion to the quantity of matter which they severally contain; that the moon likewise, according to the quantity of its matter, gravitates towards the earth; that, on the other hand, our sea gravitates towards the moon; and all the planets one towards another; and the comets in like manner towards the sun; we must, in consequence of this rule, universally allow that all bodies whatsoever are endowed with a principle of mutual gravitation. For the argument from the appearances concludes with more force for the universal gravitation of all bodies than for their impenetrability; of which, among those in the celestial regions, we have no experiments, nor any manner of observation. Not that I affirm gravity to be essential to bodies: by their *vis insita* I mean nothing but their inertia. This is immutable. Their gravity is diminished as they recede from the earth.

RULE IV

In experimental philosophy we are to look upon propositions inferred by general induction from phenomena as accurately or very nearly true, notwithstanding any contrary hypotheses that may be imagined, till such time as other phenomena occur, by which they may either be made more accurate, or liable to exceptions.

This rule we must follow, that the argument of induction may not be evaded by hypotheses.

The Place of Hypothesis in Scientific Thought [1]

The best and safest method of philosophizing seems to be, first diligently to investigate the properties of things and establish them by experiment, and then to seek hypotheses to explain them. For hypotheses ought to be fitted merely to explain the properties of things and not attempt to predetermine them, except in so far as they can be an aid to experiments. If anyone offers conjectures about the truth of things from the mere possibility of hypotheses, I do not see how anything certain can be determined in any science; for it is always possible to contrive hypotheses, one after another, which are

[1] Quotation from a letter to Gaston Pardies.

found rich in new tribulations. Wherefore I judged that one should abstain from considering hypotheses as from a fallacious argument, and that the force of their opposition must be removed, that one may arrive at a maturer and more general explanation.[2]

[2] For another and even more explicit statement of Newton's views on the impossibility of building any sound science on hypothesis, see above, p. 61.

ANTOINE LAVOISIER[1]

1 7 4 3 · 1 7 9 4

BORN IN PARIS, the son of a wealthy amateur student of science, Antoine Lavoisier had the advantage of the finest scientific education. At the age of twenty-three he won a medal from the French Academy of Science for an essay on the best means of lighting the streets of a large town. At twenty-five he was admitted to membership in the Academy. There followed many years of highly productive research, combined with service in public office. He assisted in the preparation of a mineralogical atlas of France, and started a model farm to demonstrate the value of scientific agriculture. Among his government positions was that of farmer-general of taxes and director of the national gunpowder factories. The National Assembly made use of his talents early in the Revolution, but along with other tax-collectors of the old monarchy he was condemned to the guillotine during the Reign of Terror of 1794.

As the eighteenth century drew toward its close, faith in experimentally determined facts grew to such an extent that scientists dared hope to discover all that was to be known about nature. Interest in the old, metaphysical problems of how to tell what knowledge was permanently trustworthy, or what was the true relationship of so-called cause and effect, went into the background for another century. At the same time, the increased knowledge of natural fact brought with it a need for greater care and precision in terminology. Lavoisier said, "We must trust to nothing but facts. These are presented to us by nature, and cannot deceive," but he also realized that

[1] Other selections from Lavoisier's work, dealing with the chemistry of gases and chemical nomenclature, are quoted on pp. 262-271.

the organization of the new factual learning would be greatly simplified by a clear and standardized system of nomenclature.

In the preface to his Traité Elementaire de Chimie (1789), presented in the pages which follow, Lavoisier discussed the relationship between facts, ideas, and words, in order to explain why a book originally planned as a discussion of terms turned out to be an elementary text on chemistry. He went on to express in the final paragraph his faith that the parts of chemistry, like the parts of geometry, could be closely connected together in a "complete science." The translation of his treatise presented here is that made by Robert Kerr of Edinburgh in 1799.

REASONING AND LANGUAGE

WHEN I BEGAN the following Work, my only object was to extend and explain more fully the Memoir which I read at the public meeting of the Academy of Sciences in the month of April 1787, on the necessity of reforming and completing the Nomenclature of Chemistry. While engaged in this employment, I perceived, better than I had ever done before, the justice of the following maxims of the Abbé de Condillac, in his system of Logic, and some other of his works.

"We think only through the medium of words. Languages are true analytical methods. Algebra, which is adapted to its purpose in every species of expression, in the most simple, most exact, and best manner possible, is at the same time a language and an analytical method. The art of reasoning is nothing more than a language well arranged."

Thus, while I thought myself employed only in forming a nomenclature, and while I proposed to myself nothing more than to improve the chemical language, my work transformed itself by degrees, without my being able to prevent it, into a treatise upon the Elements of Chemistry.

The impossibility of separating the nomenclature of a science from the science itself, is owing to this, that every branch of physical science must consist of three things; the series of facts which are the objects of the science; the ideas which represent these facts; and the words by which these ideas are expressed. Like three impressions of the same seal, the word ought to produce the idea, and the idea to be a picture of the fact. And, as ideas are preserved and communicated by means of words, it necessarily follows that we cannot improve the language of any science, without at the same time improving the science itself; neither can we, on the other hand, improve a science, without improving the language or nomenclature which belongs to it. However certain the facts of any science may be, and however just the ideas we may have formed of these facts, we can only communicate false or imperfect impressions of these ideas to others, while we want words by which they may be properly expressed.

To those who will consider it with attention, the first part of this treatise will afford frequent proofs of the truth of these observations. But as, in the conduct of my work, I have been obliged to observe an order of arrangement essentially differing from what has been adopted in any other chemical work yet published, it is proper that I should explain the motives which have led me to adopt that arrangement.

It is a maxim universally admitted in Geometry, and indeed in every branch of knowledge, that, in the progress of investigation, we should proceed from known facts to what is unknown. In early infancy, our ideas spring from our wants, the sensation of want exciting the idea of the object by which it is to be gratified. In this manner, from a series of sensations, observations, and analyses, a successive train of ideas arises, so linked together that an attentive observer may trace back, to a certain point, the order and connection of the whole sum of human knowledge.

When we begin the study of any science, we are in a situation, respecting that science, similar to children; and the course by which we have to advance, is precisely the same which Nature follows in the formation of their ideas. In a child, the idea is merely an effect produced by a sensation; and, in the same manner, in commencing the study of a physical science, we ought to form no idea but what is a necessary consequence and immediate effect of an experiment or observation. Besides, he who enters upon the career of science, is in a less advantageous situation than a child who is acquiring his first ideas. To the child, Nature gives various means of rectifying any mistakes he may commit respecting the salutary or hurtful qualities of the objects which surround him. On every occasion his judgments are corrected by experience; want and pain are the necessary consequences arising from false judgment; gratification and pleasure are produced by judging aright. Under such masters, we cannot fail to become well informed; and we soon learn to reason justly, when want and pain are the necessary consequences of a contrary conduct.

In the study and practice of the sciences it is entirely different; the false judgments we may form neither affect our existence nor our welfare; and we are not compelled by any physical necessity to correct them. Imagination, on the contrary, which is ever wandering beyond the bounds of truth, joined to self-love and that self-confidence we are so apt to indulge, prompt us to draw conclusions which are not immediately derived from facts; so that we become in some measure interested in deceiving ourselves. Hence it is by no means surprising that, in the science of physics in general, men have so often formed suppositions, instead of drawing conclusions. These suppositions, handed down from one age to another, acquire additional weight from the authorities by which they are supported, till at last they are received, even by men of genius, as fundamental truths.

The only method of preventing such errors from taking place, and of correcting them when formed, is to restrain and simplify our reasoning as much as possible. This depends entirely on ourselves, and the neglect of it is the only source of our mistakes. We must trust to nothing but facts. These are presented to us by Nature, and cannot deceive. We ought, in every instance, to submit our reasoning to the test of experiment, and never to search for truth but by the natural road of experiment and observation. Thus mathematicians obtain the solution of a problem, by the mere arrangement of data, and by reducing their reasoning to such simple steps, and to conclusions so very obvious, as never to lose sight of the evidence which guides them.

Thoroughly convinced of these truths, I have imposed upon myself, as a law, never to advance but from what is known to what is unknown; never to form any conclusion which is not an immediate consequence necessarily flowing from observation and experiment; and always to arrange the facts and the conclusions which are drawn from them in such an order as shall render it most easy for beginners in the study of chemistry thoroughly to understand them. Hence I have been obliged to depart from the order usually observed in courses of lectures and treatises upon chemistry; which always assume the first principles of the science as known, whereas the pupil or the reader should never be supposed to know them till they have been explained in subsequent lessons. In almost every instance, chemical authors and lecturers begin by treating of the elements of matter, and by explaining the table of affinities; without considering that, in so doing, they must bring the principal phenomena of chemistry into view at the very outset. They make use of terms which have not been defined, and suppose the science to be understood by the very persons they are only beginning to teach.

It ought likewise to be considered that very little of chemistry can be learned in a first course, which is hardly sufficient to make the language of the science familiar to the ears, or the apparatus familiar to the eyes. It is almost impossible to become a chemist in less than three or four years of constant application.

These inconveniences are occasioned, not so much by the nature of the subject, as by the method of teaching it; and chiefly to avoid them, I was induced to adopt a new arrangement of chemistry, which appeared to me more consonant to the order of Nature. I acknowledge, however, that in thus endeavoring to avoid difficulties of one kind, I have found myself involved in others of a different species, some of which I have not been able to remove; but I am persuaded that such as remain do not arise from the nature of the order I have adopted, but are rather consequences of the imperfection under which chemistry still labors. This science has many chasms, which interrupt the series of facts, and often render it extremely difficult to reconcile them with each other. It has not, like the elements of geometry, the advantage of being a complete science, the parts of which are all closely connected together. Its actual progress, however, is so rapid, and the facts, under the modern doctrine, have assumed so happy an arrangement, that we have ground to hope, even in our own times, to see it approach near to the highest state of perfection of which it is susceptible. . . .

It will, no doubt, be a matter of surprise, that in a treatise upon the elements of chemistry, there should be no chapter on the constituent and elementary parts of matter; but I may here observe that the fondness for reducing all the bodies in nature to three or four elements proceeds from a prejudice which has descended to us from the Greek philosophers. The notion of four elements, which, by the variety of their proportions, compose all the known substances in nature, is a mere hypothesis, assumed long before the first principles of experimental philosophy or of chemistry had any existence. In those days, without possessing facts, they framed systems; while we, who have collected facts, seem determined to reject even these, when they do not agree with our prejudices. The authority of those fathers of human philosophy still carry great weight, and there is reason to fear that it will even bear hard upon generations yet to come.

It is very remarkable, notwithstanding the number of philosophical chemists who have supported the doctrine of the four elements, that there is not one who has not been led, by the evidence of facts, to admit a greater number of elements into their theory. The first chemical authors, after the revival of letters,[1] considered sulphur and salt as elementary substances entering into the composition of a great number of bodies; hence, instead of four, they admitted the existence of six elements. Beccher assumed the existence of three kinds of earth; from the combination of which, in different proportions, he supposed all the varieties of metallic substances to be produced. Stahl gave a new modification to this system; and succeeding chemists have taken the liberty to make or to imagine changes and

[1] That is, after the Renaissance.

additions of a similar nature. All these chemists were carried along by the genius of the age in which they lived, being satisfied with assertions instead of proofs; or, at least, often admitting as proofs the slightest degrees of probability, unsupported by that strictly rigorous analysis which is required by modern philosophy.

All that can be said upon the number and nature of elements is, in my opinion, confined to discussions entirely of a metaphysical nature. The subject only furnishes us with indefinite problems, which may be solved in a thousand different ways, not one of which, in all probability, is consistent with nature. I shall, therefore, only add upon this subject, that if, by the term *elements*, we mean to express those simple and indivisible atoms of which matter is composed, it is extremely probable we know nothing at all about them; but, if we apply the term *elements* or *principles of bodies*, to express our idea of the last point which analysis is capable of reaching, we must admit, as elements, all the substances into which we are able to reduce bodies by decomposition. Not that we are entitled to affirm that these substances which we consider as simple may not themselves be compounded of two, or even of a greater number of more simple principles; but since these principles cannot be separated, or rather since we have not hitherto discovered the means of separating them, they act with regard to us as simple substances, and we ought never to suppose them compounded until experiment and observation have proved them to be so.

The foregoing reflections upon the progress of chemical ideas naturally apply to the words by which these ideas are expressed. Guided by the work which, in the year 1787, Messrs. de Morveau, Berthollet, de Fourcroy, and I composed upon the Nomenclature of Chemistry, I have endeavored, as much as possible, to denominate simple bodies by simple terms, and I was naturally led to name these first. It will be recollected that we were obliged to retain that name of any substance by which it had been long known in the world, and that in two cases only we took the liberty of making alterations; first, in the case of those which were but newly discovered, and had not yet obtained names, or at least which had been known but for a short time, and the names of which had not yet received the sanction of the public; and secondly, when the names which had been adopted, whether by the ancients or the moderns, appeared to us to express evidently false ideas; when they confounded the substances to which they were applied, with others possessed of different, or perhaps opposite qualities. We made no scruple, in this case, of substituting other names in their room, and the greater number of these were borrowed from the Greek language. We endeavored to frame them in such a manner as to express the most general and the most characteristic quality of the substances; and this was attended with the additional advantage both of assisting the memory of beginners, who find it difficult to remember a new word which has no meaning, and of accustoming them early to admit no word without connecting with it some determinate idea.

To those bodies which are formed by the union of several simple substances, we gave new names compounded in such a manner as the nature of the substances directed; but, as the number of known double combinations is already very considerable, the only method by which we could avoid confusion, was to divide these into classes. In the natural order of ideas, the name of the class or genus is that which expresses a quality common to a great number of individuals; the name of the species, on the contrary, expresses a quality peculiar to certain individuals only.

These distinctions are not, as some may imagine, merely metaphysical, but are established by Nature. "A child," says the Abbé de Condillac,[2] "is taught to give the name *tree* to the first which is pointed out to him. The next tree he sees presents the same idea, and he gives it the same name. This he does likewise to a third and a fourth, till at last the word *tree*, which he at first applied to an individual, comes to be employed by him as the name of a class or a genus; it becomes an abstract idea, which comprehends all trees in

[2] A contemporary French metaphysician.

general. But when he learns that all trees do not serve the same purpose, that they do not all produce the same kind of fruit, he soon distinguishes them by specific and particular names." This is the logic of all the sciences, and is very naturally applicable to chemistry.

The acids, for example, are compounded of two substances which we consider as simple; the one constitutes acidity, and is common to all acids, and, from this substance, the name of the class or the genus ought to be taken; the other is peculiar to each acid, and distinguishes it from the rest, and from this substance is to be taken the name of the species. But, in the greater number of acids, these two constituent elements, the acidifying principle and that which it acidifies, may exist in different proportions, constituting all the possible points of equilibrium or of saturation. This is the case in the sulphuric and the sulphurous acids; and these two states of the same acid we have marked by varying the termination of the specific name.

Metallic substances which have been exposed to the joint action of the air and of fire, lose their metallic luster, increase in weight, and assume an earthy appearance. In this state, like the acids, they are compounded of a principle which is common to all, and of one which is peculiar to each. In the same way, therefore, we have thought proper to class them under a generic name, derived from the common principle; for which purpose, we have adopted the term *oxyd*; and we distinguish them from each other by the particular name of the metal to which each belongs.

Combustible substances, which in acids and metallic oxyds are specific and particular principles, are capable of becoming, in their turn, common principles of a great number of compounds. The sulphurous combinations have been long the only known ones in this kind. Now, however, we know, from the experiments of Messrs. Vandermonde, Monge, and Berthollet, that carbon may be combined with iron, and perhaps with several other metals; and that from this combination, according to the proportions, may be produced steel, plumbago, &c. We know likewise, from the experiments of M. Pelletier, that phosphorus may be combined with a great number of metallic substances. These different combinations we have classed under generic names taken from the common substance, with a termination which marks this analogy, specifying them by another name taken from that substance which is proper to each.

The nomenclature of bodies compounded of three simple substances was attended with still greater difficulty; not only on account of their number, but particularly, because we cannot express the nature of their constituent principles without employing more compound names. In the bodies which form this class, such as the neutral salts, for instance, we had to consider, 1st, The acidifying principle which is common to them all; 2d, The acidifiable principle which constitutes their peculiar acid; 3d, The saline, earthy, or metallic basis, which determines the particular species of salt. Here we derived the name of each class of salts from the name of the acidifiable principle common to all the individuals of that class; and distinguished each species by the name of its peculiar saline, earthy, or metallic basis.

A salt, though compounded of the same three principles, may, nevertheless, by the mere difference of their proportion, be in three different states of saturation. The nomenclature we have adopted would have been defective, had it not expressed these different states; and this we attained chiefly by changes of termination uniformly applied to the same state of the different salts.

In short, we have advanced so far, that from the name alone may be instantly found: what the combustible substance is which enters into any combination; whether that combustible substance be combined with the acidifying principle, and in what proportion; what is the state of the acid; with what basis it is united; whether the saturation be exact, or whether the acid or the basis be in excess.

It may easily be supposed that it was not possible to attain all these different objects without departing, in some instances, from established custom, and adopting terms which, at first sight, may appear uncouth and barbarous. But we considered that the ear is soon habituated to new words, especially when they are connected with a general and rational system. The names, besides, which were formerly employed, such as *powder of algaroth, salt of alembroth, pompholix, phagadenic water, turbith mineral, colcothar,* and many others, were neither less barbarous nor less uncommon. It required a great deal of practice, and no small degree of memory, to recollect the substances to which they were applied; much more to recollect the genus of combination to which they belong. The names of *oil of tartar per diliquium, oil of vitriol, butter of arsenic and of antimony, flowers of zinc,* &c., were still more improper, because they suggested false ideas; for, in the whole mineral kingdom, and particularly in the metallic class, there exists no such thing as butters, oils, or flowers; in short, the substances to which these fallacious names were given are rank poisons. . . .

PIERRE SIMON,
MARQUIS DE LAPLACE[1]

1 7 4 9 · 1 8 2 7

By the end of the eighteenth century the "scientific method" of arriving at general truths by induction from experiment and observation had become well established. Yet admittedly there was a difference between the "truth," as far as observed, of an experimentally determined law and the perfection of eternal and absolute truth, so dear to the heart of Plato and the idealist philosophers.

How close can scientific truth ever come to the ideal or final truth was a question which needed a special method for its solution. That method was supplied by the "theory of probabilities," which Blaise Pascal and Pierre Fermat had first developed a century before as a means for solving problems of gambling with cards. Now Pierre Simon, Marquis de Laplace, made of this method a most important tool for mathematical physics.

"We see," Laplace said of it, "that the theory of probabilities is at bottom only common sense reduced to calculation; it makes us appreciate with exactitude what reasonable minds feel by a sort of instinct, often without being able to account for it. . . . It is remarkable that this science, which originated in the consideration of games of chance, should have become the most important object of human knowledge."

Laplace, the son of a farmer, rose to the position of professor of mathematics at the École Militaire in Paris, where he was a teacher of the young Napoleon Bonaparte. During the violent political

[1] For Laplace's contribution to astronomy, see p. 119.

changes of the following years in France, Laplace—unlike his contemporary, Lavoisier—managed to remain in favor with the ruling group of the moment, and won many titles and honors. He was finally made Marquis by Louis XVIII.

In the selection quoted below, he describes both the confidence he feels in the immutable working of the laws of material cause and effect, and the manner in which he has used the rule of probabilities to create a very high degree of assurance as to the truth of inductive, scientific conclusions. Although we cannot be absolutely certain, on the ground of its regular risings in the past, that the sun will rise again tomorrow, by the rule of probabilities it can be demonstrated that the chance that it will fail to rise is so slight that we need not worry over it. In the same way, the truth of many laws of science, while not to be called absolute, is for all practical purposes as well founded as if it were.

Our selection is taken from Laplace's Philosophical Essay on Probabilities, first published in 1814, and translated by F. W. Prescott and F. L. Emory in 1902.

PROBABILITIES AND
NATURAL PHILOSOPHY

§

ALL EVENTS, even those which on account of their insignificance do not seem to follow the great laws of nature, are a result of it just as necessarily as the revolutions of the sun. In ignorance of the ties which unite such events to the entire system of the universe, they have been made to depend upon final causes or upon hazard, according as they occur and are repeated with regularity, or appear without regard to order; but these imaginary causes have gradually receded with the widening bounds of knowledge and disappear entirely before sound philosophy, which sees in them only the expression of our ignorance of the true causes.

Present events are connected with preceding ones by a tie based upon the evident principle that a thing cannot occur without a cause which produces it. This axiom, known by the name of *the principle of sufficient reason,* extends even to actions which are considered indifferent; the freest will is unable without a determinative motive to give them birth; if we assume two positions with exactly similar circumstances and find that the will is active in the one and inactive in the other, we say that its choice is an effect without a cause. It is then, says Leibnitz, the blind chance of the Epicureans. The contrary opinion is an illusion of the mind, which, losing sight of the evasive reasons of the choice of the will in indifferent things, believes that choice is determined of itself and without motives.

We ought then to regard the present state of the universe as the effect of its anterior state and as the cause of the one which is to follow. Given for one instant an intelligence which could comprehend all the forces by which nature is animated and the respective situation of the beings who compose it—an intelligence sufficiently vast to submit these data to analysis—it would embrace in the same formula the movements of the greatest bodies of the universe and those of the lightest atom; for it, nothing would be uncertain and the future, as the past, would be present to its eyes. The human mind offers, in the perfection which it has been able to give to astronomy, a feeble idea of this intelligence. Its discoveries in mechanics and geometry, added to that of universal gravity, have enabled it to comprehend in the same analytical expressions the past and future states of the system of the world. Applying the same method to some other objects of its knowledge, it has succeeded in referring to general laws observed phenomena and in foreseeing those which given circumstances ought to produce. All these efforts in the search for truth tend to lead it back continually to the vast intelligence which we have just mentioned, but from which it will always remain infinitely removed. This tendency, peculiar to the human race, is that which renders it superior to animals; and their progress in this respect distinguishes nations and ages and constitutes their true glory.

Let us recall that formerly, and at no remote epoch, an unusual rain or an extreme drought, a comet having in train a very long tail, the eclipses, the aurora borealis, and in general all the unusual phenomena were regarded as so many signs of celestial wrath. Heaven was invoked in order to avert their baneful influence. No one prayed to have the planets and the sun arrested in their courses; observation had soon made apparent the futility of such prayers. But as these phenomena, occurring and disappearing at long intervals, seemed to oppose the order of nature, it was supposed that Heaven, irritated by the crimes of the earth, had created them to announce its vengeance. Thus the long tail of the comet of 1456 spread terror through Europe, already thrown into consternation by the rapid successes of the Turks, who had just overthrown the Lower Empire. This star after four revolutions has excited among us a very different interest. The knowledge of the laws of the system of the world acquired in the interval had dissipated the fears begotten by the ignorance of the true relationship of man to the universe; and Halley, having recognized the identity of this comet with those of the years 1531, 1607, and 1682, announced its next return for the end of the year 1758 or the beginning of the year 1759. The learned world awaited with impatience this return which was to confirm one of the greatest discoveries that have been made in the sciences, and fulfil the prediction of Seneca when he said, in speaking of the revolutions of those stars which fall from an enormous height: "The day will come when, by study pursued through several ages, the things now concealed will appear with evidence; and posterity will be astonished that truths so clear had escaped us." Clairaut then undertook to submit to analysis the perturbations which the comet had experienced by the action of the two great planets, Jupiter and Saturn; after immense calculations he fixed its next passage at the perihelion toward the beginning of April, 1759, which was actually verified by observation. The regularity which astronomy shows us in the movements of the comets doubtless exists also in all phenomena.

The curve described by a simple molecule of air or vapor is regulated in a manner just as certain as the planetary orbits; the only difference between them is that which comes from our ignorance.

Probability is relative, in part to this ignorance, in part to our knowledge. We know that of three or a greater number of events a single one ought to occur; but nothing induces us to believe that one of them will occur rather than the others. In this state of indecision it is impossible for us to announce their occurrence with certainty. It is, however, probable that one of these events, chosen at will, will not occur because we see several cases equally possible which exclude its occurrence, while only a single one favors it.

The theory of chance consists in reducing all the events of the same kind to a certain number of cases equally possible, that is to say, to such as we may be equally undecided about in regard to their existence, and in determining the number of cases favorable to the event whose probability is sought. The ratio of this number to that of all the cases possible is the measure of this probability, which is thus simply a fraction whose numerator is the number of favorable cases and whole denominator is the number of all the cases possible.

The preceding notion of probability supposes that, in increasing in the same ratio the number of favorable cases and that of all the cases possible, the probability remains the same. In order to convince ourselves let us take two urns, A and B, the first containing four white and two black balls, and the second containing only two white balls and one black one. We may imagine the two black balls of the first urn attached by a thread which breaks at the moment when one of them is seized in order to be drawn out, and the four white balls thus forming two similar systems. All the chances which will favor the seizure of one of the balls of the black system will lead to a black ball. If we conceive now that the threads which unite the balls do not break at all, it is clear that the number of possible chances will not change any more than that of the chances favorable to the extraction of the black balls; but two balls will be drawn from the urn at the same time; the probability of drawing a black ball from the urn A will then be the same as at first. But then we have obviously the case of urn B with the single difference that the three balls of this last urn would be replaced by three systems of two balls invariably connected.

When all the cases are favorable to an event the probability changes to certainty and its expression becomes equal to unity. Upon this condition, certainty and probability are comparable, although there may be an essential difference between the two states of the mind when a truth is rigorously demonstrated to it, or when it still perceives a small source of error.

In things which are only probable the difference of the data, which each man has in regard to them, is one of the principal causes of the diversity of opinions which prevail in regard to the same objects. Let us suppose, for example, that we have three urns,

A, B, C, one of which contains only black balls while the two others contain only white balls; a ball is to be drawn from the urn C and the probability is demanded that this ball will be black. If we do not know which of the three urns contains black balls only, so that there is no reason to believe that it is C rather than B or A, these three hypotheses will appear equally possible, and since a black ball can be drawn only in the first hypothesis, the probability of drawing is equal to one third. If it is known that the urn A contains white balls only, the indecision then extends only to the urns B and C, and the probability that the ball drawn from the urn C will be black is one half. Finally, this probability changes to certainty if we are assured that the urns A and B contain white balls only.

It is thus that an incident related to a numerous assembly finds various degrees of credence, according to the extent of knowledge of the auditors. If the man who reports it is fully convinced of it and if, by his position and character, he inspires great confidence, his statement, however extraordinary it may be, will have for the auditors who lack information, the same degree of probability as an ordinary statement made by the same man, and they will have entire faith in it. But if some one of them knows that the same incident is rejected by other equally trustworthy men, he will be in doubt and the incident will be discredited by the enlightened auditors, who will reject it whether it be in regard to facts well averred or the immutable laws of nature.

It is to the influence of the opinion of those whom the multitude judges best informed and to whom it has been accustomed to give its confidence in regard to the most important matters of life that the propagation of those errors is due which in times of ignorance have covered the face of the earth. Magic and astrology offer us two great examples. These errors inculcated in infancy, adopted without examination, and having for a basis only universal credence, have maintained themselves during a very long time; but at last the progress of science has destroyed them in the minds of enlightened men, whose opinion consequently has caused them to disappear even among the common people, through the power of imitation and habit which had so generally spread them abroad. This power, the richest resource of the moral world, establishes and conserves in a whole nation ideas entirely contrary to those which it upholds elsewhere with the same authority. What indulgence ought we not then to have for opinions different from ours, when this difference often depends only upon the various points of view where circumstances have placed us! Let us enlighten those whom we judge insufficiently instructed; but first, let us examine critically our own opinions and weigh with impartiality their respective probabilities.

The difference of opinions depends, however, upon the manner in which the influence of known data is determined. The theory of probabilities holds to considerations so delicate that it is not surprising that with the same data two persons arrive at different results, especially in very complicated questions . . .

INDEX OF SCIENTISTS
AND WRITERS

This book is divided into nine subject areas, with many cross references between the sections. Each section is treated historically and spans the period from about 1550 to 1800. The table of contents affords the best means of finding a given subject. The sections are grouped as follows: I, Astronomy; II, The Laws of Light and Heat; III, Chemistry and the Study of Gases; IV, Electricity; V, Geology; VI, Biology; VII, Human Physiology; VIII, Medicine; IX, The Philosophy of Science.